The Regulation of
Potassium Balance

Raven Press books by
Donald W. Seldin and Gerhard Giebisch

The Regulation of Potassium Balance
The Regulation of Acid-Base Balance
The Regulation of Sodium Chloride Balance
The Kidney (2 volumes)

The Regulation of
Potassium Balance

Editors

Donald W. Seldin, M.D.

William Buchanan and Systems Professor of Internal Medicine
Department of Internal Medicine
The University of Texas Southwestern Medical Center at Dallas
Dallas, Texas

Gerhard Giebisch, M.D.

Sterling Professor
Department of Cellular and Molecular Physiology
Yale University School of Medicine
New Haven, Connecticut

Raven Press   New York

Raven Press, 1185 Avenue of the Americas, New York, New York 10036

Library of Congress Cataloging-in-Publication Data

The Regulation of potassium balance.

Includes bibliographies and index.
1. Potassium—Metabolism—Disorders.   2. Potassium—Metabolism.   I. Seldin, Donald W., 1920–

II. Giebisch, Gerhard H.   [DNLM: 1. Potassium—metabolism.
2. Water-Electrolyte Balance.   QU 130 R344]
RC632.P64R44   1988   616.3'9   86-45986
ISBN 0-88167-468-0

The material contained in this volume was submitted as previously unpublished material, except in the instances in which some of the illustrative material was derived.

Great care has been taken to maintain the accuracy of the information contained in the volume. However, neither Raven Press nor the editors can be held responsible for errors or for any consequences arising from the use of the information contained herein.

Materials appearing in this book prepared by individuals as part of their official duties as U.S. Government employees are not covered by the above-mentioned copyright.

9 8 7 6 5 4 3 2 1

Preface

Disturbances of potassium metabolism are the common currency of clinical medicine. Three classes of derangements can be identified. First, potassium redistribution can lead to a distorted internal distribution of potassium even though total body stores remain unchanged. Second, potassium depletion may result from deficient intake, extrarenal losses, or wastage into the urine. Third, potassium intoxication may be the consequence of excessive potassium loads or diminished urinary excretion. This volume treats clinical disturbances of potassium metabolism, not in the context of discrete disease entities, but rather as physiologic derangements common to a whole variety of disease states.

In this volume, the processes regulating the distribution of potassium in the body are analyzed, and the mechanisms responsible for normal and abnormal apportionment between the cellular and extracellular fluid compartments are explored. Next, the factors underlying the long-range regulation and adjustments of the body potassium content are examined. Principally, this involves an analysis of the adaptive mechanisms of the kidney, with a small contribution from the colon. Finally, the spectrum of clinical syndromes of potassium deficiency and potassium excess and their consequences are considered.

The regulatory influences governing the internal distribution and renal clearance of potassium under normal circumstances and during pathologic distortion are increasingly reducible to physiologic analysis. The detailed examination of the principles determining potassium distribution and excretion presented herein will provide a rational framework to elucidate normal and disturbed potassium metabolism. We trust this will deepen the basic understanding of students of physiology, internal medicine, and urology, and broaden the diagnostic and therapeutic armamentarium of internists, nephrologists, and urologists who must grapple with these derangements.

Donald W. Seldin, M.D.
Gerhard Giebisch, M.D.

Contents

Contributors

Tomas Berl, M.D.
Professor of Medicine
Division of Renal Diseases
University of Colorado School of
Medicine
4200 East Ninth Avenue
Box C-281
Denver, Colorado 80262

Jeffrey S. Berns, M.D.
Section of Nephrology
Yale University School of Medicine
333 Cedar Street
New Haven, Connecticut 06510

David E. Clapham, M.D., Ph.D.
Assistant Professor of Pharmacology
Department of Pharmacology,
Physiology, and Biophysics
Guggenheim Bldg, 701
Mayo Foundation
Rochester, Minnesota 55905

Franklin H. Epstein, M.D.
William Applebaum Professor of
Medicine
Renal Division
Department of Medicine
Harvard Medical School and
Beth Israel Hospital
330 Brookline Avenue
Boston, Massachusetts 02215

Michael J. Field, M.D.
Senior Lecturer in Medicine
Department of Medicine
University of Sydney
Concord Hospital
New South Wales
2139 Sydney, Australia

Gerhard Giebisch, M.D.
Sterling Professor
Department of Cellular and Molecular
Physiology
Yale University School of Medicine
333 Cedar Street
New Haven, Connecticut 06510

William B. Guggino, Ph.D.
Associate Professor of Physiology
Department of Physiology
Johns Hopkins University/School of
Medicine
725 North Wolfe Street
Baltimore, Maryland 21205

John P. Hayslett, M.D.
Professor of Medicine
Section of Nephrology
Department of Internal Medicine
Yale University School of Medicine
333 Cedar Street
New Haven, Connecticut 06510

James P. Knochel, M.D.
Professor of Internal Medicine
The University of Texas Southwestern
Medical Center
Chairman, Department of Internal
Medicine
Presbyterian Hospital of Dallas
8200 Walnut Hill Lane
Dallas, Texas, 75231

Stuart L. Linas, M.D.
Associate Professor of Medicine
Department of Medicine-Nephrology
University of Colorado Health Science
Center
777 Bannock Street
Denver, Colorado 80204

Lawrence G. Palmer, Ph.D.

Department of Physiology
Cornell University Medical College
1300 York Avenue
New York, New York 10021

Robert L. Ruff, M.D. Ph.D.

Associate Professor of Neurology
Case Western Reserve University
Chief of Neurology
Cleveland Veterans Administration
  Medical Center
10701 East Boulevard
Cleveland, Ohio 44106

Victor L. Schuster, M.D.

Department of Internal Medicine and
  Veterans Administration Medical
  Center
University of Iowa
Iowa City, Iowa 52242

Donald W. Seldin, M.D.

William Buchanan and Systems
  Professor of Internal Medicine
Department of Internal Medicine
The University of Texas Southwestern
  Medical Center at Dallas
5323 Harry Hines Boulevard
Dallas, Texas 75235-9030

John B. Stokes, M.D.

Professor of Internal Medicine
Director, Division of Nephrology
College of Medicine
University of Iowa
Iowa City, Iowa 52242

Louis Tobian, Jr., M.D.

Professor of Medicine
Chief, Hypertension Section
Department of Internal Medicine
University of Minnesota Hospital
420 Delaware Street, S.E.
Minneapolis, Minnesota 55455

Christopher S. Wilcox, M.D., Ph.D.

Professor of Medicine, Pharmacology
  and Therapeutics
Division of Nephrology Hypertension
  and Transplantation
Department of Medicine, Pharmacology
  and Therapeutics
University of Florida College of
  Medicine
JHMHC Box J-224
Gainesville, Florida 32610

Mark E. Williams, M.D.

Renal Division
Department of Medicine
Joslin Diabetes Center
Harvard Medical School
1 Joslin Place
Boston, Massachusetts 02215

Normal Potassium Metabolism

The Regulation of Potassium Balance, edited
by Donald W. Seldin and Gerhard Giebisch,
Raven Press, Ltd., New York © 1989.

1

Internal Exchanges of Potassium

*Mark E. Williams and **Franklin H. Epstein

*Department of Medicine, Renal Division, Harvard Medical School,
*New England Deaconess Hospital, **Beth Israel Hospital,
Boston, Massachusetts 02215*

Internal potassium homeostasis may be defined as the regulation of potassium distribution between the intracellular and extracellular fluid compartments, apart from net gain or loss of body potassium. Just as the kidney plays the predominant role in maintaining external potassium balance, this term acknowledges that nonrenal tissues, chiefly skeletal muscle and liver, are quantitatively the primary organs involved in the regulation of internal potassium balance.

The ratio of potassium between intracellular and extracellular fluids is important not only to the behavior of electrically excitable cells, such as muscle and nerve, but also to the vital processes of all cells. These processes are regulated in large part by their cellular membrane potential, a function of the Goldman-Hodgkin-Katz equation; its most important term is the logarithm of the internal to external ionic activity of potassium.

POTASSIUM DISTRIBUTION AND FACTORS THAT PRESERVE IT (26,30)

Of the 3,500 mEq of potassium found in the body of a 70 kg human, about 98% is confined to intracellular water (Fig. 1). Of this, 80% is contained in muscle cells, at a concentration of about 150 mEq/liter. The remaining 2% of total body potassium (about 70 mEq) is located in the extracellular fluid (about 14 liters), where the normal concentration is 3.5 to 5.5 mEq/liter. The chief biologic mechanism maintaining this 30-fold potassium gradient between cell water and extracellular fluid is the Na,K-ATPase pump, situated in the plasma membrane of all animal cells. Transcellular distribution of potassium is modulated also by hormonal factors, such as insulin, catecholamines, and aldosterone, by hydrogen ion balance, plasma osmolality, intracellular potassium

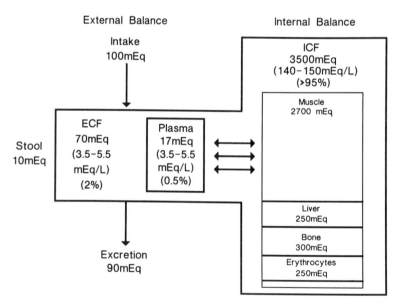

FIG. 1. Internal potassium homeostasis in a 70 kg person. The potassium concentration in the extracellular fluid (ECF) depends on both the external balance (intake and output) and the internal balance (distribution between extracellular and intracellular fluid, ICF). Factors affecting internal balance are listed in Table 1. Note that the large IC pool exists at a far greater potassium concentration than the small EC pool. The EC pool will, therefore, change more dramatically with changes in total body potassium or potassium distribution.

TABLE 1. *Factors affecting internal potassium homeostasis*

Factor	Effect on potassium
Insulin	Enhanced cell uptake
β-Catecholamines	Enhanced cell uptake
α-Catecholamines	Impaired cell uptake
Acidosis	Impaired cell uptake[a]
Alkalosis	Enhanced cell uptake[a]
External potassium balance	Loose correlation
Drugs	*See text*
Hyperosmolarity	Enhanced cell efflux

[a]Degree varies with disturbance.

content, and to a degree by factors that affect net cellular potassium flux, such as the calcium channel (Table 1). Some of these factors, such as Na, K-ATPase, aldosterone, and hydrogen ion balance, may concurrently affect the potassium activity in cells of the distal nephron, thereby influencing potassium secretion and its external balance.

Since the intracellular potassium concentration far exceeds its extracellular concentration, percentile changes in the concentration within cells will be relatively small even during extreme degrees of total body potassium surfeit, deficit, or internal redistribution. In living animal cells, therefore, the membrane potential will be determined largely by the extracellular concentration of potassium. For this reason, a variety of factors may act to preserve that concentration in the extracellular fluid.

For example, changes in extracellular potassium content equal to only 1% of total body potassium (35 mEq), if confined to the extracellular space, would alter the plasma potassium concentration by about 2.5 mEq/liter, enough to produce pronounced effects on neuromuscular function. It is well known, however, that a potassium load given to a normal human or dog has an apparent volume of distribution of 60% to 70% of body weight, roughly equivalent to total body water, instead of 20%, which represents extracellular fluid. In other words, of 35 mEq of retained potassium, only a small portion (about one quarter) will normally remain extracellular, raising its concentration by only about 1 mEq/liter. In contrast, a similar load of potassium administered to patients with deranged potassium homeostasis may produce life-threatening hyperkalemia.

In the acute defense against hyperkalemia, this internal disposal of potassium is of vital importance. It should be emphasized that even normal subjects will excrete only half of an orally or intravenously administered potassium load over 3 hr, the rest requiring extrarenal disposal within cells. Likewise, in states of progressive potassium deficit as depletion becomes more severe, more and more potassium is lost from within cells to protect the plasma concentration of potassium and to minimize alteration in its intracellular/extracellular ratio.

These examples of potassium surfeit or deficit demonstrate the homeostatic role of extrarenal factors in modulating potentially dangerous changes in plasma potassium. Of increasing clinical importance, however, is the variety of disorders related to the extrarenal factors themselves. Such disturbances are the primary topic of this chapter.

INSULIN (3,16,19)

It is not widely appreciated that insulin's effect on potassium homeostasis was first demonstrated just 2 years after its purification; serum potassium fell coincident with lowering of blood sugar when insulin was administered to diabetic patients as well as in the nondiabetic human, dog, and rabbit. Despite rare reports of severe hypokalemia in insulin-treated patients with ketoacidosis who developed paralysis, the effect of insulin on ion transport was not thoroughly investigated until the past two decades.

Cellular Mechanisms

It is accepted now that the hypokalemic action of insulin derives from its capacity to cause net potassium uptake in skeletal muscle and hepatic cells, as well as other extrarenal sites. This effect formerly was assumed to occur to preserve electrical neutrality when insulin-mediated glucose uptake produced intracellular anionic sugars.

This classic hypothesis did not explain the clinical observation that sudden lowering of serum potassium could precede the fall in blood sugar in insulin-treated diabetic coma. Furthermore, the effect of insulin on potassium movement in rat muscle occurred even in the absence of glucose; its known effect to increase sodium efflux *in vitro* also occurred without glucose. Furthermore, enhancement of potassium disposal in the intact animal was separable temporally from glucose uptake and occurred at plasma insulin concentrations having no measurable influence on uptake of glucose *in vivo*. There appear to be different receptor mechanisms for potassium and glucose transport.

In vitro, insulin is known to stimulate both potassium uptake and sodium efflux in frog and rat muscle preparations. Similar effects have been reported in rat adipose tissue and hepatocytes.

Considerable evidence, critically reviewed by Moore, suggests that, after binding to cell surface receptors, insulin accelerates monovalent cation transport by stimulating Na,K-ATPase, the sodium-potassium pump. Most convincing is the fact that both insulin-stimulated net sodium efflux and potassium influx are blocked by ouabain. *In vitro*, addition of insulin to purified plasma membrane of skeletal muscle increases the activity of the Na,K-ATPase. It remains to be determined if insulin activation of other cellular transport mechanisms, such as sodium-hydrogen exchange sensitive to amiloride, is important to sodium pump-mediated potassium uptake. Little evidence is available currently on whether insulin affects potassium permeability or potassium channels in cells.

Stimulation of active sodium-potassium transport by Na,K-ATPase could be due to a *de novo* increase in the number of sodium pump sites or to allosteric activation of existing sites. The latter theory is consistent with the rapid activation of transport that occurs and with the lack of new ouabain binding sites after exposure to insulin *in vitro*. In the rat adipocyte, a coupling to glucose transporter vesicles that undergo translocation has been suggested.

At least two molecular forms of the Na,K-ATPase catalytic subunit have been identified, named α and $\alpha(+)$. The $\alpha(+)$ subunit, present in muscle cells and adipocytes but not liver, is activated by insulin. In liver, on the other hand, the effect of insulin can be entirely accounted for by increased intracellular sodium concentration.

It should be noted that insulin is known to produce hyperpolarization of cellular membranes not only in skeletal muscle but in a variety of other tissues as well. This rapid effect appears to precede measurable increases in intracellular potassium. Although stimulation of Na,K-ATPase could account for insulin's hyperpolarizing effect, failure of ouabain to block it, at least in some studies, suggests that changes in ion permeability may be responsible. The role of hyperpolarization in mediating insulin effects on cation transport is uncertain.

In Vivo Effects

Abundant evidence exists, therefore, that insulin increases net uptake of potassium ions by several tissues *in vitro*. Since skeletal muscle is well documented to respond to insulin and is the major body reservoir for potassium, it is the most likely dominant site for insulin-stimulated extrarenal potassium disposal *in vivo*. Human forearm muscle (and adipose tissue) increase potassium uptake during arterial infusion of insulin.

It was noted a half century ago that injected potassium rapidly disappeared from the blood of cats but was followed by a secondary rise in serum potassium. Recent investigation suggests that, at least during insulin infusion, hepatic disposal plays an important role in potassium homeostasis in the first hour of exposure to insulin in humans. Splanchnic uptake accounted for two thirds of the fall in plasma potassium during euglycemic hyperinsulinemia. In the second hour, net splanchnic uptake reversed, and peripheral tissues became the dominant site of potassium disposal.

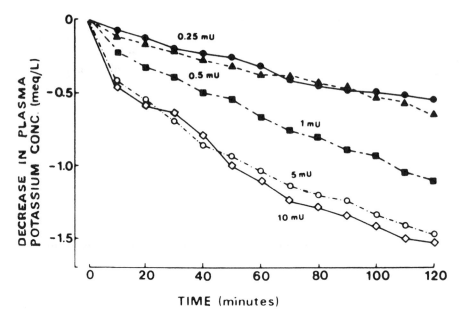

FIG. 2. Dose-related effect of euglycemic hyperinsulinemia on plasma potassium concentration. Infusion of insulin at the doses shown produced plasma insulin levels of approximately 25, 50, 100, 500, and 1,000 μU/ml above basal values. (From ref. 3.)

That the effect of insulin on extrarenal potassium homeostasis is dose-related is well established (Fig. 2). In normal subjects, neither intramuscular nor subcutaneous administration of insulin, which achieved plasma insulin levels of about 50 μU/ml, decreased the plasma potassium. Intravenous insulin injection, by comparison, produced 40-fold greater insulin levels, which were accompanied by steady state reduction in plasma potassium, with a maximal effect of about 30% occurring 50 min after insulin injection. On the other hand, much smaller increments of insulin, about threefold above basal values, during constant venous or intraarterial infusion also appear capable of augmenting potassium uptake *in vivo*.

Clinical Implications

The relevance of these findings to a given clinical situation will depend on the magnitude of potassium load requiring disposal and the elevation of insulin accompanying it. Following carbohydrate feeding, for example, increased liver uptake of potassium occurs. Since peripheral venous insulin levels for 2 hr after oral glucose loading are elevated fivefold, well within the range capable of augmenting potassium uptake, it seems likely that insulin contributes to the transient decrease in potassium that occurs in the fed state.

Because carbohydrate is not the primary source of dietary potassium, however, it is of note that even basal circulating insulin levels may be essential to disposal of an acute potassium load, since disposal is impaired when basal levels are decreased 50% by somatostatin.

During exogenous potassium challenge, the importance of insulin to potassium disposal by the intact organism deprived of endogenous insulin is well established. As expected, supraphysiologic doses of exogenous insulin are capable of restoring potassium tolerance to normal.

The ability of potassium loading to stimulate the release of pancreatic insulin directly, in amounts sufficient to contribute to disposal of that potassium, is less clear. *In vitro*, only supraphysiologic increments in potassium concentration appear to stimulate insulin release from perfused rat pancreas or incubated rabbit pancreatic slices. In humans and intact dogs, in contrast, minor increments in blood potassium appear capable of triggering pancreatic insulin secretion. Since elevations in portal venous insulin far exceed those in the peripheral circulation when insulin release is stimulated, it seems reasonable to conclude that, under conditions of significant hyperkalemia, induction of insulin release to promote potassium uptake constitutes a homeostatic feedback control system.

CATECHOLAMINES AND POTASSIUM HOMEOSTASIS (5,7,10,29)

The old observation that epinephrine lowers serum potassium in animals recently has gained new physiologic and clinical relevance. Although the rapid rise in serum potassium that followed a bolus injection of epinephrine in cats (now thought to be due to transient hepatic discharge of potassium by alpha-adrenergic stimulation), was initially emphasized, of greater significance was the sustained "after fall" in plasma potassium that he observed. The secondary decrease in potassium was found later to last throughout a 1 hr infusion of epinephrine.

Since epinephrine inhibited the renal excretion of potassium, its late hypokalemic action was attributed to net uptake of potassium by extrarenal tissues. Tissue analysis and ion flux studies supported accelerated uptake of potassium, primarily in skeletal muscle but also in heart, in response to epinephrine. *In vitro*, epinephrine was shown to stimulate potassium uptake as well as sodium efflux by isolated skeletal muscle. A similar effect was present in rat diaphragm, cat cardiac muscle, and frog sartorius but not frog cardiac muscle.

Because epinephrine may induce insulin secretion indirectly in response to concomitant changes in peripheral glucose metabolism, it was necessary to show that its hypokalemic action was independent of insulin. Independence from renin-mediated aldosterone release was established by lowering of potassium despite nephrectomy. Since extrarenal potassium disposal was impaired when nephrectomized rats were subjected to adrenalectomy or to chemical sympathectomy, both circulating adrenomedullary epinephrine and peripheral sympathetic nervous activity appeared to be important sources of sympathetic influence on potassium.

Beta-Adrenergic Effects of Epinephrine

Epinephrine itself had been shown many years earlier to stimulate both alpha- and beta-adrenergic receptors. The conclusion that its hypokalemic action was a result of beta-adrenergic receptor stimulation derived from analysis using beta agonists and antagonists. Isoproterenol, a nonspecific beta agonist, reproduced the prolonged hypokalemia earlier observed by D'Silva, and this effect was reversed by the beta-adrenergic antagonist, propranolol. Likewise, epinephrine's effects on cation flux were blocked by beta antagonists.

More specifically, agonists and antagonists recently have been used to establish that the stimulating effect of catecholamines on potassium uptake is mediated by the $beta_2$ receptor subtype. Epinephrine effects are prevented by the presence of nonselective beta antagonists, such as propranolol and timolol, as well as by the nonspecific alpha-beta blocker, labetolol. Less reversal occurs with the partially $beta_1$ selective antagonists, metoprolol and atenolol. No effect on potassium appears to be produced by the more specific $beta_1$ antagonist, practolol. In addition, the selective $beta_2$ antagonists, butoxamine and ICI-118551, are able to block the hypokalemic action of beta agonists.

Investigation of beta agonists has revealed that several $beta_2$ agonists, including salbutamol and terbutaline, lower serum potassium, unlike the $beta_1$ agonist, ITP, which has no effect. These pharmacologic studies, therefore, provide current support for $beta_2$ mediation of adrenergic effects to enhance potassium disposal.

Mechanisms of Action

The specific cellular mechanism by which cell surface $beta_2$ receptor stimulation augments transcellular potassium uptake in affected tissues has been evaluated in detail in recent years. Considerable support is now given to the proposal of Clausen that $beta_2$ stimulation initiates cyclic adenosine monophosphate (AMP) formation, which leads to activation of the sodium pump (Na,K-ATPase) and, therefore, electrogenic sodium efflux accompanied by potassium uptake. Beta receptors are known to produce their effects by stimulation of adenylate cyclase, enhancing conversion of intracellular adenosine triphosphate (ATP) to cyclic AMP. Linkage of beta receptors and cyclic AMP is supported by the ability of theophylline to potentiate the effect of epinephrine on cation transport and membrane potential, as well as by the increase in membrane potential that dibutyryl cyclic AMP and theophylline produce in rat diaphragm muscle. Epinephrine, in stimulating cation transport, is well known to cause hyperpolarization of membranes in skeletal muscle.

The sodium pump of muscle cells and lipocytes is known to be activated by cyclic AMP; for example, Na,K-ATPase activity in smooth muscle membrane fragments is enhanced by exposure to cyclic AMP. The facts that catecholamine-mediated potassium influx involves active movement of the cation against its electrochemical gradient and that ouabain blocks the ability of epinephrine to promote potassium influx strongly suggest that the sodium pump mediates beta-adrenergic effects on ion transport. The specific sequence of events linking beta stimulation to sodium pump activity remains unclear but presumably involves phosphorylation of some portion of the sodium pump after beta$_2$ receptor stimulation.

There are numerous clinical examples showing that enhanced exogenous or endogenous beta stimulation produces lowering of potassium levels. However, whether or not high potassium levels can stimulate secretion of endogenous adrenomedullary epinephrine, forming a homeostatic feedback loop, is unknown. At supraphysiologic levels *in vitro*, potassium can release catecholamines from isolated chromaffin cells and perfused adrenal glands, possibly related to the membrane depolarizing effect of high levels of potassium. Induction of tyrosine hydroxylase, the rate-limiting enzyme in catecholamine biosynthesis, by extremely high levels of potassium also has been observed. Reports that intraarterial injections of KCl augment catecholamine release in cats or, more recently, in the dog fish shark suggest a potential role for potassium as a catecholamine secretagogue *in vivo*.

Although specific stimulation of catecholamine release by potassium is not yet established, it seems clear that physiologic elevations of endogenous catecholamines, released in a variety of circumstances, do enhance cellular potassium uptake. Similar to the pharmacologic doses of epinephrine used in earlier animal reports of its protective effect during potassium loading as well as of its ability to lower basal potassium, relatively small doses in more recent human studies from our laboratory and elsewhere also have been shown to enhance potassium disposal. More recently, it has become clear that ambient potassium may be lowered when sustained epinephrine infusions (Fig. 3) elevate plasma concentrations of epinephrine to levels no higher than those observed in stressful conditions, such as myocardial infarction, surgical stress, and diabetic ketoacidosis. In comparison, acute beta blockade does not appear to elevate fasting potassium levels, suggesting that basal beta-adrenergic tone may play a limited role in potassium homeostasis in normal fasted individuals at rest.

The importance of the beta-adrenergic system, however, in disposal of excess potassium has been established by numerous observations. Potassium

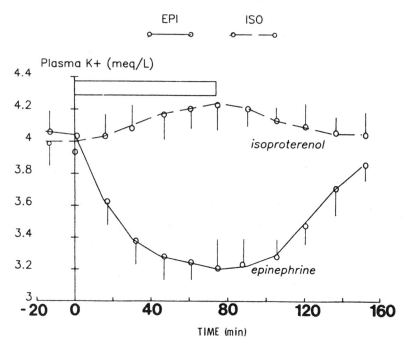

FIG. 3. Effect of epinephrine and isoproterenol infusions (long box) on the plasma potassium concentration. The contrasting effects of the two beta-agonists probably are due to the relative beta$_2$ selectivity of epinephrine at the dose given. Plasma epinephrine concentrations achieved by infusion were similar to those known to occur in myocardial infarction and other disorders. (From ref. 5.)

tolerance is increased in animals injected with beta agonists. It is also known that beta stimulation with epinephrine enhances disposal of an intravenous potassium load by normal human volunteers. Recently appreciated are two common physiologic circumstances in which endogenous catecholamines could act to defend against increments in plasma potassium. The first is postprandial disposal of dietary potassium. Feeding is associated with stimulation of the sympathetic nervous system. Since only half of the potassium ingested in a meal is excreted normally within 6 hr, enhanced beta-adrenergic-mediated extrarenal potassium disposal may help to limit elevations of serum potassium in the postprandial period. Along with enhanced potassium uptake due to insulin, this mechanism would be particularly important in subjects at risk for hyperkalemia for any reason.

The second example is the dramatic effect of catecholamines released during vigorous exertion to moderate the acute physiologic hyperkalemia of exercise. This short-term elevation of potassium, released into the circulation from working muscle, is exaggerated by beta blockade (Fig. 4), suggesting that endogenous beta-adrenergic activity does protect against extreme hyper-

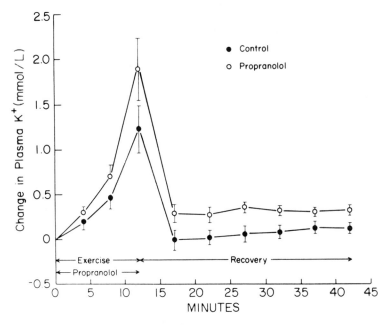

FIG. 4. Effect of adrenergic blockade on the plasma potassium concentration during vigorous exercise and recovery. Beta blockade with propranolol potentiated the rise of plasma potassium at peak exercise and prolonged its elevation during recovery. In the same subjects, alpha-blockade with phentolamine was shown to lower the peak plasma potassium level as well as the overall potassium curve. (From ref. 29.)

kalemia during exhaustive exercise. It has been well documented that catecholamines circulate in high levels during exercise.

Alpha-Adrenergic Effects

The fact that opposing beta- and alpha-adrenergic influences have in the past been reported on smooth muscle tone, glucoregulatory hormones, presynaptic membrane receptors, and changes in intracellular second messengers has warranted recent investigation into the role of alpha-adrenergics in potassium homeostasis in our laboratory. As noted previously, the early rise in plasma potassium emphasized by D'Silva in 1934 was later attributed to alpha-mediated hepatic potassium release by the mixed alpha and beta agonist epinephrine. This initial rise in potassium could be prevented by alpha blockade. In addition, phenylephrine, a pure alpha agonist, was observed to cause a sustained increase in potassium in dogs.

When we infused phenylephrine into normal human subjects who were challenged with an intravenous potassium load, the overall rise in plasma potassium was augmented by about 50% despite no change in urinary potassium, insulin, renin, or aldosterone. In separate studies, addition of the alpha antagonist, phentolamine, blocked the phenylephrine effect on potassium disposal. Neither alpha stimulation nor blockade appeared to affect the concentration of potassium in the absence of potassium loading.

Other evidence suggests that the alpha effect might contribute directly to potassium homeostasis in some circumstances. Alpha receptor stimulation during vigorous exercise contributes to the acute rise in potassium, which is maximal at peak exercise, as well as limiting the dramatic fall due to potassium re-uptake during recovery. During potassium depletion in rats, the sodium-potassium pump of skeletal muscle is suppressed by alpha-adrenergic receptors, an action that would mitigate the expected fall in plasma potassium concentration. It is speculated that enhanced alpha agonist activity might act to preserve potassium similarly during a variety of acute illnesses, such as myocardial infarction or delerium tremens, where catecholamine stimulation of both beta and alpha receptors may coexist. Whether unopposed stimulation of alpha receptors contributes to the impairment of potassium dispoal caused by beta receptor blockade remains to be determined.

Acute Illness

The clinical significance of epinephrine-induced hypokalemia is underscored by reports of hypokalemia during acute illnesses, such as myocardial infarction, as well as during medical treatment with beta agonists. For example, epinephrine infusion, producing circulating epinephrine levels similar to those found after myocardial infarction, lowers the serum potassium from 4.06 mEq/liter to 3.22 mEq/liter in normal volunteers. This ability of small doses of epinephrine to diminish potassium levels has been confirmed by Brown et al. In several studies, the frequency of hypokalemia during acute myocardial infarction has been observed to be 15% to 30%. Concomitant diuretic therapy may increase the frequency of hypokalemia during myocardial infarction as it appears to do in normal subjects who are infused experimentally with epinephrine.

Moreover, several studies have suggested that hypokalemia is an independent risk factor for cardiac arrhythmias in patients with acute myocardial infarction. Although a higher incidence of atrial fibrillation was first observed, several recent studies have reported an increased incidence of ventricular arrhythmias in hypokalemic compared to normokalemic subjects during infarction. In one report, ventricular tachycardia or fibrillation increased threefold (to 35%) and hospital mortality doubled in hypokalemic patients with myocardial infarction.

It must be appreciated, however, that hypokalemia reported during earlier studies of epinephrine infusion occurred when high concentrations of plasma epinephrine were sustained by infusion. It is unclear if elevations of plasma epinephrine during acute myocardial infarction are similarly sustained rather than transient. The contribution of circulating epinephrine to the hypokalemia that may occur during this form of acute illness, therefore, remains hypothetical. Nonetheless, pharmacologic data suggest that such acutely ill patients may be protected from the hypokalemia associated with myocardial infarction by use of beta blockade. It is not known if the beneficial effect of beta blockade reported in this setting is due to diminution in hypokalemia-related arrhythmias.

Transient lowering of potassium levels has been reported recently in other acute medical conditions in which catecholamines might stimulate beta-adrenergic receptors capable of increasing potassium uptake by cells. Pharmacologic therapy using beta$_2$ agonists, such as terbutaline, salbutamol, or albuterol, in treatment of bronchospasm and to prevent premature labor may produce unwanted lowering of potassium. Even subcutaneous bronchodilator therapy may lower potassium acutely in asthmatics. In aerosolized form, no effect appears to occur, at least in normal subjects.

Beta-Adrenergic Blockade

The clinical significance of alpha-adrenergics in potassium balance is evident in the well-established effect of beta antagonists alone to elevate plasma potassium. Already noted is the acute effect of propranolol in exaggerating the hyperkalemia of vigorous exercise. Some but not all investigators have reported a 10% to 15% increase in ambient plasma potassium during chronic beta blockade with nonselective agents. In addition, one study suggests that serum potassium may rise above 6 mEq/liter in patients on nonselective beta blockers at the time of open heart surgery. Another study suggests that hemodialysis patients demonstrate a significant increase in predialysis ambient serum potassium with the addition of propranolol. Patients receiving succinylcholine anesthesia also may be at risk.

A few studies substantiate the anticipated absence of effect on potassium of cardioselective beta$_1$ antagonists. Selected groups at risk for hyperkalemia, such as diabetics, patients with hypoaldosteronism, or those with renal failure, might be protected from significant elevations in potassium due to beta blockade by use of cardioselective agents.

Beta Agonists for Hyperkalemia

The beneficial effect of beta agonists in lowering serum potassium in the treatment and prevention of hyperkalemic periodic paralysis is now firmly established. In this condition, episodic muscle weakness is associated with hyperkalemia resulting from release of potassium from skeletal muscle, a condition presumably counteracted by therapeutic beta-mediated stimulation of potassium uptake. A similar role of acute beta agonist therapy in the medical management of severe hyperkalemia in other conditions awaits formal evaluation.

ALDOSTERONE (9,13,25)

Aldosterone, unlike catecholamines or insulin, affects potassium homeostasis primarily by increasing its urinary excretion. No significant extrarenal role of aldosterone in potassium homeostasis has been established. Four factors, however, hinder interpretation of published studies on aldosterone and internal potassium balance: (a) its dominant effect of producing potassium depletion by causing kaliuresis, (b) the concomitant removal of adrenal medullary epinephrine in studies of adrenalectomized animals, (c) the excessive mineralocorticoid doses used in many studies, and (d) failure to consider the mineralocorticoid influence on acid-base balance. Both potassium depletion and alkalosis, for example, are known to alter internal potassium balance.

Extrarenal Effects

The ability of a few extrarenal tissues to respond to mineralocorticoid has been demonstrated adequately. Both human salivary and sweat glands respond to aldosterone administration by increasing the potassium content of their secretions. Likewise, it is well known that mineralocorticoids augment colonic losses of potassium. The overall contribution of these effects to normal potassium homeostasis, is, however, minute.

In extrarenal tissues vital to internal potassium balance, no consistent effects of aldosterone have been found. *In vitro* studies of skeletal muscle have produced conflicting results on the ability of aldosterone to increase muscle potassium content by enhancing muscle potassium uptake. Little is known about mineralocorticoid effects on electrolyte transport in the liver.

Both epinephrine, from the adrenal medulla, and aldosterone, from the cortex, are removed by adrenalectomy. Since epinephrine is now recognized as promoting extrarenal potassium uptake, a series of investigations using adrenalectomized models now appears more difficult to interpret than when epinephrine effects were unacknowledged. Earlier studies in both humans and animals, suggesting that decreased renal potassium excretion did not fully account for the postadrenalectomy rise in potassium concentration, did not separately evaluate the effects of removal of aldosterone and epinephrine. Likewise, extrarenal adaptation to potassium, which is abolished by adrenalectomy, need not be attributed solely to aldosterone.

A role for aldosterone in extrarenal disposal of a potassium load has been suggested in adrenalectomized rats replaced with aldosterone, although supraphysiologic doses were used and fecal losses were not measured to help localize the target site involved.

Several animal studies have suggested that both deoxycorticosterone acetate and aldosterone administration can produce a fall in plasma potassium unrelated to increased urinary potassium excretion. These results, however, are complicated by the large doses of hormone used and by the failure to evaluate changes in acid-base balance. Aldosterone administration results in a greater portion of potassium in the body being located within cells; suggestive of internal potassium redistribution, this effect may occur during potassium depletion from any cause, during which a greater proportion of extracellular potassium is lost than of potassium lost from within cells.

Aldosterone Secretion

Despite the difficulty in demonstrating any aldosterone effect on internal potassium balance, there is little disagreement that in animals and in man, potassium is an aldosterone secretagogue. An increase in serum potassium, produced by enteral potassium loading, is known to increase aldosterone excretion in dogs. This effect of potassium has since been established *in vivo* in normal humans and *in vitro* in adrenal cortical slices and is independent of the accompanying anion. Physiologic increments in potassium concentration (<0.5 mEq/liter) produced by oral or intravenous potassium administration appear adequate to enhance aldosterone secretion, and this effect may be sustained well after the period of potassium loading. Furthermore, aldosterone production can be related directly to the intracellular potassium content of the adrenal cortex. The chief result, however, of this aldosterone response appears to be enhanced kaliuresis rather than extrarenal redistribution of potassium.

ACID-BASE (1,2,22,28)

Although acid-base balance alters renal potassium excretion, shifts of potassium across extrarenal cells are the initial mechanism by which acute acid-base disturbances affect serum potassium. It has become accepted increasingly that these fluxes derive from a variety of factors that depend not only on the primary acid-base disturbance but also in some cases on its specific etiology. Among these factors are blood pH, serum bicarbonate concentration, the anion that accompanies the hydrogen cation, and hormonal factors.

Hydrogen Ion

According to classic teaching, plasma potassium levels tend to vary directly with levels of the free hydrogen ion concentration, so that acidosis promotes hyperkalemia and alkalosis promotes hypokalemia. Early studies demonstrated the importance of pH itself in internal potassium distribution during acidosis. Potassium was shown to exit from skeletal muscle *in vitro* when the bathing medium pH was lowered, yet move into the tissue when blood, at physiologic pH, was substituted for the acidic medium. The Donnan equilibrium was involved to account for similarity in the intracellular/extracellular ratios of hydrogen and potassium ions, so that a decrease in that ratio produced by acidosis would be associated with a decrease in the ratio for potassium, i.e., an extracellular increase. An alternate mechanism, the simple exchange of hydrogen and potassium ions moving in opposite directions, seemed less likely.

That acidosis did elevate the plasma potassium concentration was thereafter supported by studies in dogs and humans, although no study measured cellular pH. In addition, several lines of evidence, reviewed by Adrogue and Madias, appear to refute any simple relationship between concentration ratios of hydrogen and potassium ions. These include tissue differences in ion movements during acidosis and dissociation of hydrogen and potassium fluxes *in vitro* and *in vivo*.

Consistent with this complex interrelationship is the poor correlation in acidemic and alkalemic states between blood pH and serum potassium concentration. The axiom that decrements in blood pH of 0.1 pH unit produce predictable 0.6 mEq/liter increases in serum potassium derived from average values in a single study of five patients with different acid-base disorders, originally a qualitative observation. Several studies support a more variable relationship between pH and serum potassium.

The importance of pH *per se* is diminished by the fact that the effect of acute respiratory acidosis in elevating potassium is much smaller in magnitude than that of metabolic acidosis, although an effect is generally present. In anephric dogs, the effect on potassium is initially small but, after 2 hr of respiratory acidosis, may increase to the range observed with metabolic acidosis.

Anion

That changes in acidity are not the sole determinant of the kalemic response to acidosis has been suggested by the disparate effects that mineral and nonmineral acidoses have on potassium. In humans and animals, infusion of organic acids produces far smaller elevations of potassium than does infusion of hydrochloric acid. The prevailing hypothesis is that the anions of organic acids, either by readily penetrating the intracellular compartment, by entering cells as intact molecules, or by being formed endogenously within cells, minimize the necessity for potassium cations to leave cells in exchange for hydrogen ions. Clinical observations on the endogenous mineral acidosis of uremia due to retention of sulfate and phosphate suggest that the change in potassium when acidosis is corrected is of the magnitude seen in experimental mineral acidosis.

In contrast, infusion of such organic acids as acetic, lactic, or beta-hydroxy-butyric acid produces a smaller kalemic response and, unlike hydrochloric acid, appears to cause no efflux of potassium from cells. One reason for this may be that ketone acids stimulate the secretion of insulin by the normal pancreas while suppressing the secretion of glucagon. Infusions of hydrochloric acid, on the other hand, do not stimulate insulin secretion but enhance plasma glucagon. For similar degrees of clinical severity, less elevation of serum potassium occurs with the endogenous organic acidoses, although the correlation of pH and serum potassium in these disorders is further complicated by prior total body potassium depletion, oliguric renal failure, hyper-catabolism, and other factors. Recent evidence in dogs suggests that moderately severe potassium depletion (as occurs in diabetic ketoacidosis) itself attenuates the increase in plasma potassium induced by metabolic acidosis.

Untreated severe diabetic ketoacidosis, for example, is characterized by marked deficits (200–300 mEq) in total body potassium, due primarily to coincident potassium losses from the gastrointestinal tract or kidneys. Despite those losses, hypokalemia is uncommon, present in only 4% of episodes in one series. Serum potassium is usually normal or elevated.

Since insulin plays a significant role in cellular shifts of potassium, insulin lack plays an important role in internal potassium homeostasis during keto-acidosis, as it does in patients with hyperosmolar nonketotic coma, who may have severe hyperkalemia without acidosis.

Similar to uncontrolled diabetes, several factors in lactic acidosis complicate the effect of acidemia *per se* on serum potassium. These include volume depletion, prerenal azotemia, hypercatabolism, concomitant diabetes, and external potassium imbalance. Although severe hyperkalemia is unusual in lactic acidosis, Perez et al. have brought attention to the absence of detailed studies on potassium homeostasis in this varied disorder. In experimental lactic acid infusion in animals and in uncomplicated postseizure lactic acidosis in humans, potassium does not increase with the appearance of acidosis. However, in other forms of lactic acidosis, such as those earlier encountered due to phenformin therapy in diabetes and other forms not associated with tissue hypoxia, mild elevation of potassium may occur. Renal insufficiency may be a contributing factor.

Patients with alcoholic ketoacidosis appear to have, as a group, a normal extracellular potassium, although significant variability exists.

The effects of rarer forms of organic acidosis on internal potassium homeostasis have been reviewed in detail by Perez et al.

Bicarbonate

Recent evidence suggests that the serum bicarbonate concentration, even at constant or isohydric pH, alters extrarenal potassium distribution and might account, in part, for the weak correlation of pH and serum potassium in many studies. Under conditions of constant blood pH, infusion of sodium bicarbonate appears to lower serum potassium, and during acidosis in rats, potassium may correlate better with serum bicarbonate than with blood pH. A similar correlation can be found in patients with hyperkalemia of diverse etiologies and in experimental acute ammonium chloride acidosis. This has been taken to indicate that bicarbonate therapy, in addition to beneficially raising pH, corrects hyperkalemia directly, perhaps via intracellular transfer with the potassium cation.

Another explanation of the same data is that it is the quantity of acid buffered by cells rather than the arterial pH that governs the release of intracellular potassium. This would account for the fact that the ratio of rise in serum potassium to fall in blood pH is inconstant from one experiment to another but tends to be higher later in the course of an acute acid load, when the reserve of cellular buffers has been exhausted. The same considerations would explain why extracellular bicarbonate, rather than arterial pH, sometimes seems to exert an independent controlling influence on extracellular potassium. Effective buffering of an acid load by intracellular and extracellular buffers, so as to produce a low serum bicarbonate and a normal arterial pH, would involve the liberation of substantial amounts of potassium cations from intracellular proteins.

Other Factors in Acidosis

In addition to pH, the type of accompanying anion, and the serum bicarbonate concentration, other factors may influence the impact of acid-base balance on extrarenal potassium. These include changes in adrenergic activity, as may occur with acute respiratory acidosis, and, as recently described during experimental ketoacidosis, effects on pancreatic secretion of both insulin and glucagon.

Alkalemia

Alkalemia is a common cause of hypokalemia; both metabolic and respiratory alkalemias cause changes in potassium, although of smaller magnitude than is seen with metabolic acidosis. The predominant cause of hypokalemia in metabolic alkalosis is negative external potassium balance, although, experimentally, alkalosis provokes a rapid decrease in potassium levels not attributable to kaliuresis.

In respiratory alkalosis, a transient initial increase in serum potassium of unclear origin is followed by hypokalemia comparable in magnitude to that of metabolic alkalosis. The importance of enhanced cellular potassium uptake has not been determined. As with metabolic alkalosis, however, the predominant mechanism appears to be negative external potassium balance, since an abrupt kaliuresis follows the onset of acute hypocapnia. Extreme hypocapneic alkalosis and hypokalemia, as seen in recently intubated patients who are overventilated, may produce serious cardiac arrhythmias.

RENAL FAILURE (4,6,11,14,18)

In healthy fasting subjects, the renal response to acute potassium loading is prompt, occurring within 3 hr, and complete, amounting to an 8 to 10-fold increase in fractional potassium clearance, adequate to return the subject to external potassium balance within 6 hr. As a result, the serum potassium level, which increases by about 1 mEq/liter for each mEq/kg body weight of potassium administered to healthy subjects, is restored to normal.

In chronic renal failure, the ability to excrete potassium is well maintained by an adaptive increase in fractional potassium excretion rates to levels near the maximal for normal subjects. However, the adapted, diseased kidney has little reserve with which to respond to increased potassium loads, which must then be retained and disposed of, at least initially, by extrarenal mechanisms.

Whether extrarenal potassium homeostasis might be similarly adapted in renal failure or might be, instead, defective, is unclear. In response to an oral potassium load, patients with chronic renal failure excrete only one-fourth to one-half the amount excreted by control subjects in 4 to 6 hr. Nonetheless, an exaggerated rise in serum potassium may not occur, suggesting normal or even enhanced extrarenal potassium disposal. A frequently cited human study with contradicting results failed to measure potassium excretion at a time when renal failure subjects had higher plasma potassium levels than did controls, after oral potassium loading. In a more recent study, anuric subjects had a greater increment in plasma potassium than normals following oral loading, consistent with impaired extrarenal disposal. However, higher basal plasma potassium levels in the renal failure group may have contributed to the exaggerated rise after oral loading.

With intravenous potassium loading, by comparison, a discernible extrarenal defect appears to emerge in rats and dogs with renal failure, although not present in all studies. These results suggest that a subtle extrarenal defect may exist but is exposed only by acute potassium loads critically dependent on extrarenal disposal.

Impaired cellular potassium uptake in renal failure could not be due to increased cellular potassium content or to high total body potassium, since both are normal or low in uremia. Nor does there appear to be peripheral resistance to insulin-mediated potassium uptake despite the known resistance to the action of insulin on glucose metabolism in renal failure. Fasting insulin levels usually are increased in renal failure. Although secretion after a glucose stimulus is enhanced, some data suggest that potassium-mediated insulin release might be impaired.

Catecholamines appear to circulate at normal levels in renal failure. However, the ability of beta-adrenergic stimulation to enhance potassium uptake normally has not been evaluated adequately. Metabolic acidosis, if present, could impair cellular potassium uptake; alkalinization has been shown to reverse this effect in anuric subjects.

Although renin production might be expected to be suppressed in patients with end-stage renal disease, it is normal or even elevated in many. Both hyperkalemia and restriction of salt appear to stimulate aldosterone production adequately (in patients who do not have isolated hyporeninemic hypoaldosteronism), and lowering of serum potassium suppresses aldosterone secretion normally.

The role of other factors in internal potassium balance in renal failure is unclear. Uremic suppression of Na,K-ATPase activity could explain low cellular potassium in several tissues, but no study has demonstrated that the improvement of the transport defect that occurs with dialysis results in enhanced extrarenal potassium disposal. It is unlikely that elevated glucagon levels in renal failure contribute to potassium intolerance.

EXTERNAL POTASSIUM BALANCE (20,24)

The purpose of this chapter is to review factors that affect internal, not external, potassium homeostasis. However, in some conditions, such as diabetic ketoacidosis, vomiting, or chronic renal failure, abnormalities of internal and external potassium homeostasis may coexist. Just as internal potassium homeostasis may affect its uptake and excretion by the kidney, it is important to recognize that its external balance, by altering cellular potassium content, can independently influence internal potassium homeostasis.

Potassium Depletion

The idealized curvilinear relationship between total body potassium and the serum potassium concentration (Fig. 5) was derived from a few measurements in hypokalemic patients with positive potassium balance during replacement therapy and from unpublished data on hyperkalemic humans and animals. It was supported by direct measurements of total body potassium in a few patients and has been confirmed more recently. Consistent with the rapid fall in serum potassium in the initial phases of potassium depletion are studies of muscle composition and membrane potential in animals indicating that in early stages of depletion, extracellular potassium loss is proportionately greater than loss of cellular potassium. Since only a small fraction of body potassium is extracellular, however, the quantity of potassium lost from the extracellular compartment is much smaller than that lost from inside cells.

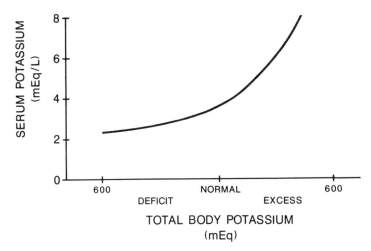

FIG. 5. Idealized relationship between the serum potassium concentration and the body potassium content. (From ref. 24.)

For example, patients in the early phases of hypokalemia (>2.5 mEq/liter) tend to display a linear relationship between total body potassium and the serum potassium concentration. It is observed that a change of 100 to 200 mEq in total body potassium (about 5%) is required to lower serum potassium by 1.0 mEq/liter. The extracellular potassium concentration would be expected to fall proportionately more (e.g., 4.0–3.0 mEq/liter) than the intracellular concentration (e.g., 140–125 mEq/liter). Because cell membrane potentials are based on the logarithm of the ratio of internal to external ionic activity of potassium (the Goldman-Hodgkin-Katz equation), excessive extracellular potassium loss would tend to hyperpolarize cells (resting membrane potential increases). This has been confirmed in studies of potassium-depleted dogs.

When potassium depletion becomes more severe so that serum levels fall below about 2.5 mEq/liter, a further 1.0 mEq/liter fall will represent a much larger 200 to 400 mEq decrement in total body potassium (greater than 10%), reflecting a greater increment of potassium loss from within cells than occurred in early phases of depletion. Decreased cell potassium content has been observed in several tissues during severe hypokalemia. Consistent with this, cells tend to depolarize (membrane potential is depressed) in dogs, and symptoms of weakness and muscle paralysis develop.

Potassium Repletion

During potassium repletion for severe hypokalemia, cellular potassium uptake is enhanced in both animals and humans, i.e., the administered potassium has an increased volume of distribution. As potassium is gained by the body and stores are higher, the cellular uptake of potassium decreases. In anuric humans, for example, cellular uptake of a potassium load decreases as total body potassium increases. More potassium then remains outside cells, and the membrane potential decreases. The important therapeutic caveat in the late phases of correction of potassium depletion is that less administered potassium is required to increase its serum concentration, which may rise suddenly to unexpected, hyperkalemic levels.

Nonetheless, as is apparent in the review by Sterns, the serum potassium alone is, at best, an extremely rough guide for estimating potassium replacement therapy, probably because other factors, such as acid-base status, influence it. A low serum potassium value (e.g., 3.0 mEq/liter) might be associated, in fact, with a range of total body deficits of a few hundred milliequivalents.

The exact mechanisms involved in this curvilinear relationship are unclear. The fall in membrane potential in severe hypokalemia might result from loss of selective potassium permeability of the muscle membrane or from impairment of the electrogenic sodium pump. During potassium depletion in rats, skeletal muscle potassium loss is associated with a reduced capacity for Na-K pumping and a reversible decrease in the number of ouabain binding sites. Hypokalemic suppression of insulin release could play a permissive role in the loss of cellular potassium during severe hypokalemia.

DRUGS (12,15,23,27)

Medications are the primary etiologic factor in as many as one third of cases of clinically significant hyperkalemia. Potassium supplements, potassium-sparing diuretics, and prostaglandin-suppressing drugs that induce hyporeninemic hypoaldosteronism account for most of these cases; relative to these, hyperkalemia due to drugs that alter internal potassium distribution would appear to be uncommon. As is true for drug-induced hyperkalemia in general, the risk of significant hyperkalemia is substantially increased in patients with diabetes mellitus, renal insufficiency, and hypoaldosteronism and in the elderly. In most other cases, the rise in potassium is mild.

Impaired Extrarenal Disposal

Hyperkalemia due to beta blockers, the most common medications that elevate potassium by extrarenal mechanisms, was discussed in an earlier section. A small, transient increase in serum potassium usually occurs in patients given depolarizing muscle relaxants, such as succinylcholine. Exaggerated increments, however, may occur in patients with central nervous system diseases, spinal cord injury, increased intracranial pressure, and a variety of other ailments. Because potassium efflux from muscle end plates occurs during normal depolarization, massive efflux of the cation from sensitized muscle can account for the hyperkalemia noted in patients with neurologic motor deficits, tetanus, or muscle damage.

Why burn patients and those with intracranial lesions not involving upper motor neurons also are at risk is not clear. One possible mechanism would be proliferation of muscle end plates in such patients. In patients at risk, succinylcholine should be used with caution, in the smallest doses possible, and with pretreatment by nondepolarizing muscle relaxants.

Arginine HCl, in doses used for correction of metabolic alkalosis, may increase serum potassium. When this cationic amino acid is taken up by cells, potassium is displaced into the extracellular fluid. Hyperkalemia is more likely in patients with renal failure, who are unable to excrete this endogenous potassium load, and in those with liver failure, who are unable to metabolize the administered arginine normally. The magnitude of potassium rise in normal subjects is under 1 mEq/liter; it is not closely correlated with pH and may occur in patients before correction of the alkalosis is accomplished. Lysine HCl also may increase serum potassium levels.

Trivial increments in potassium may occur at therapeutic or mildly toxic levels of cardiac glycosides. Blockade of Na,K-ATPase-mediated potassium uptake with normal doses of digitalis has minimal effect on the serum potassium, since glycoside binding to skeletal muscle, the major body reservoir of potassium, is limited. At toxic concentrations of digitalis, however, such as following massive overdose, hyperkalemia does occur and indicates a poor prognosis. The hyperkalemia also prevents standard treatment with potassium. Although no effect to retard potassium disposal in normal subjects with therapeutic digitalis levels has been established, it is likely that such an effect may contribute to hyperkalemia in patients at risk.

Nonsteroidal anti-inflammatory drugs produce hyperkalemia best attributed to their antikaliuretic effect, which results in positive potassium balance. Limited data suggest that in some cases, serum potassium rises out of proportion to reduced urinary potassium loss. However, no impairment of extrarenal potassium homeostasis has been demonstrated directly.

Lithium intoxication in animals is associated with a progressive elevation in serum potassium and electrocardiogram abnormalities characteristic of hyperkalemia. However, only at concentrations of plasma lithium (>10 mEq/liter) many times the therapeutic lithium levels (1 mEq/liter) attained in manic-depressive patients do these changes occur. Increments in serum potassium of under 1 mEq/liter have been reported during chronic lithium therapy, but frank hyperkalemia is rarely observed. Lithium may displace intracellular potassium from human red blood cells and from skeletal muscle.

Enhanced Extrarenal Disposal

Drug-induced lowering of serum potassium by exogenous insulin and beta-adrenergic agonists was described in detail earlier. Increased circulating catecholamine levels also appear to mediate in part the effects of methylxanthine derivatives, such as aminophylline. Hypokalemia due to beta-adrenergic stimulation may occur with severe theophylline toxicity in humans. Propranolol is reported to block hypokalemia due to theophylline toxicity in the dog. Whether therapeutic levels of aminophylline are important in acutely lowering serum potassium in humans is unclear. Other methylxanthines, such as caffeine, also might be expected to decrease potassium concentrations.

Enhanced extrarenal potassium disposal recently has been demonstrated with the calcium channel blockers, verapamil and nifedipine. Pretreatment with each drug reduced by about 40% the increment in plasma potassium produced over 1 hr by the infusion of KCl in nephrectomized rats by increasing the translocation of potassium out of the extracellular compartment. The effect was not mediated by changes in pH, bicarbonate, insulin, aldosterone, or the alpha- or beta-adrenergic systems. Diminished calcium-mediated net potassium efflux from cells may be responsible, since increased intracellular calcium enhances erythrocyte potassium permeability *in vitro* (the Gardos effect). Calcium-dependent potassium channels are present also in hepatocytes in some species; their existence in skeletal muscle is under active investigation. This study on calcium channel blockers awaits clinical correlation.

Two reports suggest that metoclopramide, the specific dopaminergic blocker, produces a prompt, though small, lowering of serum potassium when given intravenously to humans or intraarterially to rabbits. This acute effect has not been present in other reports, and no change in serum potassium is measured after 2 weeks of exposure to the drug. Nor does either dopamine itself or the dopaminergic agonist, bromocryptine, appear to influence steady state potassium levels. As reported, the acute effect of metoclopramide has preceded the rise in potassium excretion that the drug produces by blocking tonic dopaminergic inhibition of aldosterone release. Whether the drug might augment disposal of an acute potassium load is not known.

OTHER FACTORS (8,17,21)

Three other factors that may affect extrarenal potassium homeostasis clinically are hyperosmolarity, the hormone glucagon, and cellular necrosis.

Hyperosmolarity

Hypertonic potassium-free solutions administered to normal human subjects fail to lower plasma potassium, despite expanding the extracellular fluid compartment. This observation suggests that plasma potassium is maintained during the infusion by movement of potassium out of cells, impelled by an increase in its intracellular concentration because of contraction of the intracellular volume. Potassium levels are maintained even when dilutional acidosis is prevented by incorporating bicarbonate into the hypertonic infusion.

A modest rise in plasma potassium concentration (0.3–0.6 mEq/liter) can be produced in normal subjects by moderate increases in tonicity (10 mOsm/kg). The effect is of clinical importance chiefly in diabetics, in whom plasma tonicity can be raised by 40 to 50 mOsm/kg during hyperglycemia and who lack insulin-mediated potassium uptake. Glucose-induced hyperkalemia is more pronounced in diabetics deficient in aldosterone secretion or during treatment with captopril, but it may also be observed in diabetics with normal aldosterone responses. The standard 100 oral glucose tolerance test produced an average increment of 1.3 mEq/liter in plasma potassium in four such patients. The effect of hyperosmolarity on potassium homeostasis may be present in patients with cerebral edema or with renal insufficiency when treated with large quantities of hypertonic mannitol.

Glucagon

The effect of glucagon on extrarenal potassium disposal has been difficult to isolate because the hormone also influences the secretion of insulin, epinephrine, and aldosterone. Administration of glucagon to cats produces a transient rise in arterial potassium levels. The hyperkalemic response appears to be only partly due to an epinephrine-like effect of glucagon to increase liver glycogenolysis. Glucagon also induces secretion of insulin, and when this is suppressed by somatostatin, infusion of glucagon to physiologic levels tends to elevate plasma potassium slightly by an extrarenal mechanism. It is unclear if hyperglucagonemia that occurs in decompensated diabetes mellitus, uremia, and exhaustive exercise affects potassium homeostasis. In the dog, potassium-stimulated insulin release appears to be accompanied by a modest rise in circulating glucagon.

Cellular Necrosis

When renal excretion and extrarenal disposal of potassium are exceeded, release of intracellular potassium into the extracellular compartment during cellular necrosis will result in hyperkalemia. The most common sources are muscle, tumor cells, and erythrocytes.

Traumatic muscle injury from motor vehicle accidents, alcoholism, or other etiologies may produce life-threatening hyperkalemia, usually during rhabdomyolytic renal failure. Catabolic states, such as sepsis, compound fractures, burns, major surgery, or overwhelming infections, result in protein breakdown to meet increased energy demands. Skeletal muscle, the source of protein loss, may release sufficient potassium to cause severe hyperkalemia if renal excretory mechanisms are compromised.

Accelerated breakdown of a large leukemic tumor burden, especially during induction of chemotherapy, produces kaliuresis and may cause symptomatic hyperkalemia. Burkitt's lymphoma, a rapidly growing neoplasm, although not causing hyperkalemia even in azotemic patients before chemotherapy, may result in hyperkalemia within hours of treatment even in the absence of renal insufficiency. Fatal hyperkalemia has been reported after initial tumor lysis therapy in acute lymphocytic leukemia, chronic lymphocytic leukemia, and lymphosarcoma. The tumor lysis syndrome is only rarely reported after treatment of nonlymphomatous solid tumors. Intensive supportive therapy probably accounts for the absence of hyperkalemia reported in some series.

Transient hyperkalemia, in the absence of renal failure, occasionally occurs during hemolytic states, such as congenital or acquired hemolytic anemia, hemoglobinopathy, or transfusion reactions.

REFERENCES

1. Adler, S., and Fraley, D. (1977): Potassium and intracellular pH. *Kidney Int.*, 11:433–442.
2. Adrogue, H., and Madias, N. (1981): Changes in plasma potassium during acute acid-base disturbances. *Am. J. Med.*, 71:456–467.
3. Bia, M., and DeFronzo, R. (1981): Extrarenal potassium homeostasis (editorial review). *Am. J. Physiol.*, 240:F257–F268.
4. Bilbrey, G., Carter, M., White, M., Schilling, J., and Knochel, J. (1973): Potassium deficiency in chronic renal failure. *Kidney Int.*, 4:423–430.
5. Brown, M., Brown, D., and Murphy, M. (1983): Hypokalemia from beta$_2$-receptor stimulation by circulating epinephrine. *N. Engl. J. Med.*, 309:1414–1419.
6. Cheng, J.-T., Kahn, T., and Kaji, D. M. (1984): Mechanism of alteration of sodium potassium pump of erythrocytes from patients with chronic renal failure. *J. Clin. Invest.*, 74: 1811–1820.
7. Clausen, T. (1983): Adrenergic control of Na-K homeostasis. *Acta Med. Scand. (Suppl.)*, 672:111–115.
8. Cohen, L. F., Balaw, J. E., Magrath, I. T., Poplack, D. G., and Ziegler, L. T. (1980): Acute tumor lysis syndrome. *Am. J. Med.*, 68:486–491.
9. Cox, M., Sterns, R. H., and Singer, I. (1978): The defense against hyperkalemia: The roles of insulin and aldosterone. *N. Engl. J. Med.*, 299:525–532.
10. DeFronzo, R. A., Bia, M., and Birkhead, G. (1981): Epinephrine and potassium homeostasis. *Kidney Int.*, 20:83–91.
11. Fernandez, J., Oster, J R., and Perez, G. O. (1986): Impaired extrarenal disposal of an acute oral potassium load in patients with end stage renal disease on chronic hemodialysis. *Miner. Electrolyte Metab.*, 12:125–129
12. Garella, S., and Matarese, R. A. (1984): Renal effects of prostaglandins and clinical adverse effects of nonsteroidal anti-inflammatory agents. *Medicine*, 63:165–181.
13. Hiatt, N., Chapman, L., Davidson, M., and Sheinkopf, J. (1979): Adrenal hormones and the regulation of serum potassium in potassium-loaded adrenalectomized dogs. *Endocrinology*, 105:215–219.
14. Kahn, T., Kaji, D. M., Nicolis, G., Krakoff, L. R., and Stein, R. M. (1978): Factors related to potassium transport in stable chronic renal disease. *Clin. Sci. Mol. Med.*, 54:661–666.
15. Kearney, T., Manoguerra, A., Curtis, G., and Zeigler, M. (1985): Theophylline toxicity and the beta-adrenergic system. *Ann. Intern. Med.*, 102:766–769.

16. Lytton, J., Lin, J., and Guidotti, G. (1985): Identification of two molecular forms of (Na,K)-ATPase in rat adipocytes. *J. Biol. Chem.*, 260:1177–1184.
17. Massara, F., Martelli, S., Cagliero, E., Comanni, F., and Moliknatti, G. (1980): Influence of glucagon on plasma levels of potassium in man. *Diabetologia*, 19:414–417
18. Mitch, W., and Wilcox, C. (1982): Disorders of body fluids, sodium and potassium in chronic renal failure. *Am. J. Med.*, 72:536–550.
19. Moore, R. (1983): Effects of insulin upon ion transport. *Biochem. Biophys. Acta*, 737:1–49.
20. Morgan, D., Cumberbatch, M., and Swaminthan, R. (1981): The relation between plasma, erythrocytes and total body potassium in patients with hypokalemia. *Miner. Electrolyte Metab.*, 5:233–239.
21. Nicolis, G., Kahn, T., Sanchez, A., and Gabrilove, J. (1981): Glucose-induced hyperkalemia in diabetic subjects. *Arch. Intern. Med.*, 141:49–53.
22. Perez, G., Oster, J., and Vaamonde, D. (1983): Serum potassium concentration in acidemic states. *Nephron*, 27:233–243.
23. Ponce, S., Jennings, A., Madias, M., and Harrington, J. (1986): Drug-induced hyperkalemia. *Medicine*, 64:357–370.
24. Scribner, B., and Burnell, J. (1956): Interpretation of the serum potassium concentration. *Metabolism*, 5:468–479.
25. Spital, A., and Sterns, R. (1986): Paradoxical potassium depletion: A renal mechanism for extrarenal potassium adaptation. *Kidney Int.*, 30:532–537.
26. Sterns, R., Cox, M., Feig, P., and Singer, I. (1981): Internal potassium balance and the control of the plasma potassium concentration. *Medicine*, 60:339–554.
27. Sugarman, A., and Kalm, T. (1986): Calcium channel blockers enhance extrarenal potassium disposal in the rat. *Am. J. Physiol.*, 250:F695–F701.
28. Waddell, W., and Bates, R. (1969): Intracellular pH. *Physiol. Rev.*, 49:233–243.
29. Williams, M., Gervino, E., Rosa, R., et al. (1985): Catecholamine modulation of rapid potassium shifts during exercise. *N. Engl. J. Med.*, 312:823–827.
30. Williams, M., Rosa, R., and Epstein, F. H. (1986): Hyperkalemia. *Adv. Intern. Med.*, 31:265–291.

The Regulation of Potassium Balance, edited
by Donald W. Seldin and Gerhard Giebisch,
Raven Press, Ltd., New York © 1989.

2

Correlates of Potassium Exchange

James P. Knochel

Department of Internal Medicine, Southwest Medical School, Dallas, Texas 75216

Role of Potassium Ions in Regulation of Skeletal Muscle Blood Flow
Carbohydrate Metabolism in Potassium-Deficient Skeletal Muscle
  Impaired Glucose Utilization • Reduced Insulin Secretion • Reduced
  Glycogen Synthesis
Interrelationship of Blood Flow, Metabolism, Energy Production, Work,
  and Endurance in Potassium Deficiency
Exercise Hyperkalemia
Hypokalemia in the Physically Conditioned Man
Kaliogenic Hypermetabolism
Spurious Hypokalemia
References

Exchange of potassium ions across cellular membranes accounts for a large
number of important physiologic as well as pathologic events. In fact, a substantial portion of this book is dedicated to such phenomena as familial hypokalemic periodic paralysis, Gamstorp's disease, and a variety of more common
disorders that disturb the critically important intracellular-extracellular potassium concentration gradient. Less well known but of equal importance are
events discussed in this chapter dealing with the role of potassium ions in
regulation of blood flow to skeletal muscle, insulin release from the pancreas,
hyperkalemia during exercise, electrochemical characteristics of training, and
a relatively unexplored issue suggesting that release of potassium ions by
working muscle may be involved in heat production.

ROLE OF POTASSIUM IONS IN REGULATION OF
SKELETAL MUSCLE BLOOD FLOW (15,16,21,22,28,32)

Studies conducted in human volunteers nearly 50 years ago showed that
when potassium chloride was infused into a brachial artery, blood flow in the

muscle downstream from the site of infusion increased markedly. Thus, potassium appeared to be a vasodilator. It is now established that at a concentration of between 5 and 15 mEq/liter, there occurs a progressively increasing and proportionate increase of muscle blood flow. Above a concentration of 18 mEq/liter, potassium becomes a vasoconstrictor. Although several metabolic factors also have been shown to possess vasodilatory properties on skeletal muscle arterioles, including hydrogen ions, hypoxia, increased osmolality of perfusing plasma, and adenine nucleotides, the first substance that increases in interstitial fluid of the muscle bed or its venous effluent during exercise is potassium.

Studies in a number of animal species and humans have shown that when a muscle cell is depolarized immediately before contraction begins, potassium is released into the interstitial fluid bathing the muscle arterioles. Its concentration rises from a resting value in interstitial fluid that is equal to the prevailing plasma concentration up to about 15 to 18 mEq/liter during contraction (Fig. 1). It has been shown also that the concentration of potassium ions attained in interstitial fluid during exercise varies directly with the intensity of work. Although other factors mentioned previously that mediate or participate in regulation of muscle blood flow during exercise may be equally important, it seems that the burst of potassium release during the initial contractile phase

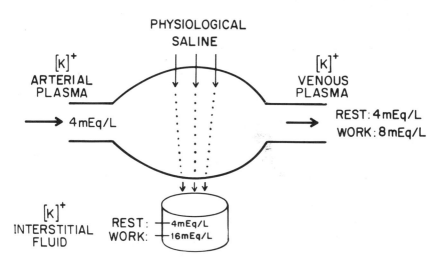

FIG. 1. Diagrammatic representation of Kjellmer's experiment showing a method to estimate interstitial fluid potassium concentration in skeletal muscle during exercise. The muscle was perfused with physiologic saline and collected by gravity (interstitial fluid). While at rest, potassium in plasma was the same as arterial plasma, indicating no net potassium release. During exercise, venous plasma [K] rose to 8 mEq/liter, and interstitial fluid [K] rose to 16 mEq/liter, indicating net potassium release. Since infusing potassium salts at concentrations up to 16 mEq/liter dilates muscle arterioles and increases muscle blood flow, it is assumed that interstitial fluid hyperkalemia produced by exercise may play a role in exercise hyperemia.

from the muscle fiber may be the single most important factor triggering the increase of muscle blood flow during exercise.

The functional significance of exercise hyperemia would appear to subserve at least three major events. Energy for muscle cell contraction and, in turn, production of work requires delivery of oxygen, glucose, and fatty acids. Without an increase of muscle blood flow, available fuel within the muscle tissue itself can provide no more than a limited supply of energy substrates. The most important endogenous fuel is glycogen, which is utilized during hard, sustained anaerobic work when demands for ATP production outstrip the quantities that can be produced solely by oxidative metabolism. Accordingly, increased muscle blood flow with proportionate increases in delivery of oxygen and readily oxidized fuels, such as glucose or fatty acids, ensures continued supply of creatine phosphate and ATP.

When substrates are utilized for those biochemical processees that provide energy for contraction, metabolites accumulate that must be removed from the cell. For example, although the initial instantaneous change in the muscle cytoplasm is an elevation of pH as the result of sodium hydrogen exchange across the cell, there then follows an accumulation of hydrogen ions resulting from production of acid metabolites and carbon dioxide. Although blood circulating through the muscle cell can buffer a substantial fraction of hydrogen ions by titration of bicarbonate and binding of carbon dioxide to hemoglobin, net removal of these substances can only be mediated by a major increase in muscle blood flow. Leakage of these metabolites from the muscle cell into the interstitial fluid and thence into capillary blood has been observed to result in a decline of arterial pH in highly trained athletes to values as low as 6.8 units and virtual disappearance of bicarbonate from the blood (Fig. 2A). The rise of lactate in venous blood matches the reduction of bicarbonate essentially mole for mole (Fig. 2B). Obviously, if muscle blood flow did not increase during exercise, metabolic processees within the cell would become quickly paralyzed because of severe hypoxia as well as declines of pH to a point at which enzymes, such as phosphofructokinase, would cease to function. Release of lactate into the venous blood correlates not only with work intensity but also with the level of venous and, consequently, interstitial hyperkalemia (Fig. 3). Delivery of lactate from skeletal muscle to the liver allows for ongoing hepatic transformation of lactate into glucose (the Cori cycle).

Besides substrate delivery and removal of metabolites, the third critical event subserved by increased muscle blood flow during exercise is cooling itself. There is no question that ischemia during work leads to major overheating of skeletal muscle cells that physiologically is most apparent in people who work under conditions of volume depletion. Such conditions reduce optimal muscle blood flow. A normal human working at 50% of his maximum rate of oxygen utilization on a treadmill may show elevations of muscle temperature up to values of 106°F (41°C). It has been clearly demon-

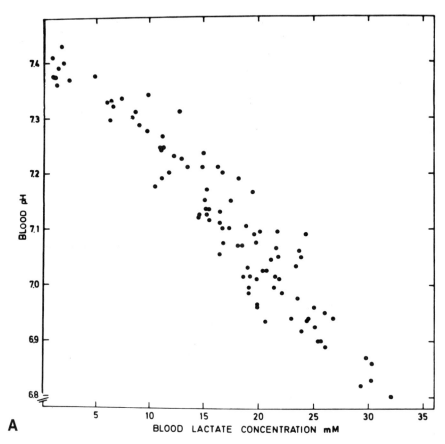

FIG. 2A. Comparison of arterial blood pH and lactate concentration in trained cross-country skiers undergoing intermittent exhaustive exercise on a treadmill. (From ref. 28.)

strated that overheating of muscle cells during exercise is associated with major reductions of biochemical as well as mechanical efficiency. By contrast, interventional cooling during exercise reduces lactate accumulation and hydrogen ion accumulation and reduces decline of ATP, yet improves mechanical work production. Furthermore, increased muscle blood flow to provide the necessary quantity of substrate delivery, removal of metabolites, and prevention of undue heating during hard, sustained work are absolute requirements to prevent injury and rhabdomyolysis. A penetrating example of heat produced by biochemical transformations is the observation that during work, when the temperature of blood emanating from working skeletal muscle and the temperature of mixed venous blood in the vena cava is 106°F, simultaneous temperature measurements of blood emanating from the hepatic venous circulation will be as a high as 108°F (42.2°C), reflecting heat production incident to gluconeogenesis in the liver. It is obvious that an integral response of the circulatory system with the critical events of potassium release and

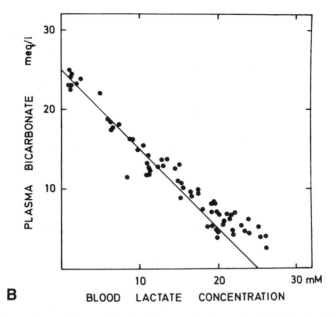

FIG. 2B. Comparison of plasma bicarbonate concentration and arterial blood lactate on same samples shown in Fig. 2A. (From ref. 28.)

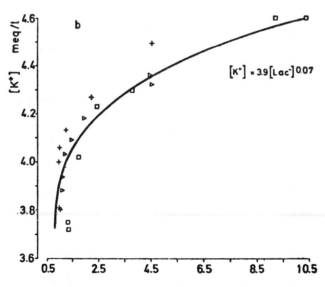

$$[K^+] = 3.9[Lac^-]^{0.07}$$

FIG. 3. A comparison of venous serum potassium values and venous lactate concentration from the exercised dog.

increased muscle blood flow during exercise determine in large part the ability of humans to survive hard work, especially when conducted under conditions of heat stress. It also points out the critical importance of avoiding water depletion, salt depletion, and potassium deficiency during hard work, especially when conducted under conditions of high environmental heat.

Perhaps the most important evidence that potassium release from contracting muscle cells is a critical factor responsible for exercise hyperemia is the fact that if a situation is established that prevents release of potassium ions from skeletal muscle cells, muscle blood flow during induced work does not rise. This effect has been elucidated by studying the effects of electrically induced exercise in the intact gracilis muscle of the dog. This is a very handy experimental model for such studies because the muscle is nourished by a single nerve and a single artery and is drained by a single vein. Thus, one can stimulate the gracilis nerve electrically in an intact animal and quantitatively examine contractile force and muscle blood flow. In normal dogs, stimulation of the gracilis nerve at supramaximal rates increases blood flow from about 7 ml/100 g/min to about 23 ml/100 g/min. Release of potassium rises from about 1.0 μEq/100 g/min at rest to 33 μEq/100 g/min during exercise. In potassium-deficient dogs or rats, neither blood flow nor potassium release rises during stimulated contractions (Fig. 4). If potassium chloride is infused into the

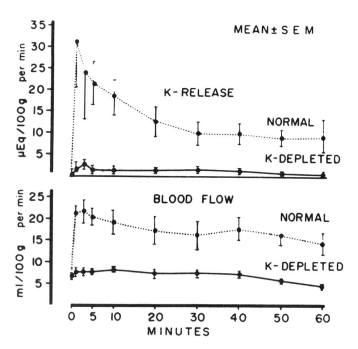

FIG. 4. Electrically induced exercise by canine gracilis muscle preparation is associated with a marked rise of potassium release and muscle blood flow. Potassium deficiency virtually eliminates these responses. (From ref. 21.)

gracilis artery of the potassium-deficient, hypokalemic dog during induced exercise, there occurs a return of muscle blood flow toward normal. Such evidence would appear strongly to support the notion that potassium release and interstitial fluid hyperkalemia are important mediators of arteriolar vasodilatation and muscle hyperemia during exercise. It can be shown that if the potassium-deficient gracilis muscle is stimulated electrically to the point of unresponsiveness and biopsied the following day, serum creatine phosphokinase activity rises and frank muscle necrosis is evident. If a normal gracilis muscle is stimulated to exhaustion and biopsies are taken the following day, the muscle appears perfectly normal and creatine phosphokinase activity remains normal. Such evidence strongly suggests that at least one important mechanism favoring development of rhabdomyolysis in the potassium-deficient animal is ischemia during exercise.

CARBOHYDRATE METABOLISM IN POTASSIUM-DEFICIENT SKELETAL MUSCLE (1,6,9–12,14,17,24,29)

The effects of potassium deficiency on carbohydrate metabolism have been studied in detail. In general terms, three major defects have been described (Table 1).

Impaired Glucose Utilization

That glucose utilization becomes impaired as a result of potassium deficiency is well recognized. In most instances, fasting plasma glucose levels are normal. However, after administration of glucose loads orally or intravenously, glucose utilization is delayed. Conn was the first to show that patients with hypokalemia and primary aldosteronism were unable to release adequate insulin in the presence of hyperglycemia. Although the question was entertained that aldosterone (or desoxycorticosterone in experimental studies) exerted a specific effect that reduced insulin release, it was clearly shown that this was a specific effect of potassium deficiency. It was shown subsequently that patients who became potassium deficient as a result of thiazide therapy also became glucose intolerant. Furthermore, in patients medicated with

TABLE 1. *Effect of potassium deficiency on carbohydrate metabolism*

1. Impairment of glucose utilization
2. Impairment of insulin release in response to hyperglycemia
3. Reduced glycogen stores in skeletal muscle

thiazides, glucose intolerance could be averted by prevention of potassium deficiency or reversed by administration of sufficient potassium supplements to correct the potassium deficiency. Thus, it was established clearly that potassium deficiency *per se* caused reduced insulin release in the face of hyperglycemia. Of clinical importance, potassium deficiency could induce simple glucose intolerance in otherwise normal individuals or, more importantly, result in gross exacerbations of glucose intolerance in patients with preexistent diabetes mellitus.

Reduced Insulin Secretion

The precise mechanism whereby potassium deficiency reduces insulin secretion in response to hyperglycemia remains to be elucidated. Studies by Robertson showed that infusions of prostaglandin E (PGE_2) into animals receiving glucose infusions markedly reduce insulin release from beta cells and thus delay metabolism of glucose. Patients with severe potassium deficiency as the result of Bartter's syndrome or dogs made seriously potassium deficient demonstrate marked overproduction of PGE_2. In potassium-deficient dogs, utilization of infused glucose is delayed, and glucogenic insulin release is substantially impaired. If the same animals are given either acetylsalicylic acid or indomethacin before administration of glucose, both glucose utilization and insulin release are quickly restored to normal, although serum potassium levels remain as low as before. Although such evidence would point toward prostaglandin-induced inhibition of insulin release from beta cells, it is possible that catecholamines could also play a role. Thus, Robertson has shown that norepinephrine reduces glucogenic insulin release from beta cells. Potassium-deficient rats show elevations of resting catecholamine levels. Since there is no known effect of acetylsalicylic acid or indomethacin on catecholamine levels, it is assumed that the mechanism whereby these drugs normalize glucose utilization and insulin release despite persistent hypokalemia is the result of inhibiting prostaglandin formation. In addition, it is noteworthy and interesting that older anecdotal studies report that occasional patients with diabetes mellitus were apparently cured after administration of acetylsalicylic acid. This strongly suggests that potassium deficiency might have been responsible for the glucose intolerance and that this, in turn, was cured by inhibition of prostaglandin synthesis.

Reduced Glycogen Synthesis

Stores of glycogen in skeletal muscle fall markedly in potassium deficiency. The first observations on intact potassium-deficient rats illustrating this phenomenon were made by Gardner et al. Potassium deficiency in these animals was induced by feeding a potassium-deficient diet. Since potassium deficiency in the rat results in a sharp reduction of food intake and reduced growth, Gardner's observation that glycogen content of skeletal muscle was reduced could have been the result of simple starvation. Furthermore, the rat is not an ideal model to study comparative effects of potassium deficiency in humans. Muscle glycogen content in the normal rat is only one tenth of that in humans. Furthermore, specific effects of severe hypokalemia and potassium deficiency, such as paralysis or rhabdomyolysis, that occur in humans are essentially not reproducible in the rat. On the other hand, in dogs, muscle glycogen metabolism appears to be identical to that of humans. Studies designed to avoid undernutrition in dogs made potassium deficient by selective reduction of dietary potassium intake along with administration of desoxycorticosterone show clearly that potassium deficiency indeed reduces glycogen content in muscle. Studies on patients who became mildly potassium deficient as the result of diuretic therapy also showed reductions in muscle glycogen content.

The precise mechanism whereby potassium deficiency reduces glycogen content of skeletal muscle has not been clearly established. Studies by Losert showed that activity of the enzyme phosphorylase phosphatase became higher in potassium deficiency. This enzyme increases glycogen turnover. In vitro, Losert's studies showed that activity of this enzyme increased in response to elevation of sodium concentration to levels observed within the cytoplasm of cells from potassium-deficient tissue. Hence, it was suggested that rather than potassium deficiency per se, the invariably associated intracellular accumulation of sodium might have been responsible for increased turnover of glycogen, thus implying that glycogen synthesis remains normal but that glycogen stores fell because of increased turnover. These observations have not been confirmed.

Although the mechanism of skeletal muscle glycogen depletion in potassium deficiency remains obscure, the clinical implications of this abnormality are very clear. Since glycogen is the most critical fuel to provide synthesis of energy in muscle during hard sustained work, glycogen depletion as a result of potassium deficiency may explain the reduced exercise endurance that occurs in potassium-deficient animals. To examine this further, we studied dogs made potassium-deficient and showed that glucose utilization by potassium-deficient muscle during work was no different from that in normal animals (Table 2). However, in potassium deficiency it could be shown that during contractile work of the isolated gracilis muscle, essentially all lactate was produced from glucose delivered to the muscle by the arterial circulation. Since glycogen is essentially absent from potassium-deficient skeletal muscle, this source of fuel and lactate is unavailable. Furthermore, since the increase of muscle blood flow that normally occurs during exercise does not occur in the potassium-deficient animal, exercise endurance is markedly reduced.

Another important consequence of potassium deficiency in skeletal muscle

TABLE 2. *Glucose uptake and lactate output in normal and potassium-deficient dogs at rest and during exercise*

	State	Normal	p	Potassium-deficiency
Glucose uptake (μmol/kg/min)	Resting	88 ± 7		91 ± 9
	Working	118 ± 14		116 ± 9
Lactate output (μmol/kg/min)	Resting	26 ± 5		32 ± 7
	Working	610 ± 80	<0.01	240 ± 60

is impairment of the physiologic process known as "glycogen supercompensa-tion." In normal humans and dogs, exercise to the point of exhaustion is asso-ciated with reduction of muscle glycogen stores to zero. A single episode of exercise sufficient to reduce glycogen content in skeletal muscle triggers a steady, progressive rebound from normal levels of about 1% wet weight to values as high as 3 to 5 g% over the course of 3 to 5 days (Fig. 5). This phenomenon of supercompensation has been used advantageously by compet-

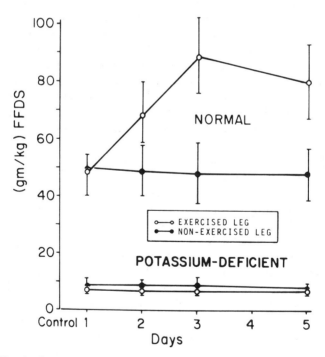

FIG. 5. Muscle glycogen content rises (supercompensation) after a single bout of exhaustive exercise in the normal dog in the exercised but not in the unexercised muscle. In potassium-deficient dogs (**bottom**), baseline values for muscle glycogen become very low and show no change after exercise.

itive runners, who deliberately unload muscle glycogen stores by exhaustive exercises 3 or 4 days before a competitive event. Then on the day before the competitive event, the runners deliberately load themselves with a high carbohydrate diet that has been shown to literally stuff the muscle with glycogen. Unquestionably, exercise endurance is enhanced by this procedure. In potassium deficiency, not only do muscle glycogen stores at rest fall to almost unmeasurable levels, but exercise of the muscle cells is not followed by supercompensation. Thus, potassium deficiency virtually eliminates one of the major biochemical adaptations to exercise training.

INTERRELATIONSHIP OF BLOOD FLOW, METABOLISM, ENERGY PRODUCTION, WORK, AND ENDURANCE IN POTASSIUM DEFICIENCY (17)

When a normal muscle is exercised, there is a close relationship among potassium released from the muscle cell, the increase of muscle blood flow, and the intensity of work. When these relationships are studied in potassium deficiency, contractile strength may be perfectly normal, although there occurs essentially no release of potassium ions and no increase in muscle blood flow. A comparison of work produced by normal and potassium-deficient gracilis muscles from dogs is shown in Fig. 6. Although the capacity to perform

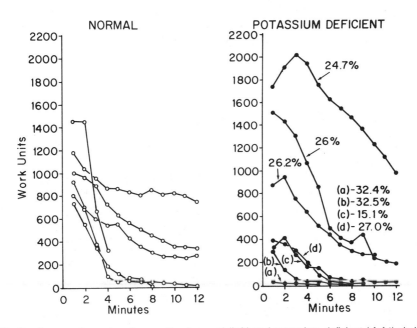

FIG. 6. A comparison of work capacity of normal (**left**) and potassium-deficient (**right**) skeletal muscle. The percentage values refer to the estimated potassium deficit that existed in each dog when the study was conducted.

work varies widely among the animals tested, it is clear that work output was normal in more than half of the animals examined despite severe potassium deficiency. This has potentially important implications. Since the metabolic products of work, including hydrogen ions and lactate, are produced in quantities proportional to the work performed, the concentration of these substances should be higher in the interstitial fluid and venous plasma of the working muscle from the potassium-deficient dogs. Figure 7 shows venous lactate concentration in normal and potassium-deficient dogs during work. It is readily seen that lactate values in venous blood become higher in the deficient animals. Nevertheless, using the venous-arterial difference and blood flow to calculate the net quantity of lactate produced by the working muscle, it can be shown that lactate production by normal muscle is essentially three times higher than that produced by the potassium-deficient animals. Table 2 illustrates these values. In addition, lactate production by potassium-deficient muscle apparently can be accounted for completely by metabolism of glucose, since each 6-carbon glucose molecule will be split into two 3-carbon molecules of lactate.

In normal animals, the uptake of glucose by skeletal muscle during work is almost exactly the same as that taken up by potassium-deficient muscle. However, in normal muscle, production of lactate is substantially higher, and this must be derived from glycogen. In these studies, the pH of the venous effluent during exercise is about 6.8. Oxygen content in the same blood sample is unmeasurable. Such data verify that work was conducted at a rate sufficient to expend all oxygen delivered and under sufficient hypoxic conditions to con-

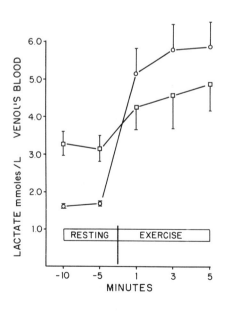

FIG. 7. Lactate concentration (means ± 1 SD) in venous blood draining exercising gracilis muscle in normal (□) and potassium-deficient (o) dogs. Although venous lactate concentration is higher, net lactate production is much less in potassium-deficient dogs (see Table 2). Venous lactate concentration is higher in deficient dogs because of blood stagnation.

sume any glycogen present in the muscle. One can conclude from these studies that metabolism of glucose at rest appears to remain intact in potassium-deficient dogs. Thus, the major defect in carbohydrate metabolism as the result of potassium deficiency is disappearance of glycogen from muscle tissue. This could explain the reduction of endurance.

EXERCISE HYPERKALEMIA
(2–5,13,18,19,23,25,26,29,31,33,35)

It was pointed out in a previous section that when a normal muscle cell contracts, potassium ions are transferred from the myoplasm into the interstitial fluid and thence into the venous circulation. When exercise is performed at moderate intensity, mixed venous potassium concentration increases by approximately 0.5 mEq/liter. At higher work levels, the rise in mixed venous potassium concentration may amount to as much as 1 or 2 mEq/liter. In extreme circumstances, especially when work has been sustained for a long period of time at high intensity, potassium concentrations in venous blood have been recorded between 9 and 10 mEq/liter (Fig. 8). Lim et al. studied the effect of propranolol on arterial potassium concentration in normal subjects after exercise. Potassium concentration in plasma was measured *in situ* with a potassium-sensitive electrode. Propranolol specifically blocks beta$_2$-adrenergic receptors in skeletal muscle and thus interferes with potassium movement back into the cells. In these studies, it was shown that without propranolol, arterial plasma potassium concentration rose from a mean value of about 4.0 mEq/liter to 5.3 mEq/liter after only 5 min of exercise on a bicycle ergometer. When medicated with propranolol, arterial plasma potassium values rose from 4.1 mEq/liter to values as high as 7.9 mEq/liter. Such changes are of sufficient magnitude to produce important electrocardiographic changes of hyperkalemia. Because of such events, it is possible that hyperkalemia during exercise could be a cause of sudden death.

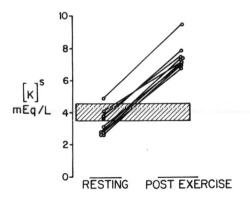

FIG. 8 An illustration of resting serum potassium values and those collected on completion of a 54 mile marathon. (From ref. 25.)

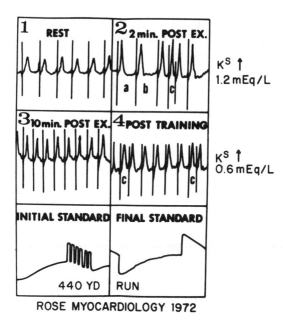

FIG. 9. A telemetered electrocardiogram in a healthy young runner before (**panels 1 to 3**) and after (**panel 4**) endurance training. Postexercise hyperkalemia was reduced by training, as also were the electrocardiographic changes compatible with hyperkalemia.

Figure 9 shows a representative telemetered electrocardiogram from a study of exercise-induced hyperkalemia during a 440 yard run in a healthy young man before and after training. Before training, his serum potassium rose 1.2 mEq/liter, and after 6 weeks, the same exercise resulted in a rise of 0.6 mEq/liter. T-wave peaking, characteristic of hyperkalemia, corresponded to the intensity of exercise hyperkalemia. That exercise hyperkalemia for a given workload is reduced after training has been observed also by Saltin et al. in human subjects and in our own laboratory on trained dogs. Nevertheless, as shown by McKechnie's studies, exhaustive exercise can still cause potentially life-threatening hyperkalemia despite training to the degree achieved by world-class competitive marathon runners.

Figure 10 illustrates the interrelation among electrolyte fluxes across the muscle cell, sodium-potassium pump activity, oxygen consumption, and membrane potential of the muscle cells during and after exercise. This shows that although venous potassium concentration may rise up to about 6 mEq/liter, the simultaneous increase of potassium concentration in the interstitial fluid may be as high as 15 mEq/liter. This value has been verified by ion-specific electrode measurements of interstitial potassium concentration in both animals and humans. As the muscle cell becomes depolarized, sodium ions flood the myoplasm and activate the sodium-potassium pump. Although potassium ions become elevated outside the muscle cell and although the sodium-po-

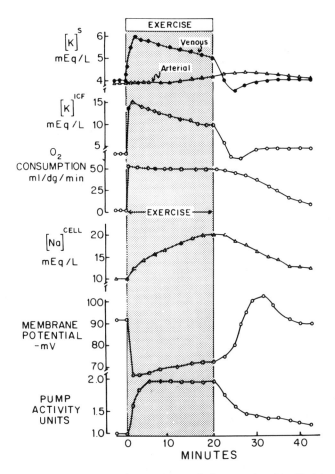

FIG. 10. Simultaneous changes before, during, and after exercise. (Modified from ref. 13.)

tassium pump is oriented so that the potassium receptor is on the outside of the cell, the maximum stimulation of the pump by potassium occurs with potassium concentrations of about 2 mEq/liter. Thus, interstitial fluid hyperkalemia probably has no direct effect on the pump. In contrast, sodium concentration in the cell rises to levels that clearly activate the sodium pump. A large portion of the increased oxygen consumption by muscle cells is used for ion transport. The best evidence for the latter statement is drawn from isolated muscle studies during work. Thus, if sodium and potassium transport is inhibited by ouabain, oxygen consumption falls hand in hand. During recovery from exercise, it is assumed that the normal stoichiometry of 3 Na^+ ions pumped out for each 2 K^+ ions pumped in persists. Continued extrusion of sodium ions at a rate greater than inward movement of potassium serves to reestablish the negatively charged interior of the cell (so-called electrogenic

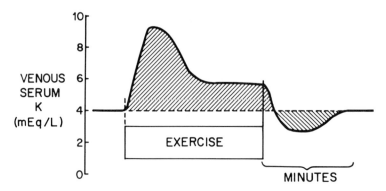

FIG. 11. Illustration of exercise-induced hyperkalemia followed by transient hypokalemia. The hypokalemia is thought to reflect the electrogenic effect of accelerated sodium transport during recovery from exercise.

effect of the pump). The electrical field generated in the cell favors a progressive reduction of venous potassium concentration. Figure 11 shows the effects of electrogenic potassium uptake, which results in a normal overshoot of cellular potassium uptake to produce frank hypokalemia before equilibrium is reestablished. Some believe that this rapid transition between normokalemia, hyperkalemia, and hypokalemia that occurs before, during, and after completion of exercise may be an important factor in the genesis of cardiac arrhythmias.

The actual quantity of sodium and potassium that interchanges across sarcoplasmic membranes during exercise is substantial. Quantitative assessments of sodium-potassium pump sites (the magnesium-dependent Na,K-ATPase) in skeletal muscle have been published by Clausen et al. The same authors have estimated maximum values for potassium release from contracting muscle cells and maximum rates by which potassium can be returned to muscle cells by the Na,K-ATPase. Data have been obtained on both human and rat muscle. In performing these studies, other mechanisms by which potassium ions could move across the sarcolemmal membrane were selectively blocked. These include calcium-sensitive K^+ channels (blocked by Ba^{2+}), passive diffusion (blocked by tetracaine), or voltage-sensitive K^+ channels (blocked by tetraethylammonium salts). The maximum capacity for potassium uptake by human muscle is 5,000 nmol/g wet weight/min. In a 70 kg man whose muscle mass approximates 28 kg, a value of 140 mmol potassium theoretically could be actively transported into skeletal muscle cells per minute. Under normal conditions, such a value would be limited by decreased muscle blood flow, energy substrate availability, and possible injury to muscle cells resulting from exercise *per se*. Under normal (not exhaustive) exercise, release of potassium from contracting skeletal muscle during exercise obviously is capable of being regulated without difficulty. However, the occurrence of potentially severe hyperkalemia clearly indicates that the system can be overwhelmed. To further illustrate the enormous capacity of this system, it has been estimated that the surface area of the sarcoplasmic reticulum in skeletal muscle, which is the site of all sodium potassium transfer, amounts to about 2 m^2/g. Extrapolated to the entire body mass of skeletal muscle, the total surface area of the sarcoplasmic reticulum is about 60,000 m^2. This is equivalent to the area of about six football fields. Studies, such as those performed by Clausen and Kjeldsen and by Hazeyama and Sparks, readily explain why interference with the Na,K-ATPase transport systems in skeletal muscle can cause exaggerated exercise hyperkalemia and cardiotoxicity. Drugs, such as propranolol, that block $beta_2$-adrenergic receptors markedly reduce the capacity of muscle cells to take up potassium. In fact, any factor that interferes with pump activity, such as hypoxia, substrate exhaustion, or alpha-adrenergic catecholamines in high concentration, theoretically can cause severe hyperkalemia during exercise.

Insulin also plays a critical role in regulation of serum potassium concentration. Zierler and Rogus were the first to show that when skeletal muscle is exposed to insulin, there follows electrical hyperpolarization. This electrical effect of insulin occurs independently of glucose. Moore and Rabovsky suggest that the initial action of insulin on the cell may be to increase permeability of sodium so that as sodium ions enter the cell, they exchange with hydrogen ions, and the interior of the cell becomes alkalinized. This increased sodium concentration inside the cell would then activate the sodium-potassium pump. Sodium ions would be transported in an outward direction at a rate that exceeds that of potassium entry. The net effect of this ionic exchange is generation of a negative electrical charge in the cell that, in turn, promotes passive diffusion of potassium ions in excess of that transported by the pump. The result is hypokalemia. More recent studies by Clausen and Flatman show that insulin stimulates active transport of Na^+ and K^+ ions even in the presence of amiloride, which blocks entry of Na^+ from the extracellular fluid. Since insulin-induced hyperpolarization occurs despite the block of Na^+ entry, the precise reason for the electrogenic effect of insulin remains unclear. Clinicians have capitalized on this effect of insulin, namely, to promote cellular uptake of potassium ions, as the cornerstone for treatment of acute hyperkalemia. It is interesting that administration of potassium ions intravenously in sufficient quantity to induce hyperkalemia causes release of insulin from the beta cells of the pancreas, so that insulin may be thought of as an internal emergency regulatory system to prevent hyperkalemia. The clinical correlate of this phenomenon is that serum potassium values ride high in the patient with diabetes mellitus who is untreated. This is especially true if the patient has a modest degree of renal insufficiency.

Although insulin is a powerful force that can drive potassium ions into cells, it probably does not play a role in regulating serum potassium concentration during exercise. During hard work, plasma insulin levels fall sharply. Although glucose uptake by skeletal muscle cells can occur independently of insulin during muscular work, the preferred substrate for ATP production in skeletal muscle during work is fatty acids. Reduction of insulin secretion by the pancreas during work probably is induced by catecholamines that normally rise during exercise. It has been shown by Robertson that infusion of norepinephrine reduces insulin release in the face of hyperglycemia. If insulin release were stimulated by hyperkalemia during exercise, one would probably die from hypoglycemia. The reduction of insulin secretion during exercise probably slows down glucose metabolism by working skeletal muscle and conserves glucose for utilization by tissues, such as the brain, that are totally dependent on glucose for ATP production.

Zierler and Rogus have examined the possibility that glucose uptake by muscle cells in the presence of insulin could be mediated by electrical hyperpolarization. In other tissues in the body, such as epithelial cells of the proximal renal tubule or small intestine, it is well known that glucose uptake is coupled with sodium transport. Although this has never been clearly demonstrated in skeletal muscle, it can be shown that administration of ouabain reduces glucose uptake. Using the sucrose gap technique to explore the effects of electrical hyperpolarization, Zierler and Rogus studied the effects of increased negative voltage induced by electrical stimulation on glucose uptake in the absence of insulin. They found that glucose uptake nearly doubled under these conditions. This suggests that insulin-stimulated proton extrusion could negatively charge the muscle cell so that Na^+ and glucose are cotransported.

In the dog and man, exercise training for endurance running results in electrical hyperpolarization of muscle cells. The average resting membrane potential of a muscle cell in the untrained state in both human and dog is about -89 mV. Training results in the elevation of this negative voltage up to values of -99 mV. Although the teleologic reason for electrical hyperpolarization of muscle cells is unknown, it is possible that this occurs for two purposes. The first would be for the purpose of blunting exercise hyperkalemia, and the second would be to promote uptake of glucose by muscle cells during the recovery period from exercise so as to restore supplies of creatine phosphate and ATP. It can be shown in dogs that potassium tolerance is induced by exercise training. Both the activity of sodium potassium ATPase and pump density in muscle sarcoplasmic membranes are increased by training. Nonetheless, the precise cause of electrical hyperpolarization as the result of exercise training is unexplained.

HYPOKALEMIA IN THE PHYSICALLY CONDITIONED MAN (20,30)

Rose was the first to observe that athletes trained for competitive running could become hypokalemic. Figure 12 illustrates data from his report. It shows that after 6 weeks of training for long-distance running, 33 of 107 men showed serum potassium values below 3.5 mEq/liter. Although Rose believed

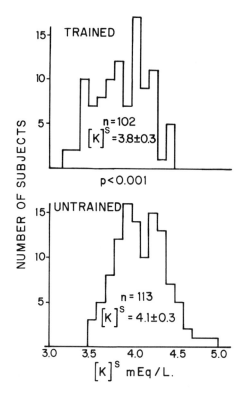

FIG. 12. Histograms illustrating the distribution of resting venous potassium values in untrained and trained long-distance runners.

this represented potassium deficiency, this would not appear to be the best explanation.

Studies conducted on young men after basic military training in the winter also showed an average value for serum potassium concentration of 3.5 mEq/liter. Since their total body potassium expressed as a function of lean body mass rose during training, it was assumed that their intracellular potassium concentration rose despite a low normal value for serum potassium. Since there is no evidence for potassium binding in cell water, the rise of intracellular potassium should have been associated with a rise of resting membrane potential. As indicated above, training does increase the electrical charge on muscle cells. It would seem likely that the electrical hyperpolarization, increased intracellular potassium, and decreased extracellular potassium concentrations are interrelated.

KALIOGENIC HYPERMETABOLISM (7,8,34)

Fenn reported a titillating observation in 1931 that there appears to be a relationship between heat production by skeletal muscle and the prevailing extracellular potassium concentration. Figure 13 shows that as extracellular

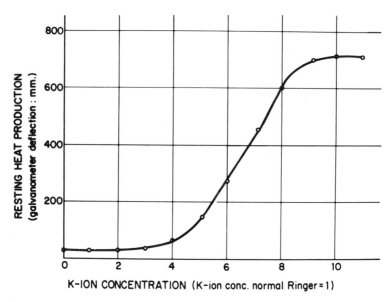

FIG. 13. Heat production *in vitro* rises if an isolated, perfused muscle is exposed to increasing levels of potassium in extracellular fluid. (From ref. 8.)

potassium concentration is successively increased from a concentration of 4 mEq/liter to approximately 8 to 9 mEq/liter, there occurs a linear response in heat production. This thermal response becomes flat above a concentration of 10 mEq/liter. It was also observed that exposure of skeletal muscle to hypertonic mannitol caused a virtually identical response in heat production and oxygen utilization. It is clearly appreciated now that if a muscle is suddenly immersed in a solution made hypertonic with a nonmetabolizable and impermeant substance, such as mannitol, water promptly flows under the osmotic force of the impermeant solute from the interior to the exterior of the cell. Since potassium concentration in muscle cell water is approximately 150 mEq/liter, the extracellular potassium concentration rises rapidly because potassium ions are simply dragged out in the process of accelerated water movement (solvent drag). Thus, essentially the same effects of hyperkalemia are generated by impermeant solute, and the effects on metabolism and heat production by the muscle cell appear to be identical. This process has an important clinical counterpart in insulin-deficient patients with diabetes mellitus. If a bolus of glucose or mannitol is administered to such a patient, the patient may immediately become hyperkalemic. Under normal conditions, introduction of a bolus of impermeable solute into the circulation may well effect removal of potassium ions from the intracellular space. However, there will occur an immediate release of insulin so that the ions are driven back into the cell. Usually, impermeant solute-induced hyperkalemia in patients with diabetes mellitus is only mild to modest. However, under certain conditions in which impaired ion transport prevails because of severe illness, such as thermal burns or generalized myopathy, substantial hyperkalemia may occur in association with acute hypertonicity.

Further studies on kaliogenic hypermetabolism have helped to provide some explanations for this interesting observation. As one would predict, increasing concentrations of extracellular potassium concentration obviously increase metabolism of the tissue in accordance with the increase in heat production. Thus, hyperkalemia *in vitro* stimulates increased metabolism of glucose and production of carbon dioxide and lactate. Additional studies have shown that as one would predict from the Nernst relationship, steadily increasing concentrations of extracellular potassium cause depolarization of the muscle cell and a corresponding rise of heat production as the muscle membrane potential falls from -90 mV to about -70 mV. This corresponds to elevation of extracellular potassium from 4 mEq/liter to 9 or 10 mEq/liter (Fig. 14). It is important to point out that these metabolic events associated with acute hyperkalemia are not associated with muscle contraction. This is important in physiologic terms, since exposure of a resting muscle to an ambient potassium concentration of 40 mEq/liter or higher results in contracture. Current evidence suggests that the most likely factor responsible for the increase of heat production and metabolism in kaliogenic hypermetabolism is the release of calcium from storage sites inside the cell. Depolarization of a

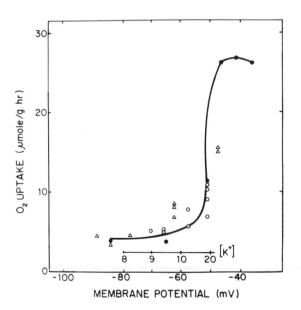

FIG. 14. *In vitro*, muscle oxygen utilization increases as potassium concentration in the surrounding fluid is increased, and resting membrane potential declines as a result of hyperkalemic depolarization.

muscle cell is associated with calcium release into the myoplasm by mechanisms that are poorly understood. Calcium thus released is thought to stimulate mitochondrial respiration. The estimated quantity of calcium ions released in the response to hyperkalemia is about 250 times smaller than the
calculated calcium release required to cause muscle cell contraction. The
respiratory stimulation induced by hyperkalemia can be blocked by depolarizing agents, such as procaine, or high concentrations in extracellular fluid of
divalent ions, such as magnesium, strontium, cobalt, or even calcium. Evidence that sodium movement and its subsequent transport outward by Na,
K-ATPase is not involved in the increased cellular respiration incident to
depolarization has been suggested by the finding that if sodium ions in extracellular fluid are replaced by choline, hypermetabolism still occurs. Evidence
that cellular depolarization *per se* does not cause hypermetabolism has been
shown by using dantrolene or deuterium to block the release of calcium from
the sarcoplasmic reticulum. If calcium release from these structures is prohib-
ited, hypermetabolism does not occur. Neither dantrolene nor deuterium
affects the membrane potential of the cell.

What practical effects might be implicated by kaliogenic hypermetabolism?
One consideration could be the disease known as "malignant hyperthermia."
This disease is a hereditary disorder characterized by instability of the sarcoplasmic reticulum of skeletal muscle cells in which marked metabolic heat
production occurs in response to either general anesthesia or administration
of depolarizing drugs. It is characterized by the rapid appearance of hyperkalemia, increased CO_2 production, metabolic acidosis, hypoxia, and a remarkable rise of body temperature up to values as high as 112°F (44.4°C). Rhabdomyolysis of severe degree invariably occurs. Untreated malignant hyperthermia attacks are usually fatal. Of great importance, the entire process can
be reversed or totally prevented by appropriate administration of dantrolene.

Hypothetically, an additional physiologic purpose of kaliogenic hyperkalemia could be the warm-up phenomenon. During exercise, the release of potassium ions from the contracting muscle cells just happens to be the optimal
concentration required to increase metabolic activity and, therefore, heat
production. It is noteworthy that patients medicated with dantrolene demonstrate decreased physical performance capacity and weakness.

SPURIOUS HYPOKALEMIA (27)

Some patients with leukemia are found to have hypokalemia as a result of *in
vitro* potassium uptake into leukemic cells. In one of our patients, serum
potassium levels were measured as low as 1.2 mEq/liter. Nearly all of these
patients have had chronic granulocytic leukemia except for one of ours who
had myelomonocytic leukemia. The event is not necessarily associated with
high white blood cell counts. There are no associated symptoms or electrocar-

diographic changes reflecting true hypokalemia. The diagnosis is established by demonstrating a normal potassium concentration in plasma that has been immediately separated from the blood sample and a progressive reduction in another sample of blood collected at the same time that has been allowed to stand 30 to 60 min. Although the mechanism for this event has not been clearly explained, it has been suggested that such leukocytes are abnormally permeable to cations and, in addition, that Na,K-ATPase activity is increased. Thus, it would appear that as sodium ions enter the cells at a rate above normal, the pump responds by extruding the sodium ions and partially exchanging them for potassium. The process is dependent upon energy consumption, since as potassium levels fall, glucose concentrations also fall and lactate levels rise. Spurious hypoglycemia and spurious lactate elevations also are noted clinically.

It should be kept in mind that leukemia may also be associated with true potassium deficiency and hypokalemia as a result of renal potassium wasting. Most of these patients have monocytic leukemia and excrete large quantities of lysozyme into the urine. Presumably, lysozyme causes proximal tubular toxicity.

REFERENCES

1. Bergstrom, J., and Hultman, E. (1966): Muscle glycogen synthesis after exercise: An enhancing factor localized to the muscle cells in man. *Nature*, 210:309–310.
2. Bottger, I., Schlein, E. M., Faloona, G. R., Knochel, J. P., and Unger, R. H. (1972): The effect of exercise on glucagon secretion. *J. Clin. Endocrinol. Metab.*, 35:117–125.
3. Clausen, T., Everts, M. E., and Kjeldsen, K. (1987): Quantification of the maximum capacity for active sodium-potassium transport in rat skeletal muscle. *J. Physiol.*, 388:163–181.
4. Clausen, T., and Flatman, J. A. (1987): Effects of insulin and epinephrine on Na^+-K^+ and glucose transport in soleus muscle. *Am. J. Physiol.*, 252:E1–E8.
5. Clausen, T., and Kjeldsen, K. (1987): Effects of potassium deficiency on Na, K homeostasis and Na^+, K^+-ATPase in muscle. In: *Current Topics in Membranes and Transport. Potassium Transport: Physiology and Pathophysiology*, edited by G. Giebisch, pp. 403–419. Academic Press, Orlando, FL.
6. Conn, J. W. (1965): Hypertension, the potassium ion and impaired carbohydrate tolerance. *N. Engl. J. Med.*, 273:1135–1143.
7. Erlij, D., Shen, W. K., Remade, P., and Schoen, H. (1982): Effects of dantrolene and D_2O on K^+-stimulated respiration of skeletal muscle. *Am. J. Physiol.*, 243:C87–C95.
8. Fenn, W. O. (1931): The oxygen consumption of muscles made nonirritable by sugar solutions. *Am. J. Physiol.*, 97:635–647.
9. Galvez, O. G., Roberts, B. W., Bay, W. H., et al. (1976): Studies of the mechanism of polyuria with hypokalemia. *Kidney Int.*, 10:583.
10. Gardner, L. I., Talbot, N. B., Cook, C. D., Berman, H., and Uribe, C. (1950): The effect of potassium deficiency on carbohydrate metabolism. *J. Lab. Clin. Med.*, 35:592–602.
11. Gaynor, M. L., Ferguson, E. R., and Knochel, J. P. (1982): The effect of prostaglandin synthesis inhibitors on glucose tolerance in potassium deficiency. *Clin. Res.*, 30:571.
12. Gullner, H. G., Lake, C. R., Gill, J. R. Jr., and Lakatua, D. J. (1982): Hypokalemia stimulates plasma epinephrine and norepinephrine in the rats. *Arch. Int. Pharmacodyn. Ther.*, 260:78–82.
13. Hazeyama, Y., and Sparks, H. V. (1979): A model of potassium ion efflux during exercise of skeletal muscle. *Am. J. Physiol.*, 236:R83–R90.

14. Helderman, J. H., Elahi, D., Andersen, D. K., et al. (1983): Prevention of the glucose intolerance of thiazide diuretics by maintenance of body potassium. *Diabetes*, 32:106–111.
15. Issekutz, B. Jr. (1970): Interrelationships of free fatty acids, lactic acid, and glucose in muscle metabolism. In: *The Physiology and Biochemistry of Muscle as a Food*, 2, edited by E. J. Briskey, R. G. Cassens, and B. B. Marsh, pp. 623–643. University of Wisconsin Press, Madison.
16. Kjellmer, I. (1965): Studies on exercise hyperemia. *Acta Physiol. Scand.*, 64:5–26.
17. Knochel, J. P. (1987): Metabolism and potassium. In: *Current Topics in Membranes and Transport. Potassium Transport: Physiology and Pathophysiology*, edited by G. Giebisch, pp. 383–400. Academic Press, Orlando, FL.
18. Knochel, J. P. (1977): Role of glucoregulatory hormones in potassium homeostasis. *Kidney Int.*, 11:443–452.
19. Knochel, J. P., Blachley, J. D., Johnson, J. H., and Carter, N. W. (1985): Muscle cell electrical hyperpolarization and reduced exercise hyperkalemia in physically conditioned dogs. *J. Clin. Invest.*, 75:740–745.
20. Knochel, J. P., Dotin, L. N., and Hamburger, R. J. (1972): Pathophysiology of intense physical conditioning in a hot climate. *J. Clin. Invest.*, 51:242–255.
21. Knochel, J. P., and Schlein, E. M. (1972): On the mechanism of rhabdomyolysis in potassium depletion. *J. Clin. Invest.*, 51:1750–1758.
22. Kozlowski, S., Brzezinska, Z., Kruk, B., Kaciuba-Uscilko, H., Greenleaf, J. E., and Nazar, K. (1985): Exercise hyperthermia as a factor limiting physical performance: Temperature effect on muscle metabolism. *J. Appl. Physiol*, 59:766–773.
23. Lim, M., Linton, R. A. F., Wolff, C. B., and Band, D. M. (1981): Propranolol, exercise, and arterial plasma potassium. *Lancet*, 2:591.
24. Losert, W. (1968): Relationships between electrolyte balance and carbohydrate metabolism. *Dtsch. Med. Wochenschr.*, 93:1723–1732.
25. McKechnie, J. K., Leary, W. P., and Joubert, S. M. (1967): Some electrocardiographic and biochemical changes recorded in marathon runners. *S. Afr. Med. J.*, 41:722–725.
26. Moore, R. D., and Rabovsky, J. L. (1979): Mechanism of insulin action on resting membrane potential of frog skeletal muscle. *Am. J. Physiol.*, 236:C249–C254.
27. Naparstek, Y., and Gutman, A. (1984): Case report: Spurious hypokalemia in myeloproliferative disorders. *Am. J. Med. Sci.*, 288:175–177.
28. Osnes, J. B., and Hermansen, L. (1972): Acid-base balance after maximal exercise of short duration. *J. Appl. Physiol.*, 32:59–63.
29. Robertson, P. (1983): Hypothesis: PGE, carbohydrate homeostasis, and insulin secretion. *Diabetes*, 32:231–234.
30. Rose, K. D. (1985): Warning for millions: Exercise can deplete body potassium. *The Physician and Sports Medicine*, pp. 67–70.
31. Rose, K. D., Dunn, F. L., and Bargen, D. (1966): Serum electrolyte relationship to electrocardiographic change in exercising athletes. *JAMA*, 195:111–114.
32. Rowell, L. B. (1986): Cardiovascular adaptations to chronic physical activity and inactivity. In: *Human Circulation: Regulation During Physical Stress*, pp. 257–286. Oxford University Press, New York.
33. Saltin, B., Blomqvist, G., Mitchell, J. H., Johnson, R. L. Jr., Wildenthal, K., and Chapman, C. B. (1968): Response to exercise after bed rest and after training. *Am. Heart Assoc. Monogr.*, 23:VII-1–78.
34. VanderKloot, W. G. (1967): Potassium-stimulated respiration and intracellular calcium release in frog skeletal muscle. *J. Physiol.*, 191:141–165.
35. Zierler, K., and Rogus, E. M. (1980): Hyperpolarization as a mediator of insulin action: Increased muscle glucose uptake induced electrically. *Am. J. Physiol.*, 239:E21–E29.

General Review Articles

36. Bia, M. J., and DeFronzo, R. A. (1981): Extrarenal potassium homeostasis. *Am. J. Physiol.*, 240:F257–F268.

37. Clausen, T. (1988): Factors regulating skeletal muscle Na,K-ATPase in man. *Kidney Int. (in press)*.

38. Knochel, J. P. (1985): Potassium gradients and neuromuscular excitability. In: *The Kidney, Physiology and Pathophysiology of Electrolyte Metabolism*, edited by D. W. Seldin and G. Giebisch, pp. 1207–1221. Raven Press, New York.

39. Sterns, R. H., Cox, M., Feig, P. U., and Singer, I. (1981): Internal potassium balance and the control of the plasma potassium concentration. *Medicine*, 60:339–354.

The Regulation of Potassium Balance, edited
by Donald W. Seldin and Gerhard Giebisch,
Raven Press, Ltd., New York © 1989.

3

Potassium and Tissue Excitability

David E. Clapham

*Cardiovascular Division, Brigham and Women's Hospital/Harvard Medical School,
Boston, Massachusetts 02115*

What Is Excitability?
  Membrane Potentials • Ion Channels • Brief Description of Patch
  Clamp Techniques • Channel Gating • Spatial Organization of Chan-
  nels • Drugs Block Channels
Action Potentials in Neurons and Skeletal Muscle
  Skeletal Muscle Excitability • Summary of Excitability in Nerve and
  Muscle
Cardiac Action Potential
  Pacemaker Activity • Summary of Cardiac Action Potentials
Short Review of Conduction
Antiarrhythmic Drugs
References

WHAT IS EXCITABILITY? (6,7,17)

Excitability is the ability of nerves, muscle, and other tissues or cells to
undergo changes that lead to a physiologic response. This definition is broad
enough to include not only the contraction of muscle or the firing of a nerve
but also such events as degranulation of mast cells and the secretion of insulin
from the pancreas. All types of cells, even plant cells, have the ability to respond to a stimulus. This response may be fast or slow, electrical or biochemical. The purpose of this chapter is to explain the more prominent physiologic
responses that occur when potassium balance is lost. Nerve and muscle are
the tissues most affected in this setting.

The practical importance of potassium balance is clear to any physician
who has seen an arrhythmia in a patient induced by too high or too low potassium concentration ($[K^+]$). Figure 1 shows a succession of electrocardiograms
(ECGs) from patients with various serum levels of potassium. The first sign of
elevated $[K^+]$ is the appearance of tall thin T waves. With continued $[K^+]$

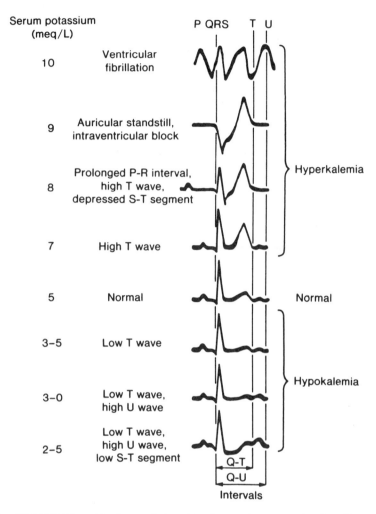

FIG. 1. Electrocardiographic changes induced by changes in serum potassium. (From ref. 1.)

increase, the P-R interval is prolonged, the S-T segment is depressed, and the QRS interval is lengthened. Finally, the P wave disappears, and the QRS complex broadens until the ECG appears sinusoidal. Ventricular fibrillation often follows. Sometimes, a very high serum potassium level may result in death despite a normal ECG, or a life-threatening arrhythmia may develop despite only modest elevation of $[K^+]$. Emergency measures are required to counteract the effects of hyperkalemia on the heart. Calcium should be administered to antagonize the cardiac toxicity of hyperkalemia. Sodium bicarbonate and glucose-insulin injections are administered to cause potassium to shift (transiently) into cells; cation exchange resins or hemodialysis is required to actually remove potassium from the body. Hypokalemia is also arrhythmo-genic and life threatening. Low serum [K$^+$] results in apparent prolongation of the Q-T interval because of an emerging U wave, T wave inversion, and sagging of the S-T segment. One goal of this chapter is to explain why high and low potassium levels give rise to arrhythmias or increased excitability of cardiac tissue, nerves, and muscle and, conversely, why certain measures counteract this excitability.

Membrane Potentials

Potassium plays a prominent role in excitability since the membrane po-tential of cells is determined largely by internal and external potassium con-centrations. The membrane potential of cells is close to the potassium equilib-rium potential (~-90 mV), since the resting membrane is mainly permeable to potassium ions rather than to sodium, chloride, calcium, or other ions.

To understand the importance of potassium in cell excitability, a review of the factors responsible for the membrane potential is necessary. Cells are enclosed by a bimolecular lipid membrane. Various proteins span the mem-brane and relay messages between the extracellular and intracellular environ-ments. The lipid bilayer is ~80 angstroms (Å) thick and lets very few ions through. In short, it is an excellent insulator.

Consider for a moment the electrolyte content of the intracellular and extracellular space (Fig. 2). The predominant cation inside the cell is potas-sium, and outside it is sodium. Calcium concentration inside the cell is extremely low (10–100 nM), whereas it is 200,000 times higher (~2 mM) outside the cell. Chloride is ~30 times higher outside the cell than inside (Table 1). Thus, for charge-carrying ions, the extracellular solution is largely sodium chloride, whereas the intracellular solution is a potassium chloride solution with low [Ca^{2+}]. Extracellular pH is ~7.4, and intracellular pH is approximately 7.2.

Ions pass through the membrane via proteinaceous holes called ion chan-nels. Suppose a cell membrane is permeable only to K$^+$ ions. The equilib-rium potential is defined as the membrane potential at which no ions flow, on average, across the membrane. This state occurs when there is no energy difference between the inside and outside of the cell. There are two relevant kinds of stored energy: chemical and electrical. Chemical energy arises from entropy; The lowest energy state occurs when the particles are distributed so that there is no concentration difference from one region to another. Random thermal motion causes particles to diffuse from regions of high concentration to regions of low concentration. Electrical energy on the other hand arises from charge separation. Potential differences drive charged ions down an electrical gradient so that positively charged ions flow away from the positive pole of a battery or from other positive charges. Now consider the situation in

A

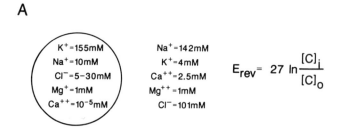

$$E_{rev} = 27 \ln \frac{[C]_i}{[C]_o}$$

B

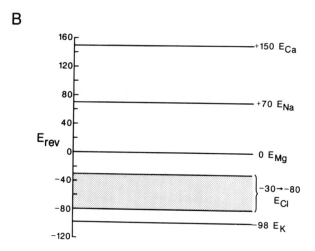

FIG. 2. A: Electrolyte content of an average mammalian cell. **B:** Nernst (equilibrium) potentials for the concentrations shown in **A.** The Nernst potential is the reversal potential for a purely ion selective channel. (E) equilibrium potential; (E_{rev}) reversal potential; ($[C]_i$) concentration inside; ($[C]_o$) concentration outside.

TABLE 1. *Approximate free extracellular and intracellular*
ion concentrations for mammalian cells

Ion	Extracellular concentration[a] (mM)	Intracellular concentration[b] (mM)	$\dfrac{[C]_o}{[C]_i}$	Nernst potential at 37°C
Na	142	10	14.2	+71
Ca	2.5	<0.0001	>25,000	>+150 mV
Mg	1	1	1	0
K	4	155	0.025	−98
Cl	101	5–30	3–20	−29 to −80

$[C]_o$, concentration outside; $[C]_i$, concentration inside.
[a] Extracellular concentrations are means from plasma or serum.
[b] Intracellular concentrations are estimates.

our idealized cell membrane with only K^+ selective channels allowing ions to flow. With 140 mM KCl inside the cell and 4 mM KCl outside the cell, K^+ ions will flow down their concentration gradients until a slight excess of cations exists in the dilute solution. The excess ions are driven there by the high concentration gradient across the membrane and are forced to migrate alone by the cation-selective nature of the ion channels. This slight excess of charge on the outside of the cell creates a negative membrane potential (inside negative). Equilibrium exists when the electrical forces exactly match and counteract the chemical forces. Thus, K^+ ions flow down their concentration gradient from inside the cell to outside the cell until a sufficient excess of charge develops to repel the cations. At this point, where electrical and chemical energy are exactly equal, no net current flows across the membrane, and an equilibrium exists. This potential equilibrium is called the Nernst potential. For a purely potassium selective membrane, the Nernst potential is expressed as follows:

$$E_K = \frac{RT}{F} \ln [K]_o/[K]_i$$

where R is the gas constant, T is the absolute temperature in degrees Kelvin, and F is the Faraday constant. RT/F is approximately 25 mV at room temperature, so that for our example:

$$E_K = 25 \text{ mV} \ln (4/145) = -90 \text{ mV}$$

Thus, a cell with only K^+ selective channels in its membrane should come to an equilibrium or resting membrane potential of -90 mV. The Nernst potential is crucial to understanding excitability in cells. Given the concentration of ions inside and outside the cells and the types and numbers of ion selective channels in the membrane, one can predict much about the electrical activity of a cell.

The idealized cell above had only K^+ selective channels in the cell membrane. Suppose that instead of being a purely K^+ selective membrane, channels that allow other ions to pass were added to the membrane. If those channels were always open, the new equilibrium potential would be dependent on the relative permeability of the various channels. The resting membrane potential would not be E_K but some other potential. This potential is predicted by an equation that is a modification of the Nernst equation, the Goldman-Hodgkin-Katz (GHK) constant field equation:

$$E_m = \frac{RT}{F} \ln \frac{P_K[K]_o + P_{Na}[Na]_o + P_{Cl}[Cl]_i}{P_K[K]_i + P_{Na}[Na]_i + P_{Cl}[Cl]_o}$$

The GHK equation takes into account the main permeant $(P = \text{permeability})$ ions at rest; Na, K, and Cl. Most cells have resting membrane potentials of -60 mV to -90 mV. Resting potentials are close to E_K, since the highest permeability of biologic membranes at rest is to potassium ions.

Obviously, cells are not static, and if other ions were allowed into the cell, for example, during an action potential, the concentration gradients would eventually be depleted. To prevent this rundown of concentration gradients, energy is required. Cells actively extrude ions by another class of proteins in the membrane; ion pumps. A classic example of an ion pump is the Na, K-ATPase pump, which under normal conditions moves sodium ions out of the cell while bringing K^+ ions back into the cell. To do so requires energy, and ATP provides the energy for the rearrangement of the pump proteins that results in Na extrusion and K^+ uptake. Other pumps in the membrane transport calcium out in exchange for sodium, or hydrogen in exchange for sodium. These pumps are much slower than channels in transporting ions across the membrane. Per protein, ion channels allow 10^6 to 10^7 ions per second to flow down their concentration gradient, whereas pumps transport ions at rates of $\sim 10^3$ ions per second. The Na,K exchange pump is electrogenic and transports 3 Na^+ ions outward and 2 K^+ ions inward per ATP hydrolyzed. Generally, pumps do not have rapid, major effects on cellular action potentials, and we will not emphasize them in future discussion of excitability. Currently there is some discussion of the role of Na, Ca exchange in arrhythmogenesis. Clinically, the importance of pumps is evident in the profound effect of digitalis or ouabain in causing long-term blockade of Na,K exchange. The end result is a change in equilibrium potentials secondary to rundown of concentration gradients.

Ion Channels

Ion pumps slowly build up the concentration gradients necessary for the resting membrane potential to be $\sim E_K$. The transmembrane potential can be changed rapidly by opening channels that allow ions to flow down their concentration gradients. Every time one of these ion selective pores opens, it tends to drive the membrane potential to its particular Nernst potential. For example, suppose a cell has only one potassium channel and one sodium channel. When the sodium channel opens, the transmembrane potential goes to E_{Na} (about +55 mV). Now if the sodium channel closes and the potassium channel opens, the membrane potential is rapidly driven to E_K (~ -90 mV). Of course, in real cells, a mixture of sodium, calcium, chloride, and potassium channels is opening. The membrane potential is determined then by the number of channels of each type and the amount of current each channel lets through the membrane.

There are a wide variety of channels in cell membranes. Channels have the common property that they are proteins that can allow millions of ions per second to flow through them. Some are specific for certain ions (selective), whereas others allow a variety of cations or cations and anions (nonselective) to pass through the cell membrane. For each channel, we can define a conductance. The conductance reflects the ease with which ions flow through the channel. A high conductance channel allows more ions to flow for a particular driving voltage than does a low conductance channel. We usually denote the single channel conductance γ to distinguish it from the conductance of the entire population of channels, G. Conductance (γ) is defined as the ratio of single channel current amplitude (i) to driving voltage (V):

$$\gamma = \frac{i}{V}$$

The units of single channel conductance are given as Siemens (ohms^{-1}). The voltage (V) in this case is the difference between the membrane potential at which no current flows through the membrane, E_{rev} (reversal potential), and the particular voltage (E) that the channel is experiencing ($V = E - E_{rev}$). The reversal potential is simply the Nernst potential for a perfectly selective ion channel.

Figure 3 shows the activity of a single potassium channel measured from a single heart cell. Each opening of a single channel is accompanied by a burst of current, seen as the boxlike transitions from the base line. Each time a channel opens at, for example, 10 mV transmembrane potential, 5 pico-amperes (pA) of current flows through it. The amplitude of each channel opening plotted against membrane voltage gives the current-voltage relation, or i-V. (Normally, i denotes single channel current, whereas I is used for net membrane currents.) The slope of the i-V relation is the single channel conductance. For this channel, the slope is about 50 picoSiemens (pS) under physiologic conditions (that is, 4 mM potassium concentration outside the cell, 140 mM K^+ concentration inside the cell). This is a relatively large conductance compared to many other ion channels but by no means the largest that has been recorded. Single channel conductances range from less than 1 pS to over 400 pS. Oddly, the selectivity of the ion channel is not paralleled by the single channel conductance. Large conductance channels may be very selective for K^+ ions. For example, a channel known as $i_{K.Ca}$, a calcium-activated single channel found in many cells, is very K^+ selective and has a conductance of ~200 pS. Its reversal potential is almost exactly E_K. On the other hand, a very nonselective channel, known as i_f has a conductance ~1 pS and a reversal potential near 0 mV. Thus, selectivity and conductance are independent. A channel is not a simple hole with variable diameter.

The conductance of a single channel is an inherent property of a channel. If one measures channel conductance in one cell type, the same channel will have a very similar, if not identical, conductance in another cell. We assume that each channel is a single gene product and that the proteins act in very similar ways in various cells. But conductance does increase with the concentration of ionic species. This is in part because there are more charge carriers at higher concentration and more current flows for a given voltage difference across the channel. This chapter is limited to discussion of channels under

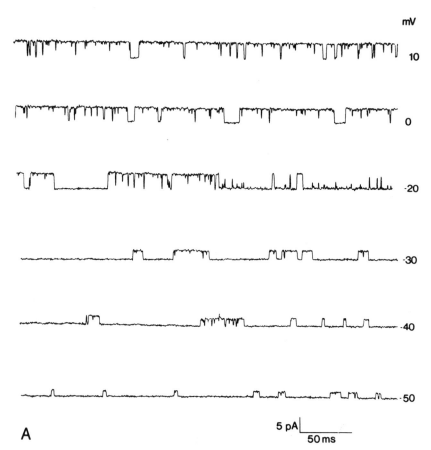

FIG. 3. A: Single potassium selective channel openings from cardiac ventricular cell membranes. Current through a small patch of membrane is measured at a constant voltage (voltage clamp). As the patch is depolarized, the driving force (E-E_K) increases, as does the single channel current (i). Note also that the probability that the channel current is in the open state also increases with depolarization. **B:** Single channel i-V relation. The slope of the i-V relation gives the single channel conductance.

physiologic concentrations of ions. Under most circumstances, the change in conductance with higher concentration of ions has little physiologic relevance. However, we will see that at least one channel changes its behavior in response to the small elevations in ion concentrations seen physiologically.

Brief Description of Patch Clamp Techniques

The workings of ion channels in cell membranes have been discovered largely through the use of voltage clamp techniques. In voltage clamp, the membrane potential is automatically held to a desired voltage set by the ex-

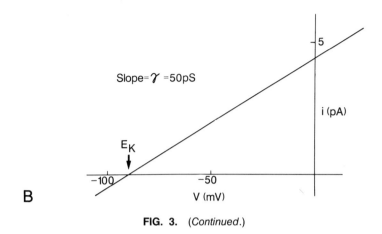

FIG. 3. (*Continued.*)

perimentalist. The current that flows to maintain this voltage is then measured. The most interesting component of this current is the part that flows through ion channels in the membrane. Recently, it has become possible to measure the ionic current through single cells or even through single ion channels. This is accomplished by placing a glass pipette (blunt tip ~1 μm in diameter) on the surface of the cell. The potential inside the pipette is controlled. The membrane potential of the tiny patch of membrane is then simply the intracellular potential minus the pipette potential. This is called a "cell-attached" patch because the cell is still intact. If the patch is broken (by suction applied to the pipette), the voltage across the entire cell membrane can be controlled, and the net ionic current can be measured (whole-cell recording). If the pipette is pulled away from the cell, a small patch of membrane stays attached to the pipette with its outside surface facing the bath. This is called an "outside-out" patch. A similar manipulation from the cell-attached state can give an "inside-out" patch. In each patch, the seal between the pipette and cell membrane is so tight that all the current is collected by the pipette. The accuracy of current measurement is such that single channel openings can be measured. These currents are in the range of 10^{-12} amperes (picoamperes).

Channel Gating

Ion channels control membrane potential by gating the flow of ions. How are the ion channels themselves controlled? Basically, there are three types of control over opening or closing (gating) of ion channels.

Voltage-Gated Ion Channels

Many ion channels open in response to changes in voltage across the membrane. Presumably, the channel protein or a charged part of the protein moves in response to the electric field applied, opening the conductive pathway and allowing ions to flow down their concentration gradient. In general, channels are either open or closed; a single ion channel does not increase its conductance in a graded fashion. However, the probability that a channel is in an open or closed state is graded with voltage. As shown in Fig. 3, the channel is mainly in a closed state, with rare openings at hyperpolarized voltages. As the membrane is depolarized, the channel spends more and more of its time in the open state until, at 10 mV, it is open more than 90% of the time. This is a clear example of voltage-dependent gating. Most voltage-gated channels move from a closed to an open state with depolarization. If the probability of a channel being open is increased with depolarization, the current flow through that channel is not necessarily increased. This is easily seen in the case where depolarization is in the direction of the channel's reversal potential. By reducing the chemical driving force, the current flow is reduced through the channel. The current through a single sodium channel increases initially with depolarization because the time the channel stays open increases, but gradually as the potential approaches E_{Na}, the driving force is smaller, and the current decreases eventually to zero at E_{Na}.

Each channel type is pulling the membrane potential to its reversal potential. The membrane potential cannot go beyond the highest reversal potentials in either the depolarized or hyperpolarized direction. Exactly where the membrane potential is at any moment in time is determined by which channel type is winning the tug-of-war. As in any tug-of-war, the winners are on the side with the largest or the most numerous pullers.

Channels also can decrease in conductance, despite depolarization, by a more complicated process. Suppose that at depolarized voltages the channel is squeezed and the channel pore allows fewer ions per second to pass. Alternatively, suppose that ions are so rapidly pushed into the channel pore that they jam the channel, much like people jamming the exit in a crowded room. In this case, the probability that the channel is open may be high, but the conductance decreases. This process is called "single channel rectification" and gives rise to a nonlinear single channel, current-voltage relation. Clear examples of rectification are seen for two types of potassium channels in heart (Fig. 4). In the case of the muscarinic-gated K^+ channel in heart, the single channel conductance decreases above E_K so that K^+ ions can flow more easily in the inward direction than in the outward direction. When magnesium is removed from the intracellular face of the channel, current passes equally well in either direction (rectification is removed). Inward rectification of potassium channels is an important point to which we will return when discussing generation of the action potential.

Most channels involved in generation of the action potential are voltage-gated. Voltage control of gating enables high-speed depolarization and propagation as well as more subtle widespread modulation of excitability in electrically coupled tissue.

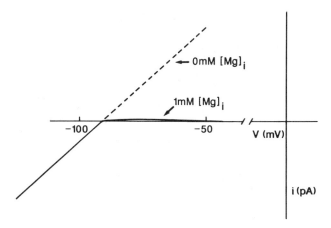

FIG. 4. Single channel rectification. In some K^+ channels, single channel current flows more easily in the inward direction than in the outward direction. When intracellular Mg^{2+} ions are removed, the channel conducts ions equally in either direction (dotted line).

Transmitter-Gated Ion Channels

Ion channels may be modulated by binding of specific molecules to receptors. When bound, these receptors may result in channel opening either directly or indirectly via a second messenger (Fig. 5). The nicotinic receptor-channel complex is an example of the first type of transmitter-gated channel. The details of the structure of the nicotinic channel are known (Fig. 6). Two acetylcholine (ACh) molecules bind to a specific subunit on the channel complex to result in a molecular rearrangement that allows Na, K, and Ca ions to flow through the channel. Since the nicotinic channel is nonselective, its reversal potential is close to zero. When ACh binds the acetylcholine channel, the channel opens and the membrane is driven toward 0 mV. Thus, nicotinic channels are excitatory; they depolarize cells to the range where sodium channels open to initiate an action potential.

The muscarinic ACh-gated K^+ channel is another transmitter-gated channel. In this case, channel gating involves an intermediate step. First, ACh binds to a muscarinic receptor. The receptor interacts with a guanosine triphosphate (GTP)-binding protein (G protein) in the membrane to allow intracellular GTP to bind to the α subunit of the G protein. The α and $\beta\gamma$ subunits then split, and the subunits cause an inward rectifying K^+ channel to open. When GTP is hydrolyzed back to guanosine diphosphate (GDP), the subunits reassociate, and the channel closes (Fig. 7). The muscarinic-gated K^+ channel in heart atria, SA, and AV nodes slows the heart rate when the vagus nerve releases ACh. Heart rate is slowed in part because this channel drives the membrane toward E_K in the hyperpolarizing direction, away from the region of regenerative inward currents.

(A) CHANNEL USING INTRINSIC SENSOR

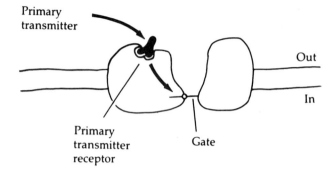

(B) CHANNEL USING REMOTE SENSOR

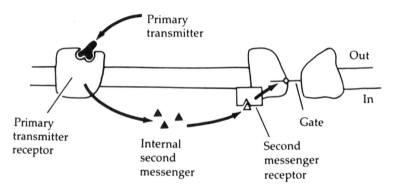

FIG. 5. Ligand-gated ion channels may be activated (**A**) by direct binding to the channel or (**B**) via generation of an intracellular second messenger. (From ref. 7.)

An even more complicated mechanism couples the beta-adrenergic receptor to a calcium channel. Epinephrine binds the beta receptor. The beta receptor interacts with a stimulatory G protein, called G_s. Presumably, GTP binds the α subunit of G_s, the α_s-GTP and $\beta\gamma$ complexes split, the active α_s-GTP complex binds the catalytic subunit of adenylyl cyclase, and cyclic AMP (cAMP) production is increased. Increased cAMP activates protein kinase A to phosphorylate a calcium channel. The phosphorylated calcium channel has a higher probability of opening in its active voltage range than does a nonphosphorylated calcium channel. In this manner, epinephrine increases calcium current and the force of contraction in heart muscle. However, increased cAMP also results in the phosphorylation of another K^+ channel (called the "delayed rectifier K^+ channel"), whose probability of opening is also increased. The net result may be an increase in calcium current but a shortening of the action potential and an increase in heart rate.

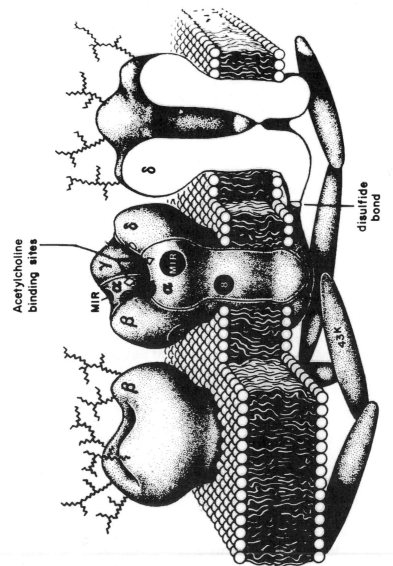

FIG. 6. A structural model of the acetylcholine-channel receptor complex. (From ref. 13.)

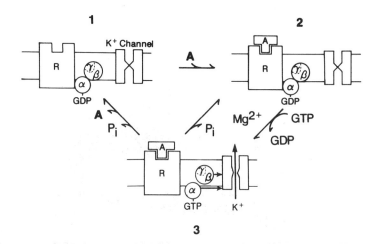

FIG. 7. The vagus nerve releases acetylcholine (ACh) on atrial and nodal cells to slow the heart rate. This is accomplished through muscarinic receptor coupling to a K^+ channel. Some of the details of coupling between receptor and channel are now known. ACh binds to the muscarinic receptor. In the presence of intracellular guanosine triphosphate (GTP) and Mg^{2+}, a GTP-binding protein splits into α and $\beta\gamma$ subunits. The subunits cause the potassium channel to open. Outward current then drives the membrane potential to E_K.

The use of second messengers to couple receptors to channels is a common theme in excitable tissues. Their use allows for a huge variety of control mechanisms, both on the rate of the enzymatic reactions and directly on channel gating. Moreover, some receptors share the same channel. For example, adenosine and ACh bind different receptors, but both open the same K^+ channel. Similarly, γ-aminobutyric acid (GABA) and glycine receptors share the same chloride channel in nervous tissue.

Intracellular Modulation of Channels

Ion channels may be activated or inactivated by various intracellular ion concentrations. The clearest example of such a channel is the ubiquitous, large conductance calcium-activated potassium channel ($i_{K.Ca}$). This channel is very selective for potassium ions and is very efficient in transferring large numbers of potassium ions out of the cell. It is activated by both voltage and intracellular calcium so that at low levels of intracellular calcium, it opens only with very large depolarizations ($\sim +40- +50$ mV). Figure 8 shows the range of activity measured for $I_{K.Ca}$ with varying voltage and [Ca]. The calcium-activated K^+ channel serves to rapidly repolarize the cell when intracellular calcium rises or when the membrane potential is very positive. Its ubiquitous nature may result from the necessity of cells to protect themselves from prolonged depolarization and calcium overload.

Another example of intracellular modulation of a channel is the ATP depletion-dependent channel found in heart cells. This channel is also K^+ selec-

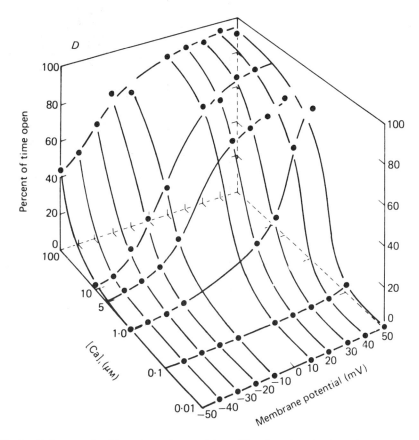

FIG. 8. Voltage and calcium dependence of $I_{K.Ca}$. The time that the $I_{K.Ca}$ channel spends in the open state is a function of both intracellular calcium concentration and transmembrane potential. (From ref. 2.)

tive with large conductance. It is normally off when ATP levels are normal (3–4 mM) within the cell but is activated when ATP is low. The obvious physiologic advantage is that the channel rapidly repolarizes the cell when the cell is metabolically exhausted. A third channel of this nature, again in heart cells, is the sodium-activated K^+ channel; $i_{K.Na}$ begins to open as intracellular sodium rises to the millimolar range. Since prolonged depolarization increases intracellular calcium and subsequently intracellular sodium via the Na,Ca pump, this channel is again activated in a tired cell and serves to repolarize it quickly. Thus, it is helpful to think of channels as enzymes whose sole purpose is to transfer ions across the membranes. These enzymes have several modulation sites that speed up or slow down the reaction.

Some well-known channels in mammalian tissue are shown in Table 2, which is divided into inward, or excitatory (under physiologic conditions), channels and outward, or stabilizing, channels.

TABLE 2. Selected channels from excitable cell membranes

Name	Charge carrier	Single channel conductance[a] (ps)	Activation mechanism	Inactivation mechanism	Intracellular modifier	Blocker
			Inward			
I_{Na}	Na	15	Voltage	Voltage		TTX[b]
I_{Na}	Na	7–10	Voltage			Amiloride
$I_{Ca(L)}$	Ca	25	Voltage	Ca?	cAMP + PKA[b]	Dihydropyridines Cd, Co^{2+}, La^{3+}, ω-conus toxin
$I_{Ca(T)}$	Ca	8	Voltage	Voltage		$Cd, Co^{2+}, La^{3+}, Ni^{2+}$
$I_{Ca(N)}$	Ca	13	Voltage	Voltage		Cd, Co^{2+}, La^{3+}, ω-conus toxin
I_f	Na, K	1	Voltage	Voltage	cAMP + PKA	
I_{Ti}	Na, K	?	$[Ca]_i$			
I_{ACh}	Na, K, Ca	40	ACh[b]	Desensitization		Curare

Outward

Current	Ion	Conductance (pS)	Activation		Modulation	Blockers
Delayed rectifier						
I_K	K	8, 15, 60		Voltage	cAMP + PKA	Cs, Ba
I_K	K	15		Voltage	cAMP, Ca	
Inward rectifier						
I_{K1}	K	4	K_o		Mg	Cs, Ba, Na, TEA[b]
I_A	K	18–22	Voltage		PKC[b]	4-AP[b], TEA
I_K (M)	K	?	Voltage	Voltage (Muscarinic ACh)		Ba^{2+}, 4AP, TEA
$I_{K,Ca}$	K	200	Voltage + $[Ca]_i$		PKC	TEA, charybdotoxin, Apamin
		30	$[Ca]_i$			
$I_{K,Na}$[b]	K	207	Na_i			
$I_{K,ATP}$[b]	K	32	Loss of ATP[b]			ATP, Ba
$I_{K,ACh}$[b]	K	4	ACh	Desensitization	Mg	(Atropine) Cs, Ba^{2+}
I_{Cl}	Cl	430	Voltage			

[a] Conductances given are for common test conditions and are not necessarily physiologic conditions (e.g., calcium channel conductances are given for 110 mm Ba^{2+}).

[b] ACh, acetylcholine; 4-AP, 4-aminopyridine; ATP, adenosine triphosphate; PKA, protein kinase A; PKC, protein kinase C; TTX, tetrodotoxin; TEA, tetraethylammonium.

Spatial Organization of Channels

The cell membrane is like an ocean of lipid, with floating, but anchored, protein buoys. Channels are not located randomly in the cell membrane but often are concentrated in various areas for specific reasons. For example, nicotinic ACh and sodium channels are much more densely localized under the synapse than elsewhere in the membrane. Once ACh channels open and cause sufficient depolarization to activate the sodium channels, propagation is assured because of their high density in this critical area. One of the most famous and spectacular localizations of ion channels occurs in the node of Ranvier in myelinated nerve. This localization provides a large inward current at nodal intervals and assures propagation of the action potential across myelinated areas of low channel density.

In the retina, a specialized glial cell has a very high density of K^+ channels on a foot process that abuts the vitreous humor. The rest of the cell body has a low density of channels. The high conductance of the foot process clamps the cell potential to E_K. Potassium accumulation from firing neurons around the cell body drives potassium into the cell body and out the foot process to equilibrate in the large space of the vitreous humor. This potassium siphoning effect is a direct result of nonuniform K^+ channel distribution.

Drugs Block Channels

Many drugs exert their effects by altering the gating of ion channels. There are several ways in which drugs modify ionic currents, but the simplest way is by channel blockade. The first example of a drug effect on a single channel is shown in Fig. 9. In this case, an ACh-activated channel was blocked by a lidocaine derivative. The channel could not close once the molecule inserted itself into the pore of the channel, nor could ions pass through the channel. The current is chopped into rapid openings and closings as drug concentration rises. However, the total time the channel stays open is not changed, since the channel cannot close from the blocked state. Other drugs may bind channels more tightly and keep the channel closed. A well-known toxin from the puffer fish, tetrodotoxin, closes sodium channels for long durations. How it closes the channel is not known in detail. Other toxins and drugs may increase total current through a channel by prolonging open time. For instance, benzodiazepines, the class of drugs represented by the well-known diazepam, increases the probability that GABA-activated chloride channels open.

Since many ion channels are common to cells, drugs typically cause side effects. In other words, drugs alter the gating of channels in cells other than the cell type intended. A related problem is that useful drugs often block more than one channel type. For example, quinidine and procaine not only block sodium channels but also have pronounced effects on many potassium

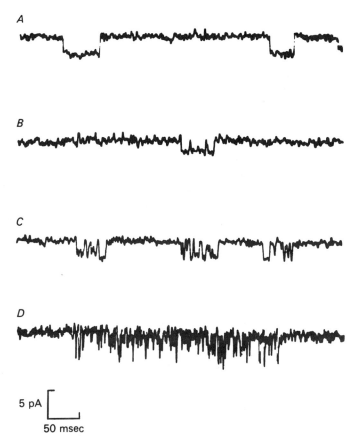

A

B

C

D

5 pA

50 msec

FIG. 9. Block of single nicotinic acetylcholine (ACh)-activated channels by the local anesthetic, QX-222. In the presence of 0.1 μM suberyldicholine (an ACh-like agonist), increasing the anesthetic from 0 (**A**) to 50 μM (**D**) concentration produces increasing blockade of the channel. The flickers to the closed state represent block of the open channel by anesthetic molecules. (From ref. 14.)

channels. Such promiscuous behavior of channel blockade accounts for varying degrees of effectiveness and often unpredictable effects of antiarrhythmic drugs.

ACTION POTENTIALS IN NEURONS AND SKELETAL MUSCLE (7)

The action potential in nerve is a rapid (1 msec) change in the transmembrane potential from a resting membrane potential of ~-70 mV to $+40$ mV and back to -70 mV. In describing the action potential of nerve, it should be made clear that this is an ideal and that many variations on this theme exist

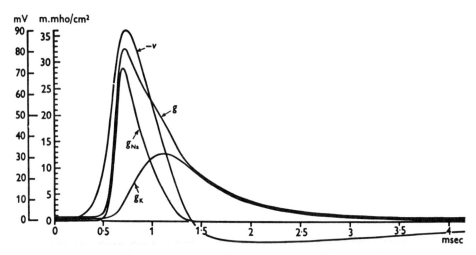

FIG. 10. The action potential (v) in squid axon as calculated from the Hodgkin-Huxley equations. g_{Na} and g_K are increases in net sodium and potassium conductance. Here, 0 mV is referenced to resting membrane potential (-60 mV). (From ref. 8.)

in various nerve cells. The nerve cell's main goal is to communicate signals rapidly from one place to another. Several electrical tricks are used to accomplish this end, but all rely on the difference in ion concentrations between inside and outside the cell. Figure 10 shows the classic squid axon nerve action potential. For mammalian nerve, the salient features are similar and are as follows. Membrane potential is brought by some stimulus to a region of potential (~-55 mV) where sodium channels begin to open rapidly. The inward sodium current is large because there are many sodium channels in the membrane highly tuned to opening at -55 mV. The channels open, sodium flows down the concentration gradient to drive the membrane potential toward E_{Na} ($+55$ mV). As the potential reaches -40 mV to -20 mV, calcium channels begin to open, albeit more slowly than the sodium channels, driving the membrane potential toward E_{Ca} ($+150$ mV). If these channels continue to open, the membrane potential would end up at some intermediate value between E_{Ca} and E_{Na}. At this point, sodium channels begin to close spontaneously (they inactivate). From their inactivated state, they cannot reopen as easily as before. Channels shuttle from closed to open to inactivated, and the sodium current is over in ~1 msec. Meanwhile, calcium channels also begin to inactivate. The membrane potential is now $\sim+40$ mV. Gradually, voltage-dependent potassium channels begin to open. Given the large driving force for potassium and the inactivation of inward currents, the potassium current becomes larger than the combined inward currents, and the net current becomes outward. Soon, only outward channels are opening. The membrane potential is rapidly driven back to E_K, where it would stay were it not for other inward conducting channels that keep the membrane potential slightly above E_K (often called "leakage channels").

In the simplest case, the action potential can occur with only two types of channels, an inward and an outward current. That more currents are involved is a clue to the rich variety of responses and controls in nerve. For example, calcium current is not necessary for conduction of a simple impulse, but calcium is the message for release of neurotransmitter at nerve terminals, for activation of calcium-dependent enzymes, and for contraction in muscle. If sodium channels are absent or blocked, an action potential can still occur, driven by calcium current. The slower activation of calcium current slows the rate of rise of the action potential and slows conduction speed. Not all sodium channels are available for activation if the membrane potential is above -90 mV. If extracellular potassium increases, E_K rises and so does the resting membrane potential. Sodium channels inactivate (have a lower probability of being in the open state) at the depolarized potentials. The more depolarized the resting membrane potential, the fewer sodium channels are able to open (available for activation), and the more the upstroke of the action potential will depend on the slower calcium current. In this way, potassium decreases the excitability of neurons and decreases the speed of nerve conduction. Similarly, lower potassium levels may increase the excitability of some neurons by hyperpolarizing the resting membrane potential, thus increasing the available sodium channels.

External calcium concentration modulates excitability. In general, raising $[Ca]_o$ stabilizes membranes by raising the threshold for excitation of nerve and muscle. Raising $[Ca]_o$ (and other divalents) changes the voltage difference across the membrane, probably by binding negatively charged groups of the glycocalyx. In the setting of combined hypocalcemia and hypokalemia, it is best to replete calcium before potassium to raise (depolarize) the threshold for excitation.

Skeletal Muscle Excitability

The action potential in skeletal muscle is similar to that in nerve. Like other excitable cells, skeletal muscle has voltage-dependent sodium, calcium, potassium, and chloride channels as well as ligand-gated channels. The skeletal muscle action potential is usually initiated by release of ACh from end plates. Nicotinic ACh channels are nonselective, with $E_{rev} \simeq 0$ mV. The opening of these channels depolarizes the cells enough for sodium channels to open and rapidly depolarize the cell in the usual fashion. Skeletal muscle contains at least two types of Ca^{2+} channels. Contraction is initiated when an action potential depolarizes the transverse tubules, a system of sarcolemmal membrane infolded into the fiber interior. Suprisingly, the surface membrane in muscle has relatively few calcium channels, and these few channels may serve only to trigger the opening of calcium channels in sarcoplasmic reticulum, releasing free calcium into the cytoplasm and initiating contraction. Thus, skeletal muscle has important internal membranes containing ion channels as well as surface membrane. After the entry of calcium, potassium channels repolarize the cell.

Hyperkalemia, as for other excitable cells, depolarizes skeletal muscle, thus causing a steady state inactivation of sodium channels. Hyperkalemia can thus reduce the force and speed of contraction. Chronic potassium depletion can cause muscle weakness and paralysis and increase susceptibility to ischemic necrosis, probably by intracellular, as well as extracellular, K^+ depletion. Hyperkalemia slows muscle contraction in a second way. Contraction of skeletal muscle is triggered by neurons. Release of ACh at the neuromuscular junction is affected by the rate of rise of the action potential. More ACh is released onto the ACh receptors in skeletal muscle in a defined time if the depolarization of the presynaptic area is fast. Hyperkalemia, by slowing the rate of rise of the presynaptic action potential, decreases the chance that enough ACh is released to fire the skeletal muscle action potential.

We have discussed potassium channels only in general terms as controlling resting membrane potential in nerve and muscle. As noted in Table 2, there are many types of potassium channels. At this point, we will ignore all transmitter-activated K^+ channels, as well as those channels that activate only under special circumstances ($i_{K.ATP}$, $i_{K.Na}$). In neurons, some potassium channels are always on. These channels show only weak voltage dependence and serve to set the resting membrane potential. These are known as "leakage" K^+ channels and may be composed of several conductance types. Other classes of K^+ channels are responsible for repolarizing the action potential and keeping its duration short (I_K). All are voltage dependent and begin to open when the membrane is depolarized above -50 mV. These voltage-dependent K^+ channels simply open on depolarization and drive the membrane potential back to E_K. How long it takes to accomplish repolarization is dependent on the balance of net inward and outward current. In nerve and muscle, repolarization is rapid.

We have discussed firing of a simple action potential. How does repetitive firing of an axon occur? How is bursting behavior explained? What modulates repetitive firing rates in axons? To answer these questions, one must understand two potassium channels: the transient outward K^+ channel (I_A), and the previously mentioned calcium-dependent K^+ channel ($I_{K.Ca}$). The clearest example of bursting pacemaking in neurons has been described for molluscan neurons (Fig. 11). In this neuron, depolarization leads to a regenerative series of action potentials. Repetitive firing at high rates gradually increases intracellular calcium until $I_{K.Ca}$ channels are activated, driving the membrane potential into a hyperpolarized range where the cell cannot fire. Slow depolarization due to inward leakage channels (or transmitter-activated inward channels) combined with calcium uptake and/or extrusion gives a slow depolarization to the range of potentials where repetitive firing can again occur.

A refinement of the rate of repetitive firing is accomplished by the A cur-

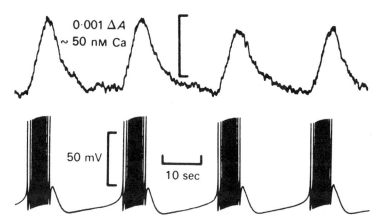

FIG. 11. Bursting is controlled by intracellular calcium level in *Aplysia* neuron. The upper trace shows the relative change in neuronal intracellular [Ca] as measured by arsenazo-III absorbance changes. The lower trace shows spontaneous bursting of action potentials. Bursting is terminated by a rise in [Ca]$_i$, which activates calcium-dependent K$^+$ channels. (From ref. 5.)

rent. This voltage-activated potassium current has the unusual property that it activates at voltages above (depolarized to) -60 mV but has already begun inactivating at voltages above -90 mV. Thus, the A current is a transient current; it opens for only a short time above -60 mV before it is closed by continued inactivation at these depolarized voltages. The net effect is a short outward current in the range of potential where the action potential is beginning to rapidly depolarize. This slows depolarization and increases the time between action potentials. It is now clear that more than one type of A current exists and that some of these currents are calcium dependent.

Summary of Excitability in Nerve and Muscle

The action potential in nerve is like a machine gun ready to fire. The cell has many ways to control when and how the gun will fire, mainly through a multitude of potassium channels. Different potassium channels are, in turn, regulated by voltage, second messengers, intracellular calcium or other cations, and transmitters. Not every neuron has the same set of channels, and the particular behavior of any one neuron is determined by the numbers and types of channels it contains. The simplest nerve may use only sodium channels and voltage-activated and voltage-independent (leakage) potassium channels to produce a simple fast spike. But even within the same nerve cell, one repertoire of channels may be used in the cell body to control the generation of the potentials, and the axon may use a different set to simply conduct the action potential to the nerve ending; yet a third set may modulate depolarization of the end plate. Despite the complexity of nerve, most nervous activity is depressed by raising extracellular potassium since potassium channels are the main determinants of resting membrane potential. Raising extracellular potassium depolarizes cells. Over some regions of potential, firing may increase as the membrane potential approaches the region where sodium channels activate. However, as extracellular potassium is further increased, fast inward conducting channels are held at potentials where they inactivate, and excitability is lost.

CARDIAC ACTION POTENTIAL (4,16)

Cardiac action potentials are strikingly different from nerve and muscle in that their action potential durations are 200 to 400 msec long. The long plateau gives the heart muscle time to empty the heart chambers (Fig. 12). There are several types of action potentials in heart. The sinoatrial and atrioventricular nodes are pacemaking cells and have slow upstroke velocities (10–15 V/sec), as well as a very slow spontaneous depolarization between action

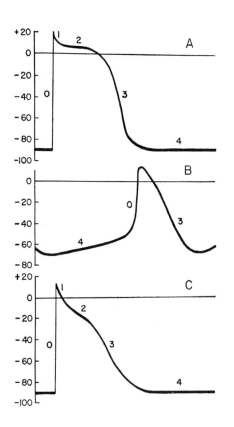

FIG. 12. Representative action potentials from (**A**) ventricle, (**B**) SA node, and (**C**) atria. Sweep speed in **B** is one-half that of **A** and **C**. (From ref. 9.)

potentials (pacemaker depolarization). At the opposite end of a continuum are ventricular action potentials with fast upstroke (200–400 V/sec) and no spontaneous depolarization between action potentials. Atrial action potentials are similar to ventricular action potentials but are of shorter duration. The action potentials of conducting cells, such as Purkinje fiber cells, look very similar to ventricular action potentials but may display spontaneous depolarization.

The fast upstroke in atrial and ventricular heart cells is accomplished, as in nerve, by sodium channels. These sodium channels are, for our purposes, practically identical in nerve, muscle, and heart. Again, as in nerve, sodium channels open rapidly to depolarize the cells to potentials where calcium channels open (Fig. 13). In atrial cells, there are two distinct calcium currents, gated by two types of calcium channels. One calcium channel opens at -50 mV but begins to inactivate as soon as it opens. This calcium current is transient, as is the sodium current, but inactivates 100 times more slowly than the sodium current ($I_{Ca.t}$). It is insensitive to block by dihydropyridines (e.g., nifedipine and nitrendipine). The other calcium channel begins to activate at ~ -20 mV and does not inactivate ($I_{Ca,L}$). It is very sensitive to block by dihydropyridines. Calcium entry initiates contraction in the usual way.

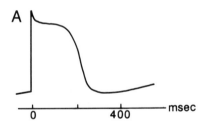

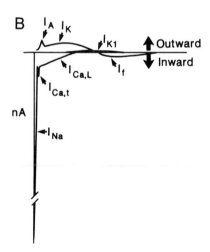

FIG. 13. A: Idealized cardiac action potential from a spontaneously beating heart cell. **B:** Ionic currents flowing through the cardiac cell membrane to produce the action potential in **A**. Time courses of currents are hypothetical and approximate.

As in nerve, once the depolarizing currents have let calcium in, repolarization is accomplished by potassium currents. Again, a large variety of potassium channels have been found in heart. An idealized view of repolarization follows, since the complete description has not been worked out for any one cell type and tissue. At the peak of the action potential, a rapidly inactivating, transient outward potassium current (similar to the A current in nerve) is responsible for rapidly repolarizing the action potential to the plateau level. Meanwhile, two voltage-activated potassium channels have begun to open. There appear to be at least two types of these voltage-activated K^+ channels in heart, one activating at -50 mV and another activating at -20 mV. Both are slow to reach a maximum open probability, and the net K^+ current is not fully on for 10 msec to 100 msec, well after the sodium current has inactivated. By the time the plateau is reached, transient outward current has inactivated, and the only currents left operating are the noninactivating K^+ currents and the calcium current(s). The plateau potential is the result of a careful balancing act between these major currents. One striking result of heart electrophysiology is that very few channels are opening during the plateau. The total conductance during the plateau region of the cardiac action potential is extremely low. Only a few hundred channels per cell are maintaining the fine balance. Finally, the potassium channels win the battle, and the membrane potential is driven back toward E_K. (Repolarization may be accelerated in some heart cells by calcium-activated K^+ channels that could be opening as intracellular calcium rises due to sarcoplasmic release of calcium.) During repolarization, the heart cell cannot be triggered to fire another action potential, since the sodium channels are still inactivated at depolarized membrane potentials. Only hyperpolarization can reprime them for activation. This period of time is the so-called absolute refractory period.

In ventricular cells, the membrane potential now stays near E_K; only activation from pacemaker cells via the cardiac conduction system can stimulate another action potential. However, other spontaneously depolarizing cells, such as the nodal cells and certain cells of the conduction system, begin to depolarize slowly.

Pacemaker Activity

Nodal cells are fundamentally different from atrial and ventricular cells in two main respects. First, nodal cells have very few leakage K^+ channels. In heart, the K^+ channels that are open at rest are called "inward rectifier" channels (see Fig. 4). Nodal cells have ~ 100-fold fewer inward rectifier channels (called I_{K1}) than do ventricular cells. As a result, there are few channels to keep the membrane potential near E_K, and the membrane potential is more depolarized than in ventricle. Second, in the node, a voltage-dependent inward current with a reversal potential near 0 mV (I_f) continually depolarizes the membrane in the range of -60 mV to -40 mV. I_f is a very slow, small current and cannot rapidly depolarize the cells, as do sodium channels. The end result in nodal cells is continuous pacemaking activity, with a slow up-stroke. The slow upstroke in nodal cells is the result of a relative lack of sodium channels, leaving the slower calcium current to depolarize the cell. Even if sodium channels were present, they would be largely inactivated at the depolarized potentials and could not participate significantly in depolarization.

The inward rectifying potassium current (I_{K1}) has a significant effect on pacemaking activity. How I_{K1} contributes to pacemaking can be understood by examining the current voltage relation for I_{K1}. I_{K1} is unusual in that in the physiologic range of membrane potential (above E_K), the net outward current becomes smaller and smaller with depolarization (Fig. 14). This current is not time dependent and thus does not inactivate. Now assume that I_{K1} is the only channel opening between -90 mV and -60 mV. As can be seen from the I-V, any depolarization induced by an inward current of any kind results in less outward current. In essence, such a cell would have an unstable membrane potential and would be driven in the depolarizing direction because of the decline in outward current. The inward rectification of I_{K1} means that a potassium current in the presence of a small inward current can cause pacemaker depolarization. Raising extracellular potassium has a pronounced effect on I_{K1}. Not only does E_K shift in the depolarizing direction, but the size of the outward current increases. Decreasing potassium concentration shifts E_K in the hyperpolarized direction and reduces the outward current. Also, since I_{K1} predominantly sets the membrane potential, extracellular potassium concentration shifts the resting membrane potential in nonpacing cells. The shift of membrane potential with $[K]_o$ is shown in Fig. 15. Note that at both low and high concentrations, the membrane potential is

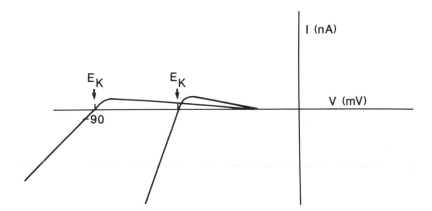

FIG. 14. Inward rectifier potassium current. The net current (I_{K1}) through the time-independent inward rectifier channels is shifted by raising extracellular potassium.

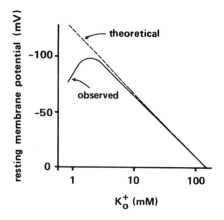

FIG. 15. Cardiac resting membrane potential as a function of $[K]_o$. Note that at very low $[K]_o$, the membrane potential is depolarized because of a decrease in the inward rectifier current (I_{K1}) and lower Na,K-ATPase pump activity. (From ref. 10.)

depolarized from a maximum at $[K]_o = 4$ mM, the normal extracellular potassium concentration. Depolarization by high $[K]_o$ is explained by I_{K1}. At low $[K]_o$, depolarization results from two factors. First, if extracellular potassium is decreased to very low levels, the Na,K-ATPase pump is hindered for lack of substrate, and the membrane potential runs down. Second, at low $[K]_o$, I_{K1} is decreased because of its sharp dependence on $[K]_o$.

The net effects of moderate hypokalemia and hyperkalemia on the action potential are shown in Fig. 16. In hyperkalemia, the fast upstroke is slowed as a result of partial inactivation of Na^+ channels at depolarized potentials. The plateau is shortened because of increased K^+ currents and reduced calcium currents. In moderate hypokalemia, there is a moderate prolongation of the action potential due to low plateau potassium currents for repolarization. These explanations of the effects of potassium imbalance on the action poten-

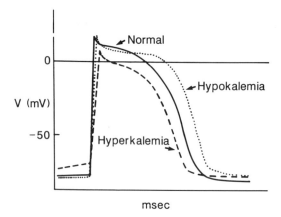

FIG. 16. Effect of hyperkalemia and hypokalemia on the cardiac action potential. High potassium depolarizes the membranes, slows upstroke velocity, and shortens the action potential duration. Low potassium prolongs the action potential. (After ref. 10.)

tial are rough approximations. In reality, all membrane currents are affected by $[K]_o$, and a complete model of the action potential is needed for more precise predictions.

Summary of Cardiac Action Potentials

In this section, some of the main themes in cardiac excitability and action potential generation have been discussed. We are far from completely understanding cardiac action potentials. To do so requires knowing every channel type in a particular cardiac cell, the number of such channels, their modification by intracellular and extracellular factors, and how they act in unison. Several computer-generated models of cardiac action potentials summarize the complex behaviors of even the incompletely understood, reduced system. Nevertheless, the main factors are known, and much can be predicted by understanding the few simple points outlined. Potassium balance is important to heart cells because (a) heart cells are depolarized by raising or reducing potassium outside the narrow physiologic range, (b) depolarization of resting membrane potential can turn triggered cells into spontaneously depolarizing cells by moving the transmembrane voltage into regions where inward currents activate, and (c) raising or lowering extracellular potassium has a profound effect on the inward rectifier and thus effects the role of pacemaker depolarization.

Since there are many cell types in the heart, potassium alterations affect each cell in different ways. A slight rise in potassium may not affect a nodal cell very significantly, but it may shift normally quiescent Purkinje cells in the conduction system into spontaneous pacemaker activity. The result would be premature ventricular contractions or escape from nodal control. Similarly, larger increases in extracellular potassium may depolarize conduction system or venticular cells to such an extent that sodium channels begin to inactivate, reducing the available current necessary to produce rapid depolarization. Spread of excitation would then be slowed, and contractility would be reduced. If regions of the heart are not very well coupled, for example, due to prior infarction, such a loss of conduction speed might release these cells from control, leading to their spontaneous activity as separate pacemakers. At very high levels of potassium, heart cells would be depolarized to the extent that all conduction would be slowed, leading to the poorly coordinated slow activity seen as a sinusoidal ECG pattern. Finally, conduction could be so slowed that cells would dissociate into islands of activity, perhaps enhanced by gap junction closure secondary to rising intracellular calcium and acidification. This state is called fibrillation.

SHORT REVIEW OF CONDUCTION

Conduction speed is governed by three main factors: the speed of the upstroke of the action potential, the resistance along the conduction route, and the resistance across the insulator, i.e., resistance orthogonal to the conduction pathway. The faster the upstroke, the larger the effective voltage to provide current to travel down the conduction pathway. In nerve, the conduction pathway is the inside of the cell body and axon. Loss of current in the orthogonal direction is prevented by the high resistance of the membrane and, in some axons, by the myelin insulation. The fastest conduction is seen in myelinated axons with large internal diameters (low path resistance). Nodes of unmyelinated areas with high channel density act as amplification relay stations that increase the current available for transmission down the axon. A further improvement is provided by scarcity of ion channels under myelinated areas.

In nerve, high potassium lowers the upstroke velocity (by lowering membrane potential and inactivating sodium channels) and increases leakage across the axon under the myelin. Conduction in skeletal muscle is similar to nerve except that there is no specialized insulator. However, skeletal muscle cells are fused from many single cells, allowing for a low internal resistance. Cardiac tissue, on the other hand, is composed of single cells connected by specialized ion channels called "gap junctions." The single gap junction channel conductance is large (~100 pS), and the channel is usually open. It may be closed by large swings in voltage, pH, or calcium concentration in either of the cells it connects. Despite the disadvantage that gap junctional conductance between cells can never be as large as through a continuous axon or between fused muscle cells, gap junctions do allow heart cells to disconnect themselves from the tissue. Damaged areas of heart can thus be disconnected electrically from normal heart tissue. Although the role of gap junctions in arrhythmias is unclear, these high resistance areas must contribute to loss of communication between heart cells under special circumstances. If extracellular potassium rises and conduction speed declines, the coupling of heart cells becomes more tenuous, perhaps giving rise to islands of spontaneous independent activity. Whether these gap junctions close to contribute to fibrillation of cardiac tissue is unknown.

ANTIARRHYTHMIC DRUGS

It follows from the foregoing discussion that just as there are many mechanisms for arrhythmias, there are many ways in which antiarrhythmic drugs work. Almost all antiarrhythmic drugs block channels in heart cells. At present, except for transmitters, such as adenosine, that open muscarinic-gated potassium channels, there are no common antiarrhythmic drugs that open channels. If a common theme is present among antiarrhythmic durgs, it is that they depress excitability. For example, lidocaine, procaine, and quinidine all block sodium channels. Verapamil and the dihydropyridines block calcium channels. These drugs are remakably nonspecific. Quinidine, for example, has been shown to depress sodium, calcium, and several kinds of potassium currents. Mechanisms of channel blockade by drugs also are not simple. Several drugs, such as verapamil and lidocaine, block channels in a voltage-dependent fashion. Block is greater at depolarized voltages than at hyperpolarized voltages. The more depolarized the cell, the more likely are the channels to be blocked by the drug. The cells firing most often should thus be most affected, as in rapidly firing atrial cells during atrial flutter.

Besides depressing excitability, some antiarrhythmic drugs may work by enhancing conduction. By blocking potassium channels, the propagation of the action potential should be enhanced, since the membrane resistance is increased. More current is now available for transmission to other heart cells across the membrane into the intercellular space. In other words, potassium channel blockade makes the membrane a better insulator. Antifibrillatory drugs, such as bretyllium (ventricle) and quinidine (atrial), work partially through this mechanism.

ACKNOWLEDGMENTS

The author gratefully acknowledges the assistance of Ms. Paula Dolan for typing the manuscript and Chaya Joshi and Diomedes Logothetis for their comments on the text. This work was supported in part by NIH grant HL34873.

REFERENCES

1. Barker, L., Burton, J., and Zieve, P. (1982): *Principles of Ambulatory Medicine*. Williams & Wilkins, Baltimore MD.
2. Barrett, J. N., Magleby, K. L., and Pallotta, B. S. (1982): Properties of single calcium-activated potassium channels in cultured rat muscle. *J. Physiol. (Lond.)*, 331:211–230.
3. Carmeliet, E., and Vereecke, J. (1979): Electrogenesis of the action potential and automaticity. In: *Handbook of Physiology*, section 2, edited by R. Berne, N. Sperelakis, and S. Geiger, pp. 269–334, Waverly Press, Baltimore.
4. Clapham, D. (1987): A brief review of single channel measurements from isolated heart cells. In: *The Heart Cell in Culture*, edited by A. Pinson. pp. 159–169, CRC Press, Boca Raton, FL.
5. Gorman, A. L. F., and Thomas, M. V. (1978): Changes in the intracellular concentration of free calcium ions in a pacemaker neurone, measured with the metallochromic indicator dye arsenazo III. *J. Physiol. (Lond.)*, 275:357–376.
6. Hammill, O. P., Marty, A., Neher, B., Sakmann, B., and Sigworth, F. J. (1981): Improved patch clamp techniques for high resolution current recording from cells and cell-free membrane patches. *Pflugers Arch.*, 391:85–100.
7. Hille, B. (1984): *Ionic Channels of Excitable Membranes*. Sinauer Assoc., Sunderland, MA.
8. Hodgkin, A. L., and Huxley, A. F. (1952): A quantitative description of membrane current and its application to conduction and excitation in nerve. *J. Physiol. (Lond.)*, 117:500–544.
9. Hoffman, B. F., and Cranefield, P. F. (1960): *Electrophysiology of the Heart*. New York, McGraw-Hill.
10. Katz, A. (1977): *Physiology of the Heart*. Raven Press, New York.
11. Logothetis, D., Kurachi, Y., Galper, J., Neer, E., and Clapham, D. (1987): The $\beta\gamma$ subunits

of GTP-binding proteins activate the muscarinic K^+ channel in heart. *Nature*, 325:321–326.

12. Marriott, D. H. (1977): *Practical Electrocardiography*. Williams & Wilkins, Baltimore, MD.
13. Montal, M., Anholt, R., and Labarca, P. (1986): The reconstituted acetylcholine receptor. In: *Ion Channel Reconstitution*, edited by C. Miller, pp. 157–204. Plenum Press, New York.
14. Neher, E., and Steinbach, J. H. (1978): Local anesthetics transiently block currents through single acetylcholine-receptor channels. *J. Physiol. (Lond.)*, 277:153–176.
15. Noble, D. (1975): *The Initiation of the Heartbeat*. Clarendon Press, Oxford.
16. Noble, D. (1984): The surprising heart: A review of recent progress in cardiac electrophysiology. *J. Physiol. (Lond.)*, 353:1–50.
17. Sakmann, B., and Neher, E. (1983): *Single Channel Recording*. Plenum Press, New York.

The Regulation of Potassium Balance, edited by Donald W. Seldin and Gerhard Giebisch, Raven Press, Ltd., New York © 1989.

4

The Regulation of Intracellular Potassium

Lawrence G. Palmer

Department of Physiology, Cornell University Medical College, New York, New York 10021

Basis for Regulation of Cell Potassium
  Donnan Equilibrium • Pump-Leak Hypothesis • Permeability and Conductance
Potassium Influx Mechanisms
  Na,K Pump • Na,K,Cl Cotransport
Potassium Efflux Mechanisms
  Potassium Channels • KCl Cotransport
References

BASIS FOR REGULATION OF CELL POTASSIUM (1,15–18)

Almost all animal cells accumulate potassium within their cytoplasm to concentrations far exceeding those in their environment, in most cases, the plasma or interstitial fluid. This phenomenon and its explanation have intrigued physiologists for decades. Basically two formalisms have been put forward to account for high cell potassium. The first visualizes the cell as a so-called Donnan or Gibbs-Donnan equilibrium system, in which the high potassium is required to balance the net negative charge on the cellular macromolecules. The second is a pump-leak hypothesis, in which cell potassium is thought to be determined by the balance of active and passive transport processes across the cell membrane. The latter viewpoint is by far the more popular and useful one from the point of view of modern physiology and is used for most of this chapter. Since the Donnan system is of both historical and heuristic interest, however, the two hypotheses concerning the regulation of potassium accumulation are compared.

A. DONNAN SYSTEM

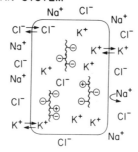

B. PUMP-LEAK SYSTEM

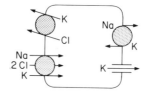

C. EPITHELIAL PUMP-LEAK SYSTEM

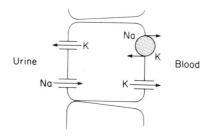

FIG. 1. Donnan and pump-leak representations of cell potassium. **A:** According to the Donnan theory, K is accumulated within the cell to neutralize the excess negative charge on cellular macromolecules. Na, the most abundant extracellular cation, does not contribute to this neutralization, since the cell membrane is impermeant, or effectively impermeant, to Na. **B:** According to the pump-leak hypothesis, cell K is determined by the balance between various specific membrane transport processes that move K into and out of the cell. Pictured here are four major K transport systems. The Na-K pump and the Na/K/2Cl cotransport systems both mediate net K movement into the cell, whereas K channels and K/Cl cotransport mediate net outward K flux. **C:** In an epithelial cell, the asymmetrical placement of pump and leak units can result in the transepithelial transport of K. In the mammalian renal cortical collecting tubule cell illustrated here, pump units are found exclusively in the basal-lateral cell membrane, whereas K channels are present in both membranes. The net result is that part of the K pumped into the cell in exchange for Na leaks out of the cell into the urine. The overall process contributes to K secretion by this nephron segment.

Donnan Equilibrium (1,16)

The application of the physical chemical principles of equilibrium in aqueous solutions formulated by Gibbs and Donnan was elucidated by Boyle and Conway. The distribution of ions between cells and their environment is considered to be determined by three factors. First, there is no osmotic gradient between the cell and the interstitial fluids (osmotic balance). Second, the positively and negatively charged ions and macromolecules must balance both in the cell and out (electroneutrality). Finally, all permeant species must be in electrochemical equilibrium across the cell membrane. (In the treatment of Boyle and Conway, K and Cl were considered to be permeant, whereas Na was considered to be impermeant.) It could be shown that, given these three laws and with knowledge of the osmotic activity and charge of the macromolecules and other impermeant species within the cell, the volume and content of K and Cl of the cell can be calculated (Fig. 1A).

According to this view, K must be high in the cell because the impermeant species in the cytoplasm carry a net negative charge. This charge is carried predominantly by the amino acid residues of proteins and by phosphate compounds, such as ATP and creatinine phosphate. This negative charge must be balanced by an excess of positive charge from a permeant species, and K is the only permeant positive ion. Since K is to be accumulated in the cell without an accompanying anion, Cl must be excluded from the cytoplasm. To accumulate K and exclude Cl while keeping both ions at electrochemical equilibrium, the cell must maintain an electrical potential that is negative with respect to the interstitial fluid, attracting cations and repelling anions. The magnitude of the potential is predicted from the ratio of intracellular to extracellular K according to the Nernst equation:

$$RT/F \ln([K]_o/[K]_i) = RT/F \ln([Cl]_i/[Cl]_o) = V_m$$

where the subscripts i and o refer to the intracellular and extracellular concentrations, respectively, and V_m is the membrane potential. The key point is that although both K and Cl concentrations are different in cell and outside the cell, these ions are both at equilibrium across the cell membrane because the electrical driving force exactly cancels the chemical driving forces established by the concentration gradients. The above equation can be simplified to

$$[K]_o[Cl]_o = [K]_i[Cl]_i,$$

signifying that the product of K and Cl concentrations must be the same on both sides of the membrane, independent of the membrane potential.

Na, on the other hand, does not equilibrate across the membrane because it is impermeant (or effectively impermeant; see below). This is another key feature of the Donnan model. Just as the accumulation of K in the cell is required to balance the charge of the intracellular macromolecules, the exclu-

sion of Na from the cell is necessary to balance the osmolarity of these impermeant cytoplasmic solutes.

Boyle and Conway showed that in frog skeletal muscle, the Donnan assumptions could account reasonably well for cell K and Cl concentrations and
cell volume both in the normal state of the cells and following a number of
experimental perturbations. The theory also provides a natural explanation for
the apparent exchange of cell K for H during, for example, chronic acidosis. If
cellular as well as extracellular pH were to be lowered, the net negative
charge on the cellular macromolecules would decrease, and the amount of K
needed for neutralization of the charge would diminish, resulting in release of
K from the cell.

The strict interpretation of the Gibbs-Donnan equilibrium hypothesis of
cell electrolytes fails on at least two counts. First, it assumes that the Na ion is
impermeant, which it is not. This is not a fatal flaw, however, since, as we
now know, Na is actively pumped from the cell at the expense of metabolic
energy and can be considered to be effectively impermeant. When Na ion
enters the cell, it is automatically extruded, which is equivalent to its having
not entered in the first place. A second flaw is that in many cell types, the use
of K-sensitive ion-selective microelectrodes has indicated that K is generally
accumulated in the cytoplasm at concentrations that exceed that predicted by
electrochemical equilibrium (Table 1). Thus the movement of K, as well as
that of Na, is coupled to cellular metabolism, and the simple physical chemical principles of the Gibbs-Donnan equilibrium are insufficient to describe K
accumulation.

The reason that the theory works reasonably well under many conditions
is that assumptions behind the theory are in many instances very nearly cor-

TABLE 1. *Intracellular potassium activities in various cells*

Tissue	a_K (mM)[a]	V_m(mV)	Outward electrochemical gradient (mV)
Frog skeletal muscle	95	-85	18
Aplysia neuron	165	-50	30
Rabbit cardiac ventrical muscle	83	-75	4
Frog oocyte	120	-43	47
Salamander proximal tubule	55	-64	22
Rabbit thick ascending limb of Henle's loop	113	-60	15
Human erythrocyte	110	-9	81

[a]K^+ ion activities (a_K) were measured with ion-selective electrodes except in the case of erythrocytes, where the concentration of K in cell water was multiplied by an assumed cytoplasmic
activity coefficient of 0.73. Membrane potentials (V_m) were measured with conventional intracellular micropipettes, except in the erythrocytes, where it was estimated from the distribution
of Cl^- ions. All measurements were made with appropriate physiologic K activities in the extracellular fluid. The outward electrochemical gradient represents the driving force for K^+ exit
from the cell and indicates the degree to which the ions are out of equilibrium between the
cell and its surrounding environment.

rect. Osmotic balance and electroneutrality conditions are in fact met, and although K is not in general at electrochemical equilibrium across the cell membrane, it is often not too far away from equilibrium. In this sense, the Gibbs-Donnan equilibrium is still a reasonable, although imperfect, way to envision the distribution of K between the cell and its environment.

Another way of looking at cell K accumulation is that of the association-induction hypothesis of Ling. This idea shares with that of the Donnan system the concept that cell K is determined mainly by an equilibrium distribution of the ion between cell and environment. A major difference is that Ling does not envision the cell K to be freely dissolved in the cell water. Rather, K neutralizes the negative charges of the cellular macromolecules by interacting strongly and specifically with them. The ability of cell proteins to bind K and their strong preference for binding K over Na is considered to be an important aspect of the living state. This view challenges the whole notion that membranes and membrane transport processes determine cell ion composition. It is not widely held.

Pump-Leak Hypothesis (1,15,17)

A more complete account of the distribution of K between the cell and the interstitial compartment can be obtained by considering cell K to result from a balance of a number of different processes that move K either into or out of the cell across the cell membrane. This was first formulated as the so-called pump-leak hypothesis, which held that the concentration of K (or any other solute) in the cell is determined by a balancing of processes by which the ions move against their activity gradient (the pump rate) and those by which they move down the gradient (the leak rate). The cell concentration reaches a steady state when these two rates are equal.

A more modern view of membrane function breaks these concepts of pump and leak down to the specific transport mechanisms by which ions enter and leave the cell. Here the cell is visualized as being surrounded by a lipid bilayer membrane that forms an effective barrier to the movement of virtually all physiologically important ions. In the bilayer is embedded a number of proteins that span the membrane and carry out specific transport tasks. These proteins can be thought of as enzymes that catalyze the translocation, rather than the chemical modification, of solutes.

The processes can be grouped into three major categories.

1. Active transport systems are directly linked to the use of metabolic energy.[1] Most commonly, this involves the hydrolysis of ATP to ADP and

---

[1]The obligatory coupling to metabolism is used here as the definition of active transport. An alternative definition, as a process that moves a solute against an electrochemical activity gradient, would include as active (or secondary active) coupled processes, such as those described subsequently.

phosphate, coupled directly to the movement of an ion or ions across the membrane. This ion movement can go against a concentration gradient or against an opposing electrical field, since the energy lost from ATP (or another source) compensates for that gained by the uphill transport of solutes.

2. Coupled transport systems depend on the simultaneous movement of other solutes in either the same direction (cotransport) or in opposite directions (countertransport or antiport). Examples include uptake of glucose and amino acids through Na-coupled transport in the kidney and intestine and coupled Na,H and Na,Ca exchange in a variety of cell types. Although not directly linked to metabolic processes, coupled systems can move one ion uphill if a coupled ion moves downhill. The total energy gained or lost by all the solutes transported determines the driving force for the whole process.

3. Passive transport systems always move ions in the direction of their electrochemical activity gradients independent of the gradients or flows of other solutes. This type of transport commonly involves ion channels.[2]

In the case of K, four major routes by which the ion can move into or out of the cell have been identified. These are illustrated schematically in Fig. 1B. K can move into the cell through the ATP-driven Na,K pump or via a cotransport system with Na and Cl. In the latter case, the driving force is provided by the Na gradient. K exit from the cell is through K-selective ion channels or by a cotransport system with Cl. Cell K concentration is thus determined by the rates of these four processes and any others that can facilitate K movement. Regulation of cell K can be accomplished by altering any of these transport mechanisms and all of them are subject to regulation.

Finally, a special case of the pump-leak hypothesis is illustrated in Fig. 1C, which shows an epithelial cell with asymmetrically distributed transport units. The cell is capable of secreting K. Cell K is still determined by the relative rates of pump and leak, but in this case K can be transported across the epithelium, with the absolute rates of influx and efflux determining the overall rate of transepithelial K transport.

The pump-leak principle is further illustrated in Table 2, in which the rates of K movement in two cell types, the erythrocyte and epithelial cells from the renal thick ascending limb of the loop of Henle (TALH), are compared. As shown in Table 1, both cells maintain high intracellular K concentration, but with very different rates of influx and efflux. The high rates of K influx into the TALH cell are dictated by the primary function of the cell, which is the rapid reabsorption of NaCl from the urine. K moves into the cell across the apical membrane by cotransport with Na and Cl and across the basal-lateral

---

[2]Some solutes can cross cell membranes by simple diffusion through the lipid bilayer. For example, dissolved CO_2 and O_2 are thought to cross the membrane without the aid of specific transport systems. K and most other ions diffuse very slowly through the lipid, so that unfacilitated transport is not of quantitative importance in determining K balance.

TABLE 2. *Comparison of transport rates for potassium in erythrocytes and renal (TALH) cells*

	Erythrocyte[a]	Talh cell[a]
K influx (= efflux)	3×10^4 ions/sec·cell	8×10^8 ions/sec·cell
No. of Na, K pumps	500/cell	40,000,000/cell
Membrane conductance	20 mS/cm^2	$<10^{-5}$ mS/cm^2
Turnover time for cell K	50 hr	30 sec

[a]Figures represent approximate values under physiologic, steady state conditions for human erythrocyte and rabbit TALH cell. Turnover time is the amount of time required for a unidirectional K flux equal to the total K content of the cell.

membrane in exchange for Na via the Na,K pump. K leaves the cell through K channels, mostly in the apical membrane, and through K, Cl cotransport, mainly across the basal-lateral membrane. Since there is no net transepithelial K transport, the two rates of influx must be equal to each other and to the two rates of efflux.

The basal-lateral membrane of the TALH cell has one of the highest known densities of Na,K pumps (about 40 million per cell) whereas the pump density of the erythrocyte is about 500 per cell, five orders of magnitude lower. The electrical conductance, which reflects the density and activity of ion channels in the membranes, is also much higher in the TALH cell. Thus, the red cell balances a low pump rate with a low leak rate, whereas the kidney cell must balance much higher rates of both influx and efflux. In the TALH cell, the turnover time for cell K, defined as the time required for an amount of K equal to the cell K to enter or leave the cell, is measured in seconds, whereas that for the red cell is measured in hours.

Permeability and Conductance

The rate of movement of K across a membrane from a higher to a lower concentration defines the ion's permeability:

$$J_K = P_K \Delta C_K$$

where J_K is the net flux of potassium, ΔC_K is the concentration difference, and P_K is the permeability coefficient. The permeability will be determined by the number and properties of both the channels and the cotransporters in the membrane that carry K. When cotransporters are present, the K permeability will also depend on the concentrations of cotransported ions (e.g., Na and Cl) present.

This simple relationship between J_K and ΔC_K holds only when there is no electrical driving force or voltage difference across the membrane. The presence of a voltage difference will drive K ions through channels even in the absence of a concentration difference. The usual equation is written as

$$I_K = FJ_K = G_K \Delta V$$

where I_K is the electrical current carried by K, ΔV is the voltage difference, and G_K is the conductance of the membrane to K. G_K will be determined by the K concentration and the number of conducting K channels in the membrane. Most of the cotransporters are thought to be neutral, that is, they carry equal numbers of positive and negative charges across the membrane. Thus, K flux through them will not be driven by a voltage difference, and they will not contribute to the conductance.

The major difference between conductance and permeability is in how the parameters are measured. Conductance is estimated by imposing a change in the transmembrane voltage and monitoring the resulting change in ionic current across the membrane. Permeability is measured by imposing a concentration difference and monitoring the flux of ions. Frequently, isotopes are used to measure permeability. Addition of an isotope to one side of a membrane creates a concentration difference for the isotopes. The resulting flux is conveniently measured by the appearance of isotope on the other side of the membrane.

For channel-mediated transport, permeability and conductance give similar but not identical information. For example, G_K will in general increase with the K concentration, whereas P_K is independent of concentration at least for the simplest cases. Transport mediated by cotransporters will have an associated permeability but no conductance.

The rest of this chapter considers in some detail the various processes that mediate K transport in various animal cells, divided into the processes that normally catalyze net K influx and those that normally catalyze net efflux from the cell. This division is somewhat artificial in that all the mechanisms are at least to some extent reversible through changes in ion gradients and, in the case of the Na,K pump, the metabolic state. Nevertheless, the division may be helpful in understanding how K movements are balanced during normal cellular operations.

POTASSIUM INFLUX MECHANISMS (1,2,4,6,7,9,10,13)

Na/K Pump (1,2,4,6,7,13)

The most common and best studied route for K influx into cells is via the Na-coupled, ATP-dependent enzyme known as the Na,K pump or Na,K-ATPase. This is a clear-cut example of an active transport mechanism, in that movements of both Na and K take place against their electrochemical activity gradients at the expense of ATP hydrolysis. The Na,K pump is found almost

TABLE 3. *Elementary properties of the Na, K pump*

Chemical	
Molecular weight	α = 95,000; β = 35,000 + carbohydrate
Subunit stoichiometry	1:1 (or 2:2?)
Transport	
Stoichiometry	3 Na:2 K:1 ATP
Maximum turnover	~500 Na (330 K)/sec
Half-maximal stimulation	
Na	10–50 mM
K	< 1 mM
ATP	< 1 mM

universally in all types of animal cells and is a major route for Na exit from the cell, as well as for K influx.

The pump has been identified as a protein with two different subunits (Table 3). The large subunit (~100 kilodalton, kD) is sufficient to enzymatically split ATP in the presence of Na and K and is thus called the "catalytic subunit." The smaller subunit (35 kD protein plus carbohydrate) is heavily glycosylated. Its function is unknown. The two subunits copurify with each other and can be reconstituted together into artificial lipid vesicles. These reconstituted pumps catalyze the simultaneous breakdown of ATP and transmembrane movements of Na and K, indicating that the two subunits probably are sufficient to account for the biologic activity of the pump. A good deal is known about the pump proteins, including their amino acid sequence, molecular shape, and tertiary structure, which are not reviewed here.

Basic Mechanism (4,6,7,10)

The basic idea thought to underlie the operation of the pump is that the protein can exist in two basic conformations that can interconvert. Both forms contain binding sites for Na and K ions. In one form, the binding sites face the cytoplasm and have high affinity for Na and low affinity for K. Thus, the pump can be loaded with Na and not with K, even when intracellular K is high and intracellular Na is low. When the protein shifts conformation, the binding sites face the outside. This is accompanied by a lowered affinity for Na, so that Na tends to be released into the extracellular solution, and an increased affinity for K, which loads onto the pump and can be carried into the cytoplasm. To keep up this cycle (Fig. 2A), the pump requires energy input, which comes from ATP. When loaded with Na from the cytoplasm, the pump can accept a phosphate moiety from ATP. This phosphorylated enzyme is thought to be in a high energy state. The energy of the phosphate bond (to

A. CHANNEL

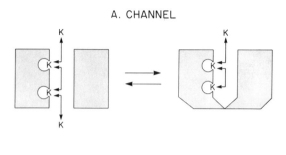

B. COTRANSPORT

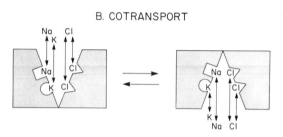

FIG. 2. Schematic representation of the three basic transport mechanisms discussed in this chapter. Three features are common to all three mechanisms. First, the transporters are membrane-spanning proteins containing special regions of a hydrophilic nature through which the ions can move. Second, the transported ions can interact with specific binding sites within the hydrophilic regions. Third, the transporters can undergo conformational changes that affect the exchange of bound ions with the outside or the cytoplasmic solutions. **A:** Ion channels. The conceptually simplest mechanism is that of a channel, where ions can move continuously from one side of the membrane to another through the pore of the transport molecule, although in most cases the transported ions are thought to bind to sites within the pore that determine in part the specificity of the pore for different ions. Most channels can undergo conformational transitions to a closed or nonconducting state. These transitions can be influenced by trans-membrane voltage, the concentration of Ca or other cytoplasmic ions, the phosphorylation state of the channel, and so on, but not necessarily by the transported ions themselves. The conformational change is not a step in the translocation process, which is limited by the movement of ions onto and off their binding sites. Thus translocation through a channel can be fast, with rates of 10^6 ions/sec or more through each pore. **B:** Cotransport systems. The Na/K/2Cl system is illustrated here. Two essential features distinguish this type of mechanism from that of a channel. First, the ions do not have access to both the extracellular and cytoplasmic solutions at the same time. A corollary of this is that the conformational change, which shifts the access from one side of the membrane to the other, is an essential step in the translocation process. Thus, this type of mechanism is generally much slower than that of a channel. Second, the binding of the translocated ions to their sites on the transport protein influences the conformational change. In this case, all four ions must bind before the transition can take place. This accounts for the obligatory cotransport of the four ions. Presumably, the completely unloaded molecule also can make this transition, bringing the transporter back to its original position, and allows the net transfer of ions across the membrane. K/Cl cotransport could be envisioned in a similar way, but without the binding or translocation of the Na or the second Cl ion. This mechanism is presented for its simplicity and is not meant to account for all the kinetic data available for these mechanisms.

C. PUMP

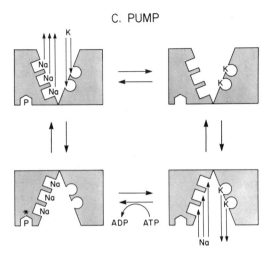

FIG. 2. (*Continued.*) **C:** Na/K pump. The pump is envisioned as a mechanism similar to that of the cotransport system except that here a countertransport system is employed. Thus, the conformational transition governing the side to which ions have access can occur when the transporter is loaded with either Na or K, but not both. The other important difference is that the affinity of the sites changes depending on which side of the membrane they are facing. When facing the intracellular medium, the sites have high affinity for Na and low affinity for K. The relative affinities are reversed when the sites face the extracellular side. This allows Na and K to be moved against their concentration gradients but requires that the transporter be energized at some point to keep the cycle going in the clockwise direction. This is done by phosphorylating the protein at the expense of ATP. The kinetics of the Na-K pump have been thoroughly studied, and many details and intermediate reaction steps are left out here for simplicity. Again, the physical picture presented here is meant only heuristically.

an aspartyl group on the alpha subunit) decreases after translocation of the Na binding sites to the external surface.

Some of the steps in the pump cycle are readily reversible. Thus the pump can, particularly in the absence of K, catalyze an exchange of cytoplasmic for extracellular Na. Exchange of K also has been documented. Both of these exchange processes can proceed without hydrolysis of ATP. In addition, the entire cycle can be reversed if the normal ion gradients are artificially exaggerated and the ADP/ATP ratio is made large. In this case, Na influx and K efflux are coupled to the synthesis of ATP from ADP and inorganic phosphate. These altered modes have been achieved mostly in red cell ghosts in which both the external and cytoplasmic sides of the membrane can be manipulated and involve conditions unlikely to apply during the normal life of the cell.

In preparations well suited for studying both ion fluxes and ATP hydrolysis, including red blood cell ghosts and pump-containing artificial liposomes, the operation of the pump involves the translocation of 3 Na ions and 2 K ions for each molecule of ATP hydrolyzed. It is widely believed that this fixed stoichi-

TABLE 4. *Energetics of Na, K pump*

Process	Free energy change
Move 3 Na against chemical gradient $RT \ln$	$\dfrac{145}{10} =$ 4,800 Kcal
Move 2 K against chemical gradient $RT \ln$	$\dfrac{140}{5} =$ 4,100 Kcal
Move 1 + against electrical gradient of 60 mV FV	
	= 1,400 Kcal
TOTAL	10,300 Kcal
Split 1 ATP	− 13,000 Kcal
NET	− 2,700 Kcal

ometry pertains to the normal operation of the pump in all cells. There are, however, reports of variable Na:K transport and Na:ATP ratios in some systems. A complete discussion is beyond the scope of this chapter.

The thermodynamics of the pump are summarized in Table 4. Given the expected free energy of hydrolysis of ATP under conditions in the cell (13 Kcal/mole) there is sufficient energy to move 3 Na ions out of the cell against a chemical gradient of 10 to 145 mM together with the movement of 2 K ions into the cell against a gradient of 5 to 140 mM. The process will also move 1 net positive charge out of the cell against an electrical gradient of 60 mV. Table 4 also indicates that the pumping process is efficient, converting well over 50% of the energy of ATP hydrolysis into useful work, specifically the establishment of ion gradients.

The most important aspect of the pharmacology of the pump, from the standpoints both of studying the pump and of manipulating it *in vivo*, is its interaction with cardiotonic steroids (e.g., digitalis, strophanthidin, or ouabain). These drugs stop the pump by binding with fairly high affinity and 1:1 stoichiometry to the enzyme. There is strong evidence that inhibition of the pump underlies the positive inotropic action of this class of drugs, since the resulting increase in intracellular Na will result in increased Ca available to activate the contractile apparatus. As discussed below, there is some evidence for endogenous substances that act in a similar way to block the pump and may play a role in its regulation.

Distribution and Functions

As indicated previously, the Na,K pump is found throughout the animal kingdom. Since most animal cells have low intracellular Na concentrations relative to that of their environment or interstitial spaces and the pump is largely responsible for maintaining low Na, it follows that the pump should be present in the plasma membranes of almost every cell in quantities large enough to cope with the leakage of Na into the cell through other pathways. The exception is the so-called low K erythrocytes from sheep and goats, which have an unusually high Na content. This is attributable in part to a reduced number of pumps and in part to an alteration in the pumps involving a reduced selectivity of the Na binding sites for Na over K.

The primary function of the Na,K pump in most cells is to keep intracellular Na concentrations low and intracellular K concentrations high. As discussed in Chapter 5, this contributes to the maintenance of cell volume. Many cells also make use of the gradient for Na established by the pump for other purposes including electrical excitability, the concentration of amino acids within the cytoplasm via cotransport with Na, and the lowering of intracellular Ca via countertransport with Na. Finally, the Na pump drives the transepithelial reabsorption of Na as well as of sugars and amino acids by the kidney and intestine.

An important feature of the distribution of Na,K pumps in epithelial cells is their segregation to one side of the cell, usually the basal-lateral side. In many epithelia, this segregation underlies the net reabsorption of Na ions, which can enter across the mucosal membrane via ion channels or cotransport processes and leave via the pump into the interstitial space. In some cases (Fig. 1C), it can serve also to secrete K, which enters the cells through the pump and exits through the apical membrane K channels. The pumps are confined to the basal-lateral side of certain fluid-secreting epithelia; the one well-documented exception to this distribution of pumps on epithelia occurs in the choroid plexus. This tissue transports Na backwards, that is, from blood to cerebrospinal fluid, and has its pump on the wrong or apical side.

Regulation

The Na,K pump activity is determined to a large extent by two factors: the intracellular Na concentration and the number of pumps in the membrane (Fig. 3). The cell Na concentration is, in turn, determined by a balance between the pumping rate and the rate at which Na enters the cells. The number of pumps is subject to regulation in both epithelial and nonepithelial cells by a variety of hormones and by both acute and chronic changes in the intracellular environment.

The concentrations of K and ATP required to activate the pump to half-maximal levels are both less than 1 mM, as judged by measurements of ATPase activity in broken cell preparations. Since the concentration of K in the extracellular fluid and of ATP in the cytoplasm are both well above 1 mM under physiologic conditions, the pump normally has enough of both of these

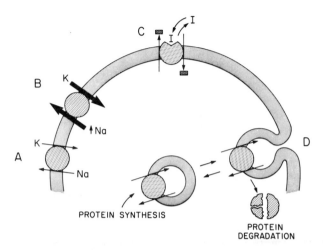

FIG. 3. Modes of regulation of pump activity. **A:** A pump operating normally in the membrane. **B:** A pump whose turnover rate has been increased by elevation of intracellular Na. **C:** A pump in which cation fluxes have been blocked by the binding of an extracellular inhibitor (I). **D:** Pumps can be moved into the plasma membrane from intracellular vesicles. This is presumably the route by which newly synthesized pumps get to the plasma membrane. Changes in the degradation rate of the pump protein also can influence the number of pumps in the membrane. In some cases, the vesicles might hold spare pumps that can be reversibly inserted into the membrane as needed. It is not known if modification of the pump, such as by phosphorylation, can change the rate at which ions are transported.

substrates to function at near optimum rates. On the other hand, the Na concentration for half-maximal activity, which would correspond to the intracellular concentration, is in the range of 10 to 50 mM.

Since intracellular Na concentrations of most cells are around 10 to 20 mM, any increase in cell Na will activate the pump, stimulating both the extrusion of Na and the influx of K. The excess K will have to leave the cell through the K exit pathways, notably K channels. To some extent, this can be accomplished by an increase in the driving force for K that will result from an increased cell K concentration. In some cases, further increase in K efflux can be effected by a regulatory response resulting in the activation of K channels. In either case, the result can be a coupling of Na and K fluxes into and out of the cell. This is of particular importance in certain epithelia, such as the renal cortical collecting tubule (Fig. 1C), where the transepithelial fluxes of Na and K are coupled. A primary increase in the apical membrane Na permeability will result in a stimulation of the pump, an increased K entry across the basal-lateral membrane, and an increased K exit, which will be in part across the apical membrane, constituting K secretion into the urine.

Factors that influence the number of pumps in the membrane are summarized briefly here (see Chapter 1).

Steroids

Adrenal steroids play an important role in maintaining and regulating the number of pumps, particularly in the kidney. Adrenalectomy results in a fall in the number of pump sites throughout the kidney. Aldosterone replacement can restore pump activity in some segments, notably, the cortical collecting tubule, by interaction with mineralocorticoid receptors. In an analogous tissue, the toad urinary bladder, the increase in the number of pumps involves the enhanced production of specific mRNA coding for the pump proteins. Extreme changes in adrenal status, from adrenalectomy to chronic mineralocorticoid replacement at pharmacologic levels, can alter the pump activity by 10-fold in the cortical collecting tubule. In other cases, glucocorticoid receptors and/or the delivery of Na to a particular segment appears to be involved. This topic is discussed more fully in Chapter 1.

Thyroid hormone

In mammals, thyroid hormone induces the synthesis of the pump in a variety of tissues, including liver, kidney, heart, and skeletal muscle. Again, the synthesis involves the enhanced production of specific mRNAs coding for the pump. This process is thought to be involved in the thermogenic response to thyroid hormone, since in many of these organs the pumping of Na and K across the cell membrane accounts for a large fraction (up to 50%) of the cells' metabolic activity.

Insulin

Insulin enhances pump activity in adipose tissue and skeletal muscle. The mechanism appears to involve either an unmasking of latent pump sites or an increase in the turnover rate of the pump rather than the synthesis of new pump units. This action of insulin may underlie the ability of this hormone to shift K from the extracellular to the intracellular compartment, an important component of nonrenal K homeostasis.

Circulating inhibitors

Circulating factors that may affect electrolyte balance by inhibiting the Na,K pump have been postulated to play a role in hypertension. Such inhibitors have been referred to as potential third factors in regulating Na excretion by the kidney, the other two factors being changes in glomerular filtration rate and changes in plasma aldosterone levels. The precise nature, origin, and importance of these endogenous ouabain-like substances are still unclear.

Chronic changes in cell electrolytes

Several cell types when challenged with an increase in cell Na and decrease in cell K exhibit a homeostatic response in which the number of Na,K pumps is increased. This appears to involve an increase in the rate of synthesis and subsequent translation of mRNA coding for the pump. A decrease in the rate of degradation of pump proteins also may contribute. The net result is a return of the cell Na and K contents toward normal.

Na,K,Cl Cotransport

A recently discovered pathway for K entry across cell membranes involves the obligatory cotransport of K with Na and Cl (Table 5). This transporter can move four ions—one Na, one K, and two Cl ions—across the membrane at the same time, with no net movement of electrical charge. The mechanism has been described both in epithelial cells, where it is involved in transepithelial salt and fluid movement, and in nonepithelial cells, where it participates in volume regulation.

Basic Mechanism

The basic mechanism appears to be passive in the sense that the driving force for transport can be accounted for by the electrochemical gradients for all three ions involved. Since under most conditions Na ions are far from equilibrium, with movement into the cell favored, and K and Cl are relatively close to equilibrium, the transporter will tend to move all three ions into the cell. This is then an example of a secondary active transport mechanism in which the movement of K (and Cl) against an electrochemical activity gradient is driven by the gradient for another ion, Na. The Na gradient is in turn established by the primary active transport system, the Na-K pump, which ultimately couples both processes to metabolic energy in the form of ATP, in

TABLE 5. *Properties of Na/K/Cl cotransporter*

Stoichiometry	1 Na:1 K:2 Cl
Half-maximal stimulation:	
K	4–10 mM
Na	4–20 mM
Cl	20–100 mM
Modulators	
Increase	ATP, cAMP, ↑ cell volume, serum, EGF,
Decreased	furosemide, bumetazide, ethacrynic acid

EGF, Epidermal growth factor.

one case directly and in the other case indirectly. Similar systems can move solutes, such as glucose and some amino acids, into the cell coupled to the inward movement of Na ions. The Na,K,2Cl can, under the appropriately directed ion gradients, also move all three ions out of the cell.

As mentioned previously, the system appears to be rather tightly coupled in that all four ions must move across the membrane together. This has been shown in two ways. First, when net movements of Na, K, and Cl through this system can be accurately measured, they appear to occur with a ratio of 1:1:2. This has been particularly well documented in Ehrlich ascites tumor cells, where the mechanism was first discovered, and in MDCK cells. Second, the movement of ions by this transporter does not affect cell membrane potentials, nor does the rate of movement appear to be affected by the membrane potential. This implies that the process does not move any net electrical charge, which is consistent with a well-coupled system with 1:1:2 stoichiometry.

The requirement for the three different ions appears to be absolute. In particular, Na and K cannot replace each other, implying that the sites of interaction of the cations with the transporter, shown in Fig. 2 as binding sites, are distinct. Rb can replace K in the stimulation of the transporter, and Li can replace Na, although not with full effectiveness. Cl can be replaced only by Br.

An important and useful pharmacologic hallmark of the so-called triple cotransporter is its sensitivity to the loop diuretics, furosemide and the more potent analogs bumetanide and piretanide. This suggests that salt transport in the loop of Henle uses this transport system. Thus, inhibition of transport by these drugs sometimes can be used to ascertain the activity of the triple cotransporter under different conditions or to dissect movement through the triple cotransporter from movement through other systems. The specificity of these agents for the triple cotransporter is not fully established, however. Although many processes involving cotransport of Na, K, and Cl in various combinations (K,Cl cotransport, Na,K cotransport, Na,Na exchange) have been demonstrated to be inhibited by loop diuretics, it is possible that some of these systems may be identical with the triple cotransporter.

Distribution and Physiologic Significance

The Na,K,2Cl cotransport system appears to be a crucial component of cell volume regulatory systems in some cells, notably the avian erythrocyte. In these cells, osmotic shrinkage activates the transporter, with the subsequent movement of ions and water into the cell, correcting the volume perturbation. The cotransporter is well suited to the purpose of increasing the amount of osmotically active solute in the cell, since each cycle brings in four ions. This process also appears to have an important role in regulatory volume increases in the frog skin epithelium and in Ehrlich ascites tumor cells.

The cotransporter also plays a major role in the transepithelial movement of ions and water in some tissues. As mentioned, this mechanism is involved in the reabsorption of NaCl by the thick ascending limb of the loop of Henle. The triple cotransporter is situated in the luminal membrane of these renal cells and mediates movement of all three ions into the cell from the urine (*see* Fig. 3 in Chap. 5). The K transported into the cells mostly recycles across the luminal membrane, which has a high K permeability. The Na and Cl, on the other hand, exit primarily across the basal-lateral membrane via the Na,K pump and Cl channels, respectively, accounting for the net reabsorption of salt. Other reabsorptive epithelia that make use of the Na,K,2Cl transporter include the flounder intestine and the MDCK cell line derived from dog kidney. In the shark rectal gland, this process is reversed. The triple co-transporter is situated in the basal-lateral membrane, whereas the Cl channels are in the apical membrane. This arrangement results in the secretion of Cl-rich fluid by this organ. A similar mechanism underlies the secretion of fluid by the large intestine.

Some cell types for which there is good evidence for the existence of the Na,K,2Cl transporter are listed in Table 6. Since this transport mechanism was discovered only recently, it is not yet known how widely distributed it is. As mentioned previously, its identity or nonidentity with various other furo-semide-sensitive cotransport systems remains to be completely established.

Energetics

In performing its apparent physiologic tasks of volume control and trans-epithelial salt transport, the cotransport system would not necessarily need to move K. In the loop of Henle, only the Na and Cl cross the epithelium to any great extent, with the K being mostly recycled across the luminal membrane.

TABLE 6. *Distribution of Na/K/Cl transporter*

Erythrocytes
  Duck
  Turkey
  Rat
  Human
Epithelia
  Frog skin (basal-lateral)
  Rabbit renal MTAL (apical)
  Shark rectal gland (basal-lateral)
  Flounder intestine (apical)
  MDCK cells (apical)
Ehrlich ascites, tumor cells, smooth muscle

MTAL, Medullary thick ascending limb.

In terms of increasing cell volume, a simple Na,Cl cotransport system also would appear to be sufficient to mediate a net influx of solute into the cell.

The inclusion of K in the triple transporter in the 1:1:2 stoichiometry observed could, however, help to maximize the energetic efficiency of the whole process, at the same time keeping it electrically neutral. Since cell Cl is generally much closer to electrochemical equilibrium across the cell membrane than is Na, the coupled movement of 1 Na and 1 Cl into the cell will waste a large part of the energy required to pump the Na back out of the cell. In fact, the Na gradient is generally sufficient to move 2 Cl ions into the cell for each Na. A Na,2Cl cotransport system, however, would involve the transfer of charge across the membrane, and movements of charge can encounter additional energy barriers within the hydrophobic environment of the membrane. Since K is generally relatively close to equilibrium across the membrane, it can be included in the cotransport scheme to keep the process electrically neutral at a small energetic cost.

Regulation

The most striking cellular process regulating the triple cotransporter is that of cell shrinkage. In both the duck erythrocyte and the frog skin epithelium, reduction of cell volume leads to an activation of Na,K,2Cl cotransport despite the fact that the driving force for the inward movements of these ions will, if anything, decrease due to the higher concentrations of these solutes in the cell when water is drawn out. The result of the activation is the accumulation of K and Cl (the Na is largely recycled through the Na,K pump) and the concomitant increase in cell water until the volume approaches the preshrunken level. The cotransporter can be activated by volume changes of less than 10%. The nature of the signal that acts directly on the transporter is not known. The role of the transporter in volume regulation is discussed further in Chapter 5.

In the duck erythrocyte, the transporter is also influenced by cAMP levels. Transport rates are enhanced when cAMP levels are raised either with catecholamines or with exogenous addition of dibutyryl cAMP. This regulatory process does not seem to be identical with that involving volume changes, since cAMP levels are unchanged during shrinkage. The nucleotide may, however, alter the set point at which volume activation can occur. The transporter is dependent also on the presence of normal levels of ATP in the cell, although ATP hydrolysis is not required for its operation. It is possible that ATP is an allosteric regulator of the protein, either by itself or as a phosphorylating agent.

There is an indication that the transporter may be activated during stimulation of the growth of quiescent cells in culture by serum or epidermal growth factor. This maneuver, which may involve the activation of protein kinase C, provokes in cells an increase in K influx and cell volume that is sensitive to furosemide. The swelling of the cells may be involved in the subsequent stimulation of cell division induced by these factors.

It is less clear if the cotransporter is regulated in epithelial cells, such as in the loop of Henle, in which it is tonically active. Although salt transport by the loop is under the influence of ADH, this hormone may affect the exit of Cl from the cell rather than the entry of ions across the luminal membrane.

POTASSIUM EFFLUX MECHANISMS (5,8–10,12,14)

Potassium Channels (5,8,12,14)

Ion channels provide a major route for K transport across most cell membranes. In addition, because ions moving through channels conduct electrical charge, these channels play a major role in determining the membrane potential of the cell. There are many different types of K channels. These transport systems are under the influence of a large variety of different control mechanisms.

An ion channel is defined as a transmembrane protein with a hole in the middle through which ions can pass by electrodiffusion. The hole or pore presumably has an environment that is much more waterlike than that of the lipid membrane, thus facilitating the partition of ions into the channel and the movement of ions through it. In practice, there are few instances in which a native membrane protein actually has been shown to contain a pore. However, it is generally accepted both on theoretical grounds and on the basis of comparisons with artificial pore-forming molecules that any system that can transport 1 million or more ions per second through an individual transport unit or protein is likely to involve a channel mechanism. The techniques of noise analysis and more recently of patch clamp recordings have permitted the measurements of currents through individual transport proteins in many different cell types and have established the existence of many different types of channels according to this operational definition. It is likely that most transport systems that are conductive, that is, that carry an electrical current, and where ion movements are not directly coupled to metabolism or to the movement of other solutes are ion channels.

Although the diversity of K channels is emphasized, there are a number of characteristics that the various channel types share. The single channel conductance, measured with patch clamp or noise techniques, reflects the number of ions that pass through the channel per second per unit of electrical driving force. Under physiologic conditions, with high K concentration in the cell and relatively low K outside the cell, most of the well-documented K channel types have single channel conductances in the range of 5 to 100 pS (1 $pS = 10^{-12}$ ohm^{-1}). Maximal conductances, with high K on both sides of the membrane, are generally larger. Second, most K channels are highly selective for K over other alkali metal cations. Na is generally conducted very poorly by these channels. In most cases, Rb is transported to some extent, although less readily than K. Third, many K channels are blocked by one or more of the classic blocking ions Ba^{2+}, TEA^+, or Cs^+, although the concentrations at which these ions block conduction and the side of the membrane from which they are most effective vary from channel to channel. These ions are thought to block K transport by entering the channels without going completely through, sticking in the mouth of the pore like a plug. Fourth, most if not all K channels (or any other kind of channel) can undergo spontaneous transitions between open and closed states. In other words, ion channels are not open all the time but switch back and forth from conducting to nonconducting states. The kinetics of these transitions vary considerably from channel to channel, and the alteration of these kinetics by a variety of factors often plays an important role in the regulation of channel activity (Fig. 4).

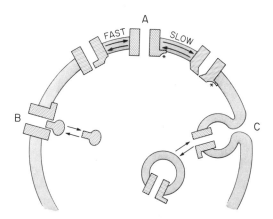

FIG. 4. Modes of regulation of channel activity. **A:** Shifts in the open-closed kinetics of the channel. The channel is viewed as being in equilibrium between an open state (center) and two closed states (left and right). This representation is arbitrary, and different channels can have different numbers of open and closed states. The closed state on the left is in rapid equilibrium with the open state. This equilibrium can be affected by the membrane potential, the binding of intracellular Ca, the binding of an extracellular ligand, or other rapidly reversible events. In this case, the equilibrium between the open state and the closed state on the right is slow and might involve the covalent modification of the channel, for example, by phosphorylation. These are the most common and best studied types of channel regulation. **B:** Some substances can block open channels by competing with the conducted ions for entry into the pore. In Ca-activated K channel, intracellular Na can reduce channel conductance in this way. Protons could also block channels during intracellular or extracellular acidosis. **C:** Channels can be inserted into the membrane from intracellular stores in submembrane vesicles. The vesicles can be either a storage place for spare channels or an intermediate compartment for newly synthesized channels.

Potassium Channel Types (5)

Channels have been classified by their single channel conductance, their open-closed kinetics, their sensitivity to channel blockers, and the factors that regulate their activity. A basic catalog of K channel types has evolved largely from studies with excitable membranes, although many of these channel types are shared between excitable and nonexcitable cells. The major types are listed in Table 7 and summarized below.

Delayed rectifier

This is the K channel described in the classic papers of Hodgkin and Huxley, which is open during the action potential of the squid axon and which is responsible for the rapid repolarization of the membrane potential after a spike has been fired. The delay refers to the period of several milliseconds between the opening of Na channels and the upstroke of the action potential and the increase in K conductance associated with the activation of these K channels. The term rectifier in this context refers to the fact that since the channels are mostly closed when the membrane potential is hyperpolarized but open when the membrane is depolarized, the channel will carry an outward current of K that will be much larger than the inward current evoked by an equivalent but oppositely directed driving force. This channel type is found in nerve and muscle; its distribution in nonexcitable tissues is unclear. However, as shown in Table 7, many K channels share the property of activation by membrane depolarization.

Inward rectifier

This channel type, unlike the delayed rectifier, carries K current into the cell more efficiently than out of the cell. Thus, when the cell membrane is hyperpolarized, the conductance through these channels is high, and K can move into the cells. When the membrane is depolarized, conductance is low and K exit is prevented. This voltage dependence may be an inherent property of the open channel rather than an effect of voltage on the open-closed transition rates, as in the delayed rectifier. Inward rectifier channels are found in skeletal muscle and in cardiac muscle, where they are involved in the spontaneous depolarization of the membranes of some cardiac cells, leading to rhythmic electrical activity. In addition, inward rectifiers with very similar properties are found in the eggs of starfish and tunicates, where they may be involved in the fertilization process.

Calcium-activated potassium channels

Many cell types express K channels that are activated by cytoplasmic Ca. The most prominent of this class of K channels is a high conductance channel called "maxi K" channel, which is activated synergistically by membrane depolarization and by increases in cell Ca. These channels are found in the

TABLE 7. Characteristics of various channel types

Channel	Single-channel conductance (pS)[a]	Modulators[b]	Blockers[c]	Distribution
Delayed rectifier	4–60	Depolarization	TEA[d] (i,o), Ba (i,o), Cs (i,o), 4-AP	Nerve, skeletal muscle, cardiac muscle
Inward rectifier	5–10	Depolarization	TEA (o), Cs (o), Ba (o)	Skeletal muscle, cardiac muscle, invertebrate eggs
Inward rectifier	65–100	ATP (inhibits)		Islet cells, heart
Maxi Ca-activated	100–200	Ca, depolarization	TEA (o), CTX (o), Cs (o), Ba (i), Na (i), quinidine	Skeletal muscle, smooth muscle, nerve, renal epithelia, secretory epithelia
Small Ca-activated	50	Ca, depolarization, protein kinase A		Snail neuron
Small Ca-activated	20	Ca	Quinine	Erythrocytes
Muscarinic K	50	Depolarization, ACh		Cardiac muscle
A-current	?	Depolarization	TEA (i,o), 4-AP, quinidine	Nerve
Renal b/1	20–40	Hyperpolarization, stretch	Ba (o)	Proximal tubule, basal-lateral membrane
S	55	Protein kinase A (inhibits)		Aplysia neuron

[a]Conductance in pS = 10^{-12} Siemans under physiologic conditions.
[b]Modulators are stimulatory except where noted.
[c]i = cytoplasmic side, o = extracellular side.
[d]4-AP, 4-aminopyridine; CTX, charybdotoxin; ACh, acetylcholine; TEA, tetraethylammonium.

transverse tubules of skeletal muscle and in vertebrate neurons, where they aid in membrane repolarization after an action potential, particularly when cell Ca is increased during or subsequent to the action potential. They have been observed also in smooth muscle, pituitary cells, adrenal chromaffin cells, and both secretory (e.g., the salivary and lacrimal glands) and reabsorptive (e.g., the renal cortical collecting tubule and loop of Henle) epithelial cells. Other Ca-activated channels, which can be distinguished from the maxi channel on the basis of single channel conductance, selectivity, voltage dependence, or pharmacology, also have been described, particularly in red cells and nerve.

Other potassium channels

Some other well-defined channel types are listed in Table 7. With the application of patch clamp techniques to a wide variety of cells, new channels are being rapidly discovered. In addition, K can move through channels that are relatively indiscriminate toward monovalent cations. The most familiar example of this type of channel is the nicotinic, acetylcholine-activated channel of the neuromuscular junction, but a number of other nonselective cation channels also have been described. Finally, although the activation of different K channels during an action potential has been extensively studied in many excitable cells, the K channels responsible for maintaining the resting membrane potential and the resting K conductance are less well understood both in excitable and in nonexcitable cells.

From Table 7 it is clear that there is a large variety of channels specialized to carry K. The list is far from complete, and new types and variants on these basic types are being discovered rapidly. In contrast, the Na-selective class of channels contains only two basic examples. A given cell can have several types of K channels. This is particularly well illustrated in the vertebrate neuron and the lens epithelium, both of which express at least four different K channels. Conversely, at least some channel types can be found in membranes from a variety of different cells. The prime example of this is the Ca-activated maxi K channel, which is widely distributed among diverse cell types.

Regulation of Potassium Channels

The regulation of K channels is important in many aspects of cell function. In excitable cells, activation of K channels on membrane depolarization tends to repolarize the cell membrane and shorten the action potential. Slower changes in K channel activity result in the spontaneous depolarization of cardiac pacemaker cells, which govern the beating of the heart. Changes in the resting potential of neurons, which can alter the excitability of the cells and may be important in learning, are accomplished, in part, by regulation of K channels. Finally, transepithelial K transport, which is ultimately responsible for determining the K content of the body fluids, is affected by changes in K channel function.

There are a number of ways in which channels can be regulated. These include changes in the number of channels in the membrane, changes in single channel conductance, and changes in the fraction of time a channel spends in the open rather than the closed state. In practice, it is not always possible to distinguish an increase in the number of channels, as by an insertion of channels into the membrane, from the recruitment of channels from a permanent or long-lived closed state to an open state. Most regulatory systems studied to date involve changes either in channel number or in channel kinetics or gating. Alterations in single channel conductance appear to be relatively rare.

Some of the more common factors that determine K channel activity follow.

Voltage

As alluded to previously, the functioning of many K channels is affected by membrane voltage. The classic Hodgkin-Huxley (delayed rectifier) K channel, M channels that also are regulated by muscarinic agonists, and the ubiquitous Ca-activated K channel are all activated by depolarization of the membrane. The activation is the result of an increase in the fraction of time the channel spends in the open rather than the closed state. In general, the functional relevance of this voltage gating process is to aid in the repolarization of the cell after a depolarizing stimulus. Although the most obvious examples are in nerve and muscle where the depolarization results from an action potential, the same type of K channel activation may serve to repolarize secretory cells, such as those in the lacrimal or salivary glands or pancreas, and at least one depolarization-activated K channel, the Ca-activated maxi channel, is seen in all of these cell types.

In the basal-lateral membranes of renal proximal tubule, gating of K channels has the opposite voltage dependence, so that the channels are open more often when the membrane is hyperpolarized. The physiologic significance of this voltage dependence is unclear.

As mentioned previously, the inward rectifier class of K channels also conducts K better when the membrane is relatively hyperpolarized, but in this case the change may be in the conductance of the open channel to K, rather than in the gating kinetics. This phenomenon may be of particular importance in the heart, where depolarization of the membrane potential will reduce the K conductance, leading to a further depolarization. This destabilization of the membrane potential underlies the spontaneous, rhythmic firing of action potentials in cardiac pacemaker cells.

Calcium

The activation of membrane K conductance by intracellular Ca was first described for red cells by Gardos in the 1950s. Subsequently, the so-called

Gardos effect has been observed in a wide variety of cell types. Ironically, whereas in most cells this effect is probably mediated by the high conductance or maxi Ca-activated K channels, the Ca-activated channel in the red cell seems to be different, being of much lower conductance.

The mechanism of activation by Ca appears to involve the direct binding of Ca to the channel, promoting the open state. The effect is observed with channels both in excised membrane patches and reconstituted in planar lipid bilayers and does not require substrates or cofactors, such as ATP, arguing against a Ca-dependent phosphorylation mechanism. Sr, but not Mg, can substitute for Ca in this activation process, whereas Ba strongly inhibits the maxi channels.

The maxi channels are activated by both Ca and depolarization, and these effects are synergistic. Thus, when the membrane is depolarized, it can be activated by lower concentrations of Ca. In neurons and secretory cells where cell activation involves depolarization by opening of Ca channels, both the membrane potential change and the influx of Ca into the cell will tend to open the K channels and elicit the membrane repolarization effect. The repolarization also tends to shut off the inward flow of Ca.

Phosphorylation

The activity of some K channels is modulated by phosphorylation, particularly by cAMP-dependent protein kinase reactions. One well-studied example is that of a voltage-independent K channel in *Aplysia* sensory neurons, which is inactivated in the presence of serotonin or by intracellular injection of its second messenger, cAMP, or of the catalytic subunit of cAMP-dependent protein kinase. The effect can be observed also in cell-free membrane patches, in which addition of the catalytic subunit and ATP closes the channels. This suggests that the phosphorylation site may be on the channel itself or a closely associated membrane-bound regulatory protein.

In snail neurons, a Ca-activated K channel of small conductance is activated by phosphorylation. As with the *Aplysia* channel, this effect could be demonstrated in cell-free membrane patches with the addition of exogenous catalytic subunit. There are numerous other examples of K currents or conductances in various cell types that are affected by cAMP or hormones that have cAMP as a second messenger, and the list of channels that apparently can be modulated by direct phosphorylation will presumably grow with the use of the patch clamp technique for studying channels in cell-free systems.

Neurotransmitters

In other cases, neurotransmitters or hormones may activate K channels more directly, without the need for a second messenger. This type of regulation has been described for the muscarinic activation of K channels in heart and for stimulation of K conductance in hippocampal cells by GABA. In both cases, it appears that the ligands bind to a receptor that is directly coupled to the target channel by GTP-binding proteins. This phenomenon has been described only recently, and it remains to be seen how general or widespread it is.

Volume

K channels can be activated by cell swelling, and this phenomenon may in some cases be important in cell volume regulation. One well-studied case is that of human lymphocytes in which cell swelling leads to parallel increases in K and Cl permeability, which, in contrast to those in other cell types, appear to be independent conductive mechanisms. It is not so clear what channel type is involved or to what extent the effect of swelling on K channels is mediated by a swelling-induced increase in cell Ca.

Adenosine triphosphate

In pancreatic islet cells, K conductance is modulated by extracellular glucose by a mechanism that probably involves cellular metabolism. K channels that are closed by millimolar concentrations of ATP in excised membrane patches have been described in these cells. This regulation is presumably important in the depolarization-induced release of insulin in these cells. Although this is a specialized function of islet cells, K channels that are closed by ATP also have been described in heart and renal tubules.

Intracellular ions and pH

The maxi Ca-activated K channel is blocked by physiologic concentrations of intracellular Na ions. Thus, changes in cell Na could potentially regulate these channels. The physiologic importance of this phenomenon and its generalization to other channel types are unknown. In some cases intracellular pH can affect K channels, K conductance being diminished during acidification. Such an effect on apical K channels in the distal nephron (Fig. 1C) may underlie the decrease in renal K excretion during acidosis.

Mineralocorticoids

Regulation of K conductance on a longer time scale has been observed in renal cortical collecting tubules that secrete K using a mechanism that involves an apical membrane K conductance. Both the K secretion rate and the membrane K conductance are increased when the mineralocorticoid status of the animal is enhanced by steroid injection or a low salt diet. This response may involve the *de novo* synthesis of new K channels.

TABLE 8. *Elementary properties of K, Cl cotransport*

Stoichiometry	1 K:1 Cl
Half-maximal stimulation	
K	10–40
Cl	?
Modulators	
Increase	SH reagents, ↑ cell volume
Decrease	Furosemide, bumetanide, intracellular Ca, anti-L_L

K,Cl Cotransport (9,10)

A second route for K exit from the cell involves a coupled movement with Cl (Table 8). This mechanism has obvious similarities with the Na,K,2Cl cotransport system discussed previously, with the crucial difference that here there is no coupling with Na; only K and Cl appear to be transported. Since both K and Cl are, in most cases, accumulated within the cell at concentrations above those of electrochemical equilibrium, not having Na in the cotransport system means that K and Cl will be transported out of the cell rather than into the cell.

Basic Mechanism

The basic mechanism of K,Cl cotransport has been relatively little studied. It is similar to that of the K,Na,2Cl transporter in that the process appears to be electroneutral, suggesting that K and Cl are moved with an obligatory 1:1 stoichiometry. The direction of movement is determined by the sum of the driving forces for K and Cl. The net outward movement of KCl can be stopped and reversed by increasing the external K concentration. Again as in the Na,K,2Cl system, the ion specificity is high, with K being replaceable only with Rb and Cl only with Br.

Distribution and Physiologic Significance

In analogy with the Na,K,2Cl transporter, the K,Cl transporter appears in some cases to be rather inactive at normal cell volumes but much more active when volume is perturbed. In the case of Na,K,2Cl transport, the mechanism is activated by cell shrinkage and leads to the accumulation of solute in the cytoplasm and, hence, to an increase in cell volume. In the case of the K,Cl system, the transporter is activated by cell swelling. This leads to a loss of KCl and water from the cell and a return of volume toward the normal level.

Thus the two mechanisms, which may be very similar in their basic operation and even in their pharmacology, move KCl in opposite directions and serve opposite physiologic purposes. K,Cl cotransport stimulated by cell swelling has been demonstrated in avian and low-K sheep erythrocytes and in Ehrlich ascites tumor cells and has been proposed in rabbit cortical collecting tubule and *Necturus* gallbladder. A fuller description of the role of cotransport systems in the control of cell volume is contained in Chapter 5.

In the thick ascending limb of Henle's loop, the triple cotransporter is tonically active and serves to transport solutes into the cell from the urine even at normal cell volumes. K,Cl cotransport also may be tonically active in the kidney. In both the proximal tubule and the thick ascending limb there is a large transcellular flux of NaCl, and the Cl movement out of the cell in the reabsorptive direction may be facilitated by cotransport with K. Whether the tonically active K,Cl cotransporters in the kidney and those responsible for volume regulation in other cell types are identical is not yet known.

The known distribution of the K,Cl cotransporter is shown in Table 9. In most cases this transport activity is activated by osmotic cell swelling. The system may turn out to be more widespread as it is looked for in other cell types.

Without any knowledge of the nature of the proteins catalyzing K,Cl and Na,K,2Cl cotransport, it is not possible to say if they are truly separate species or if they might reflect the same protein operating in different modes. The similarity of the basic mechanisms of transport, their ion specificities, and their sensitivity to loop diuretics all suggest that the systems are at least closely related. However, the presence of the K,Cl system in low K sheep erythrocytes in the apparent absence of Na-dependent cotransport may indicate that the proteins involved ultimately are different.

TABLE 9. *Distribution of K, Cl transporter*

Erythrocytes
  Duck
  Trout
  Sheep ⎫
  Pig   ⎬ reticulocytes
  Dog
  Sheep (low K)
  Human
Rabbit renal proximal tubule, TALH, cortical collecting tubule
  (basal-lateral)
Necturus gallbladder
MDCK cells
Ehrlich ascites tumor cells

Regulation

The stimulation of K,Cl transport by cell swelling has been discussed. The system is quite sensitive and can respond to cell volume changes of 5% or less. As in the case of the Na,K,2Cl transporter, the details of this activation are unknown. It is not clear if the cotransporter can respond directly to changes in cell volume or whether some second messenger is involved in transducing the volume change signal.

K,Cl cotransport can be activated by chemical modification of the membrane by sulfhydryl reagents such as N-ethylmaleimide (NEM). In sheep red cells, the stimulations by NEM and by hyposmotic cell swelling are additive. It is not yet known whether NEM is mimicking a physiologic reaction with the sulfhydryl side groups of the protein.

Intracellular Ca also has a powerful influence on this transport system. Reducing cell Ca stimulates K,Cl cotransport; this effect is not additive with that of NEM. Increasing cell Ca inhibits both basal and NEM-stimulated transport by this system.

Finally, there is a specific antibody (anti-L_L) that blocks K,Cl transport in sheep red cells. The identity or relationship of the L_L antigen with the cotransport molecule has not been established.

REFERENCES

1. Blaustein, M. P., and Hamlyn, J. M. (1984): Sodium transport inhibition, cell calcium, and hypertension. The natriuretic hormone/Na^+-Ca^{2+} exchange/hypertension hypothesis. *Am. J. Med.*, 77(4A):45–59.
2. Edelman, I. S. (1976): Transition from the poikilotherm to the homeotherm: Possible role of sodium transport and thyroid hormone. *Fed. Proc.*, 35:2180–2184.
3. Geck, P., and Heinz, E. (1986): The Na-K-2Cl cotransport system (Topical Review). *J. Membr. Biol.*, 91:97–105.
4. Glynn, I. M., and Karlish, S. J. D. (1975): The sodium pump. *Annu. Rev. Physiol.*, 37:13–53.
5. Hille, B. (1984): *Ion Channels of Excitable Membranes.* Sinauer Associates, Sunderland, MA.
6. Jorgensen, P. L. (1980): Sodium and potassium ion pump in kidney tubules. *Physiol. Rev.*, 60:864–917.
7. Jorgensen, P. L. (1986): Structure, function and regulation of Na,K-ATPase in the kidney. *Kidney Int.*, 29:10–20.
8. Latorre, R., and Miller, C. (1983): Conduction and selectivity in potassium channels (Topical Review). *J. Membr. Biol.*, 71:11–30.
9. Lauf, P. K. (1985): K^+:Cl^- cotransport: Sulfhydryls, divalent cations, and the mechanism of volume activation in a red cell. *J. Membr. Biol.*, 88:1–13.
10. Lauf, P. K. (1986): Chloride-dependent cation cotransport and cellular differentiation: A comparative approach. *Curr. Top. Membr. Transport*, 27:89–125.
11. Saier, M. H. Jr., and Boyden, D. A. (1984): Mechanism, regulation and physiological significance of the loop diuretic-sensitive NaCl/KCl symport system in animal cells. *Mol. Cell. Biochem.*, 59:11–32.
12. Sakmann, B., and Neher, E. (1983): *Single Channel Recording.* Plenum Press, New York.
13. Sweadner, K. J., and Goldin, S. M. (1980): Active transport of sodium and potassium ions: Mechanisms, function and regulation. *N. Engl. J. Med.*, 302:777–783.

14. Van Driessche, W., and Zeiske, W. (1985): Ionic channels in epithelial cell membranes. *Physiol. Rev.*, 65:833–903.

General Review Articles

15. Alberts, B., Bray, D., Lewis, J., Raff, M., Roberts, K., and Watson, J. D. (1983): *The Molecular Biology of the Cell*, Chap. 6. Garland Publishing, New York.
16. Boyle, P. J., and Conway, E. J. (1941): Potassium accumulation in muscle and associated changes. *J. Physiol.*, 100:1–63.
17. Friedman, M. H. (1986): *Principles and Models of Biological Transport*. Springer-Verlag, New York.
18. Kernan, R. P. (1965): *Cell K*. Butterworth, London.

The Regulation of Potassium Balance, edited
by Donald W. Seldin and Gerhard Giebisch,
Raven Press, Ltd., New York © 1989.

5

Potassium and Cell Volume

William B. Guggino

*Department of Physiology, The Johns Hopkins University School of Medicine,
Baltimore, Maryland 21205*

The size and shape of all cells in an organism must be carefully maintained
so that each can fit into the body as a whole. Since most cells contain between
50% and 80% water, the size and to some extent the shape of a cell will be
determined by the total amount of water contained within the cytoplasm. In
plants and bacteria, volume changes are buffered by the cell wall covering the
external face of the plasma membrane and the pressure generated within the
cell. But animal cells do not have rigid coats. Instead they are compliant,
which makes them able to withstand only very small changes in internal
pressure before they change in size. As a consequence, in plants and bacteria,
factors that tend to cause water to move out of or into cells, such as desicca-
tion or overhydration, would, at first, translate into differences in internal
pressure, whereas in animal cells, these same factors would cause changes in
water content and cell volume. Consequently, the key to the control of cell
size in animal cells is to maintain, within narrow limits, the volume of intracellular water. Because animal cells are freely permeable to water, at least on
the surface facing the blood, they must control water volume by manipulating
intracellular solute content. Furthermore, because all animal cells are bathed
in an extracellular fluid (ECF) that is very different from intracellular fluid

(ICF) and because ECF may vary in composition with the state of hydration, cells must expend energy to maintain volume.

This chapter addresses the role of intracellular potassium in volume regulation. The following topics are discussed: the relationship between osmolality and cell volume, why a cell must expend energy to maintain volume in normal osmotic conditions, and the consequences of the adjustments a cell must make following changes in ECF osmolality.

OSMOLALITY AND CELL VOLUME (10,13)

The movement of water from one body compartment to another can be described by the following equation:

$$J = Lp(\Delta P - \Delta \pi) \tag{1}$$

where J is the rate of fluid movement across a compartment, Lp the hydraulic permeability coefficient that describes the relative ease with which water can move across a barrier, ΔP is the hydrostatic pressure difference, and $\Delta \pi$ is the osmotic pressure difference. An example of osmotically driven water flow is illustrated in Fig. 1. A membrane permeable to water but not to sucrose separates two compartments whose ends are sealed by watertight pistons (Fig. 1A). Pushing on piston 2 will cause water to move into compartment 1. This will increase the internal hydrostatic pressure in compartment 2, squeezing water into compartment 1. Water also will move into compartment 1 if sucrose is added to compartment 1. Since in Fig. 1B both pistons can slide, the movement of water into compartment 1 will increase its volume until the concentration of sucrose is equal in both compartments. If one of the pistons is fixed (Fig. 1C), addition of sucrose to compartment 1 will not result in water flow; instead the hydrostatic pressure in the compartment will increase. The resulting pressure difference between the two compartments is defined as the osmotic pressure difference. Thus the $\Delta \pi$ is defined at the ΔP necessary to make $J = 0$.

Since most animal cell membranes cannot support large hydrostatic pressure gradients, ΔP is approximately zero. Thus Eq. 1 can be rewritten

$$J = -Lp(\Delta \pi). \tag{2}$$

Applying the van't Hoff formulation, which states that

$$\Delta \pi = RT \Delta C \tag{3}$$

where ΔC is the solute concentration difference across the cell membrane to Eq. 2 gives

$$J = -Lp(RT \cdot \Delta C) \tag{4}$$

Because water is freely exchangeable across cell membranes in the steady state ($J = 0$), the total solute concentration in ECF and ICF will be approxi-

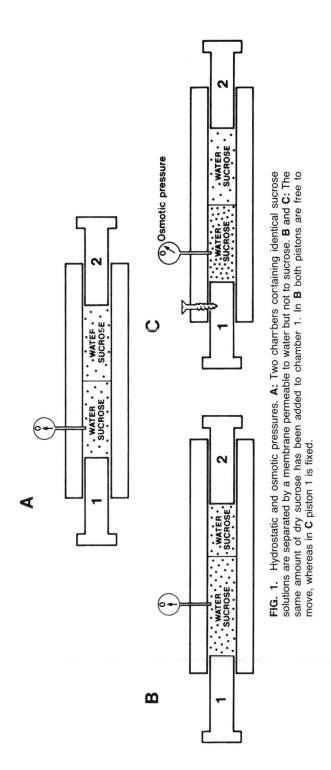

FIG. 1. Hydrostatic and osmotic pressures. **A:** Two chambers containing identical sucrose solutions are separated by a membrane permeable to water but not to sucrose. **B** and **C:** The same amount of dry sucrose has been added to chamber 1. In **B** both pistons are free to move, whereas in **C** piston 1 is fixed.

mately the same. According to Eq. 4, for water to move between ICF and ECF, the total solute concentration in at least one of the compartments must change. As a rule, water will move from a compartment that has a lower total solute concentration (higher water activity) to another with a higher total solute concentration (lower water activity) until the activity in the two compartments is again the same. However, whether water moves after a change in solute concentration will also depend on the reflection coefficient of the solute. The latter, which can vary between 0 and 1, is a measure of the permeability of a particular solute to a membrane. For example, solutes with reflection coefficients of 1 are impermeable to a cell membrane; the membrane is very effective in reflecting such molecules. If the concentration of such a solute were increased in ECF (Fig. 2), decreasing ECF water activity, water will move from ICF to ECF until the activity of water is again the same in both compartments. The result will be a decrease in cell volume. On the other hand, solutes with reflection coefficients close to zero are just as permeable to a cell membrane as water. If such a solute were added to ECF (Fig. 2), it would rapidly distribute between ICF and ECF without significant changes in cell volume. Thus, solutes with reflection coefficients close to 1 are very effective in causing water movements across cell membranes, whereas the lower the reflection coefficient the smaller the rate of water movement for the same initial solute concentration difference. Including the reflection coefficient (σ) in Eq. 4 gives:

$$J = -Lp(RT \cdot \sigma \cdot \Delta C) \qquad [5]$$

Osmolality depends on the total number of particles in a solution rather than on their chemical properties. On the other hand, tonicity is the effective osmotic pressure in relation to a given cell membrane, considering both total solute concentration and reflection coefficient. Thus, the reflection coefficient

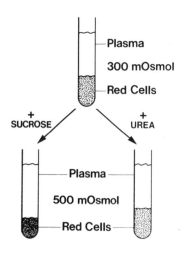

FIG. 2. The effect on red blood cell volume of increasing extracellular osmolality from 300 to 500 mOsm by adding either sucrose (left tube) or urea (right tube). Assuming that red blood cell water is about 80%, the addition of sucrose will reduce the hematocrit from 40% to 27%, whereas a similar increase using urea will not affect cell volume.

could also be defined as the tonicity/osmolality. Only when the reflection coefficient of a solute is 1 are the terms synonymous.

K^+ in mammalian cells is freely permeable across most cell membranes, yet it behaves as if it had a rather high reflection coefficient. This special characteristic of intracellular K^+ and several other solutes within the body (e.g., ECF Na^+) is brought about by the action of Na,K pumps, which do not allow K^+ to distribute evenly across all body compartments. Instead, as discussed in Chapter 4, the pump, which requires energy in the form of ATP, keeps most of the body K^+ within cells, making K^+ an important intracellular osmolyte. Because K^+ is both a major intracellular osmolyte and highly permeable across cell membranes, it is used by cells along with Cl^- to control volume in both isotonic and anisotonic media. We will see in the following sections how cells use these special characteristics of K^+ to control cell volume.

VOLUME REGULATION IN ISOTONIC SOLUTIONS (18,19,23)

Osmotic Crisis

All cells in the body contain significant quantities of polyvalent macromolecules that are restricted to the cell interior and are absolutely required for cell replication and normal function. At normal cell pH, most of these macromolecules have a net negative charge. Because these molecules are negatively charged, they influence the concentration of smaller permeable cations and anions in the cell in a way described by Gibbs and Donnan several years ago and outlined in detail in Chapter 4. To maintain electroneutrality, the sum of valences of the more permeable intracellular anions, such as Cl^- and HCO_3^-, and cations, such as Na^+, K^+, and Ca^{2+}, along with the macromolecules must equal that of the ECF. Because macromolecules are much less abundant in ECF than in ICF, the quantity and the concentration of small anions such as Cl^- will be much greater in ECF than in ICF. Na,K pumps maintain the steady state of high intracellular K^+ and low Na^+ by continually compensating for the loss of K^+ and the influx of Na^+ caused by the movement of both ions down favorable electrochemical gradients. The combination of ionic gradients and permeabilities determines the resting membrane potential, which in most cells is interior negative, generated in large part by the diffusion potential for K^+ and the greater permeability of the membrane to K^+ over Na^+. The negativity of membrane potential helps to maintain a low concentration of intracellular small anions. Therefore, most cells are in a steady state, with the influx of ions balanced by the efflux.

This steady state situation is maintained as long as Na,K pumps are operating normally. However, if inhibited by the cardiac glycoside ouabain, or by a pathologic condition, such as anoxia, most cells will swell. Let us examine

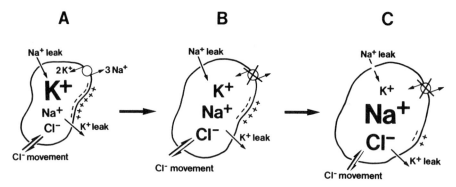

FIG. 3. The influence of pump inhibition on cell volume. Stopping the pump will decrease intracellular K^+ content and increase the content of Na^+, Cl^-, and water. **A** is a normal cell, **B** is the same cell after short-term Na,K pump inhibition where there is an exchange of Na^+ for K^+, and **C** is the same cell after longer-term pump inhibition where Na^+ entry exceeds the K^+ leak, causing a net entry of NaCl and cell swelling.

this osmotic crisis in more detail in Fig. 3. Once the pump is inhibited, there is no longer any transport to balance the leak of K^+ out of the cell and the tendency of Na^+ to move into the cell. Hence, initially there is a loss of intracellular K^+ in exchange for extracellular Na^+. The diminished intracellular K^+ activity reduces the K^+ diffusion potential and depolarizes the membrane potential. The depolarization of the membrane potential allows small anions, predominantly Cl^-, to enter. Because the polyanionic macromolecules in the ICF cannot exchange with those in the ECF, additional Na^+ must follow Cl^- to maintain electroneutrality. Thus, after pump inhibition, Na^+ enters the cell in two ways, in exchange for K^+ and in association with Cl^-. The increased content of osmotically active particles within the cell leads to an influx of water and cell swelling.

Because the rate of cell swelling after pump inhibition depends on the permeability of the cell membrane to Na^+, K^+, and Cl^-, not all cells swell immediately after pump inhibition. In those that do not swell or swell only very slowly, the anion permeability may be low, or alternatively, the cell in an attempt to guard against such swelling may reduce either K^+ or Na^+ permeability following pump inhibition. Toad bladder epithelial cells are a classic example of cells that do not swell after tissue incubation with ouabain. Although the primary effect of ouabain treatment is to inhibit the pump, there is a secondary inhibition of Na^+ permeability that limits the net uptake of Na^+, Cl^-, and water.

This can be mimicked experimentally in the amphibian diluting segment or in the analogous segment, the mammalian thick ascending limb of the kidney (Fig. 4). Normally, in this segment, Na^+, K^+, and Cl^- enter the cell across the apical cell membrane simultaneously via a cotransporter that is inhibited by loop diuretics, such as furosemide. The Na,K pump on the basolateral cell

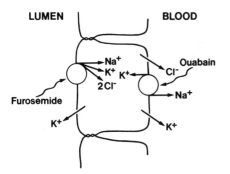

LUMEN   **BLOOD**

FIG. 4. Transport model for the *Amphiuma* diluting segment and the mammalian thick ascending limb of the kidney.

membrane pumps the Na^+ out of the cell. K^+ can leak out of the cell via apical or basolateral conductances, and Cl^- leaves by way of a basolateral Cl^- conductance or a K,Cl cotransporter. Under normal conditions, the influx of ions in diluting segment cells is balanced by the efflux; the cells are in a steady state. Exposure of diluting segment cells to the cardiac glycoside, ouabain, inhibits the Na,K pump swelling the cells. Since the cells swell, it follows that ouabain upset the steady state, resulting in an influx of ions greater than the efflux. The resulting increase in intracellular ion content draws water into the cells, increasing volume. Ouabain will not swell these cells if before pump inhibition, the apical cotransporter, the major system by which Na^+ can enter the cells, is blocked by furosemide. This shows that if Na^+ cannot enter diluting segment cells either in exchange for K^+ or accompanying Cl^-, the cells will not swell. Although a low plasma membrane Na^+ permeability is a good way to resist brief episodes of pump inhibition, it is not compatible with life, since cells must have a Na^+ permeability for nervous activity, muscle contraction, and net movement of Na^+ in such organs as the kidney, gut, and airways.

There are mammalian cells that do not have Na,K pumps. In those cells, other types of energy requiring pumps are used to avoid swelling. For example, dog and cat red blood cells have inverted ion gradients (high Na^+, low K^+), but can extrude Na^+ to maintain volume via a Ca^{2+}-dependent Na^+ transporter.

Homeostatic Volume Regulation in Epithelial Cells

Epithelial cells similar to all other cells in the body must balance the potential osmotic crisis that can occur after pump inhibition. However, epithelial cells, whose primary function is to transport ions from one fluid compartment to another, must also balance the movement of ions across both apical and basolateral cell membranes. The thick ascending limb of the mammalian kidney transports NaCl from the urine back into the blood. This segment, which has one of the highest transport rates of any epithelial tissue, can vary the rate of transepithelial transport in response to changes in the metabolic state of the animal. For example, in the mouse medullary thick ascending limb, the rate of net NaCl transport may triple after stimulation by antidiuretic hormone. To avoid changes in volume during normal or after perturbed transepithelial transport, thick ascending limb cells must maintain a constant intracellular ion content by balancing the influx of ions across the apical cell membrane with efflux across the basolateral cell membrane. This is accomplished by carefully matching the rate of entry of solutes with the rate of exit.

This phenomenon can be illustrated experimentally in the diluting segment by very rapidly perfusing furosemide in the apical solution (Fig. 4). Furosemide blocks the apical cotransporter, rapidly reducing entry of Na^+, K^+, and Cl^- into the cell. Despite this rapid reduction in entry, which should reduce intracellular ion content and shrink the cell if the exit of ions continued unabated, cell volume changes very little. Because volume does not change after furosemide treatment, the efflux of ions must have been reduced as rapidly as entry of ions in order to maintain a constant intracellular ion content. Clearly, the signal that allows apical and basolateral membranes to communicate must act very quickly to couple the rates of transport across both membranes.

Another aspect of this control process is the link between the rate of the Na,K pump and the leak pathways for K^+. In many epithelial cells, changes in the net transport of ions inevitably must be accompanied by changes in the pump rate, since it is the Na,K pump that supplies the energy for most of the net transport of ions. Since the pump transports 3 Na^+ for every 2 K^+, alterations in pump rate without affecting the leak pathways will tend to hydrate or dehydrate a cell and change the diffusion potential for ions within the cell. Consequently, to vary the rate of net Na^+ transport without creating significant alterations in volume and intracellular Na^+, the entry rate for Na^+ must change in parallel with the pump rate. Similarly, altered pumping would certainly modify intracellular K^+ content and cell volume unless the leak pathways for K^+ were increased also to keep the cell in balance. Since most epithelial cells do not undergo sustained swelling or shrinking during transepithelial transport, it follows that the transport rates of both pump and Na^+ and K^+ leak pathways must be coupled. This phenomenon is particularly evident in both the small intestine and the cortical collecting tubule of the kidney. For example, in the small intestine, glucose absorption is coupled to Na^+. The reintroduction of glucose to a substrate-starved small intestine stimulates net Na^+ absorption. This increase in net Na^+ absorption is accompanied by a large increase in the K^+ conductance of the basolateral cell membrane. Likewise, stimulation of the cortical collecting tubule with aldosterone stimulates net Na^+ absorption by stimulating the entry of Na^+ across the apical cell membrane, the apical K^+ conductance, and the Na,K pump on the basolateral cell membrane. In both tissues, increases in K^+ conductance enhance the leak of K^+ from the cell.

VOLUME REGULATION IN ANISOTONIC MEDIA
(1–9,11,12,14–17,20–22,24–26)

We have examined the steps that a cell must take to control volume in isotonic solutions. This is the most common situation in the mammal because the osmolality of ECF in most of the organism normally is maintained within narrow limits through the action of antidiuretic hormone. The fine control of ECF usually prevents exposure of most cells in the body to all but only minor variations in osmolality. However, many situations exist where ECF osmolality is not nearly so constant. For example, in some vertebrates, especially those aquatic animals that live in brackish water or those that migrate between fresh and salt water, ECF osmolality may not be constant but could vary depending on the environment. Moreover, in order for mammals to conserve water during water stress by excreting urine with a higher osmolality than plasma, solutes are concentrated in the ECF of the renal medulla. The osmolality of this fluid, which can be as much as 5 to 7 times normal osmolality, is not constant but can vary depending on the state of hydration of the organism or after application of loop diuretics, such as furosemide. Finally, in certain pathologic states, such as hyponatremia and hypernatremia, even in mammals, ECF osmolality can vary. These situations of changing ECF osmolality make it essential that many cells have the capability to control volume in anisotonic solutions.

Influence of Anisotonic Media on Cell Volume

Unless a cell can control volume in anisotonic media, it will shrink or swell according to the following relationship, which considers the cell to behave as an osmometer

$$mOsm_1(V_1 - b) = mOsm_2(V_2 - b) \qquad [6]$$

where $mOsm_1$ and $mOsm_2$ are the initial and final osmolalities of ECF, V_1 and V_2 are the initial and final cell volumes, and b is nonsolvent water, which is approximately 20% of most cells. (Assumed in the equation is that the change from $mOsm_1$ and $mOsm_2$ is brought about by solutes with reflection coefficients that are 1 or are effectively 1, as has been discussed.) Figure 5, which was derived from Eq. 6, shows that there is a linear relationship between cell volume and ECF osmolality in cells that do not regulate volume. Figure 5 also shows the measured steady state volume versus ECF osmolality in the proximal tubule of the *Necturus* kidney. Notice that *Necturus* proximal tubule cells change volume in either hypoosmotic or hyperosmotic ECF much less than predicted from Eq. 6, suggesting that they can resist volume changes in anisotonic solutions. However, regulation is only partial because there are significant changes in volume in anisotonic solutions. There are

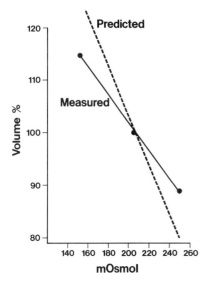

FIG. 5. Measured (solid line) and predicted (broken line) percent cell volume plotted versus extracellular fluid (ECF) osmolality. Measured values were obtained from *Necturus* proximal tubule cells, and predicted values were determined from Eq. 6. Normal ECF osmolality in *Necturus* is about 205 mOsm. Notice that these proximal tubule cells can resist changes in cell volume induced by changes in osmolality but do not regulate their volume completely.

other tissues that are much more effective volume regulators than the kidney cells. For example, *Necturus* gallbladder cells exposed to similar changes in ECF osmolality return to within a few percent of their original volume.

In addition, although the mammalian proximal tubule of the kidney resides in the renal cortex, a portion of the kidney that does not experience large fluctuations in interstitial fluid osmolality, it can resist changes in volume when exposed to hypoosmotic solutions but appears not to be able to control volume when exposed to hyperosmotic solutions. Perhaps the proximal tubule retains some of the mechanisms of hypoosmotic volume regulation and uses them in transepithelial transport. In contrast, in the medullary thick ascending limb of the kidney, volume regulatory mechanisms are well developed in response to both hypotonic and hypertonic solutions. Thus, processes controlling volume in anisotonic solutions vary in effectiveness from tissue to tissue in the same animal.

To regulate volume in response to changes in ECF osmolality, cells must alter intracellular solute content in parallel with the change in extracellular solute content. For example, if ECF osmolality decreases, cells must reduce intracellular solutes to avoid volume changes. Likewise, after increases in ECF osmolality, intracellular solute content also must rise. This strategy is very different from isotonic regulation discussed in the previous section. In isotonic regulation, cells must balance the influx and efflux of solutes to maintain a constant intracellular solute content against steep ionic concentration differences across the membrane that tend to upset the balance. In contrast, cells regulating in anisotonic media must purposefully upset this balance and alter content.

In some cells, a significant portion of the adjustment in solute content occurs via the manipulation of organic molecules within the cell. For example, large amounts of glycerolphosphorylcholine, betaine, inositol, and sorbitol are present in the mammalian renal medulla during antidiuresis, which helps the cells to withstand the hyperosmotic solutions in the renal medulla. The strategy is to vary the transport and either the breakdown or synthesis of these organic molecules after changes in ECF osmolality, thereby altering the number of osmotically active particles within the cell. These particles then play an important role in controlling the amount of water in the cell.

However, in many tissues, inorganic ions are the major effectors of volume control in anisotonic solutions. The strategy here is to vary intracellular ion content via the action of specific solute transporters in the cell membrane. The transporters may in some cells operate only during volume regulation, or, in others, they may be involved in the normal functioning of the cells, with their rates being enhanced during volume regulation.

Volume Maintenance in Hypotonic Solutions

Many cells placed in a hypotonic solution (Fig. 6) swell initially to a value close to that expected from Eq. 6 and then gradually return close to their original volume. The initial increase in volume is due to water entering the cells, whereas the recovery involves the subsequent net loss of solutes accompanied by water. This typical pattern represents a rapid movement of water owing to the very high water permeability of some cell membranes and a much slower secondary movement of ions. In other cells with lower water permeabilities, significant changes in intracellular solutes can occur during the initial phase, reducing the magnitude of the initial volume transient below

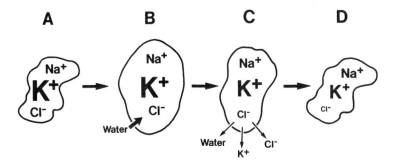

FIG. 6. The effect on intracellular K^+, Na^+, and Cl^- content of reducing extracellular fluid (ECF) osmolality (**A**, normal; **B, C, D**, hypotonic). Immediately after a reduction of ECF osmolality (**B**), water enters the cell with little or no effect on intracellular ion content. In this initial phase, the cell swells near to that predicted for an osmometer (Eq. 6). Subsequently (**C**), K^+ and Cl^- are lost, reducing the intracellular content of both ions with little effect on intracellular Na^+ content. When the cell attains its regulated volume (**D**), the additional efflux of ions cease; the cells are again in a steady state.

that predicted from Eq. 6. In many cells, the secondary phase, commonly called a volume regulatory decrease (VRD), is associated with a reduction in both intracellular K^+ and Cl^- content. The reduction in KCl content, which could occur by reducing entry, typically takes place by a simultaneous stimulation of the leak pathways for K^+, Cl^-, or both.

In some cells, the increased efflux of K^+ and Cl^- occurs via separate conductive pathways, with the two fluxes coupled indirectly by the diffusion potential of each ion and the cell membrane potential, as is the case with lymphocytes, lymphoblasts, and the mammalian proximal tubule (Fig. 7). The volume-induced increase in membrane conductance can occur either by enhancing the movements of ions through the membrane via ion channels already functioning to generate the resting membrane conductance or by inducing channels that are quiescent at normal osmolalities. Frequently, the induction of new channels in the membrane involves the insertion of a submembrane population of channel-containing vesicles that are moved into the membrane by the physical stretching of the membrane. VRD induced by K^+ and Cl^- channels is inhibited by Ba^{2+}, a blocker of many types of K^+ channels, and by removal of Cl^- from the medium.

Red blood cells from different species demonstrate the diversity of mechanisms affecting KCl loss. For example, in avian red blood cells, KCl loss occurs by means of a single cotransporter that moves both ions simultaneously (Fig. 7). Since the transport of K^+ and Cl^- occurs on the same protein, the process is electroneutral, with ion movement dependent only on the differences in the concentration of ions across the membrane. In *Amphiuma* red

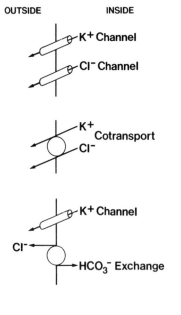

FIG. 7. Models of the transporters involved in hypotonic volume regulation.

blood cells, two electroneutral exchangers, a K,H, and a Cl,HCO$_3$ exchanger, operate together, whereas in human red blood cells, a combination of Ca^{2+}-activated K$^+$ channels and Cl-HCO$_3$ exchangers bring about KCl loss.

For cells to undergo VRD via the loss of K$^+$ and Cl$^-$, there must be sufficient electrochemical energy to drive the ions out of the cell. This is not usually a problem for K$^+$, since the Na,K pump keeps intracellular K$^+$ concentrations in most cells above electrochemical equilibrium. However, intracellular Cl$^-$ concentration in most cells is inherently low between 10 and 30 mM, and ECF Cl$^-$ concentration is much higher at about 110 mM. This requires that cells take special steps to drive Cl$^-$ out of the cell. Some cells solve the problem by having other transporters, for example, the apical cotransporter in the diluting segment (Fig. 4), which moves Cl$^-$ into the cell. These transporters couple the movement of Cl$^-$ to Na$^+$ using the chemical potential for Na$^+$ across the membrane to raise intracellular Cl$^-$ above equilibrium concentrations and to make the efflux energetically favorable. In cells where the efflux is not energetically favorable, transport of Cl$^-$ can be coupled directly to the movement of another ion, such as occurs in the K,Cl cotransporter, in which the energy for Cl$^-$ efflux is derived from the chemical potential for K$^+$. Thus, cells can use two strategies to provide energy for Cl$^-$ efflux: either raise intracellular Cl$^-$ or couple it to the movement of another ion.

Control of Volume in Hypertonic Solutions

Although many cells can withstand decreases in osmolality, far fewer cells can control volume in response to hypertonic solutions. As was discussed, a good example of this phenomenon is the mammalian proximal tubule. In hypotonic solutions, mammalian proximal tubule cells swell and undergo a distinct VRD, almost completely regaining their original volume. In contrast, if exposed to hyperosmotic solutions, proximal tubule cells shrink and remain so until the osmolality is restored back to normal.

Figure 8 illustrates the response of cells that can regulate volume in hypertonic solutions. Again there are two phases, an initial shrinking immediately after the increase in ECF osmolality followed by an increase in volume near to the original volume. The initial shrinking is caused by the movement of water out of cells, whereas the later return to near normal volume, termed VRI for volume regulatory increase, involves the movement of solutes accompanied by water into the cell. Similar to the situation in hypotonic solutions, the magnitude of the initial decrease in volume depends on the water permeability and the speed of the ion regulatory response.

Most commonly, for example, in mammalian medullary thick ascending limb, *Necturus* gallbladder, and *Amphiuma* red blood cells, the increased intracellular solute occurs via an enhanced movement of Na$^+$ and Cl$^-$ into

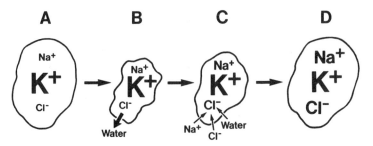

FIG. 8. The effect of increasing extracellular fluid (ECF) osmolality (**A**, normal; **B, C, D,** hypertonic). Immediately after the increase in ECF osmolality (**B**), water leaves the cell without significant alterations in intracellular ion content. Subsequently (**C**), Na^+ and Cl^- enter the cell, increasing intracellular ion content drawing water into the cell. When the cell reaches its final volume (**D**), the cell is again in a steady state, ending the net influx of NaCl.

the cell. In contrast to VRD, which frequently occurs via conductive pathways for K^+ and Cl^-, VRI almost always involves the electroneutral transport of Na^+ and Cl^-. The transport can involve a cotransporter that moves either Na^+ and Cl^- or Na^+, K^+, and Cl^- into the cell simultaneously but more frequently results from the parallel operation of two exchangers, Na,H and Cl,HCO_3 (Fig. 9). The net effect of parallel Na,H, and Cl,HCO_3 exchangers is the transport of NaCl into the cell in exchange for the movement out of the cell of H^+ and HCO_3^-. A characteristic of these cells is that removal of either Na^+, Cl^-, or HCO_3^- from the medium bathing the cells or application of the diuretic amiloride, which blocks Na,H exchange, abolishes VRI. In cells that employ the parallel exchangers to regulate volume, the exchangers are either quiescent at normal osmolality, being stimulated to operate by hypertonicity, or, most often, participate in other cell functions, such as regulation of intracellular pH, as in the *Necturus* gallbladder. In either case, the hypertonicity must signal the operation of the two exchangers not only to enhance the rate of influx of Na^+ and Cl^- but also to coordinate the rates.

In some cells Na,K,Cl cotransporters are involved in volume regulation in hypertonic media. For example, in duck red blood cells, the cotransporter is not very active unless stimulated either by epinephrine or by cell shrinking. On stimulation, the cotransporter can move solute into the cell, leading to a VRI. Interestingly, although present in the apical cell membrane of the mouse medullary thick ascending limb, this same cotransporter is only involved in the net transport of NaCl across the epithelium (Fig. 4) and not in volume regulation. When mouse medullary cells are exposed to hypertonic solutions, cell solute concentration increases not by enhancing apical Na,K,Cl cotransport but by inducing parallel Na,H and Cl,HCO_3 exchangers that drive NaCl into the cell, affecting solute transport across the epithelium. The induction of new transporters separates the net transport function from volume regulation.

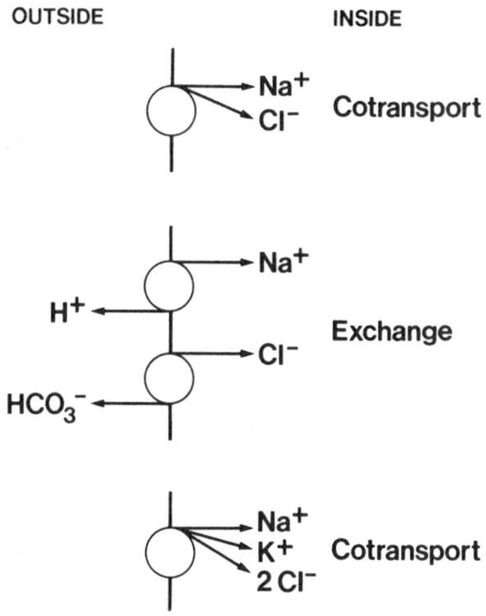

OUTSIDE INSIDE

FIG. 9. Models of some of the transporters that evoke volume regulatory increase.

Role of Na,K Pump in Anisotonic Volume Regulation

All the transporters involved in anisotonic volume regulation derive energy for the flow of ions from the electrical and chemical potentials of ions generated ultimately by the Na,K pump. In hypotonic volume regulation, the pump establishes a K^+ diffusion potential across plasma membranes, which allows for the loss of both ions via separate conductances or cotransport. Also, by pumping three Na^+ out of the cell for two K^+, it removes an osmotically active solute from the cell such that enhanced Na^+ pumping also can contribute significantly to decreased intracellular solute content during VRD. In hypertonic volume regulation, the Na,K pump also generates the concentration differences that allow for the movement of Na^+ and Cl^- into cells either via a single cotransporter or via parallel exchangers.

The pump also may be involved in a tertiary phase of volume regulation, namely, the return to steady state in the new osmolality after either VRD or VRI. In both these cases, volume regulation upsets the intracellular K^+/Na^+ ratio, which the pump may restore. For example, the increase in intracellular Na^+ as a result of VRI may stimulate the pump to exchange some of the increased Na^+ for K^+, nearly restoring the original K^+/Na^+ ratio.

Finally, it is possible for cells to regulate their volume in anisotonic solutions without Na,K pumps. However, since anisotonic volume regulation is a process that operates by ions moving down their electrochemical potentials, some other energy-requiring pump, such as Na,Ca exchange or H^+ pumps, must be present to establish the ion concentration differences across the cell membrane.

Factors Affecting Volume Regulation

The processes involved in regulating cell volume require a sensor that determines each individual cell's optimal volume and determines whether a cell is overhydrated or dehydrated, a signal that is specific for the state of hydration and the effectors that actually evoke ion rearrangements. There is very little known about the sensor or the signal, although it is likely that the degree of membrane stretch probably sensed by microtubules and microfilaments located near the intracellular face of the membrane may be involved in detecting changes in volume. One interesting example is the class of stretch-activated channels. These K^+ selective channels, which are normally quiescent, are activated by stretching the membrane. Since exposure to anisotonic solutions usually causes an initial change in cell volume, perhaps the degree of membrane stretch could be an important signal. However, owing to the complexity of volume regulation and the different kinds of effectors involved, there are likely to be several signaling molecules that play a role, including intracellular Ca^{2+}, which has been shown to be important in volume regulation in the toad bladder epithelium.

Because Na,K pumps and ionic gradients are important in volume regulation, the metabolic state of a cell also will determine the ability of a cell to control its volume. Obviously, cells depleted of metabolic energy will have a hard time controlling volume if the ion gradients across the cell membrane are disturbed. Finally, some hormones also will enhance the ability of cells to volume regulate. For example, in avian cells, epinephrine stimulates Na,K,Cl cotransport, and in the mouse medullary thick ascending limb, antidiuretic hormone enhances net NaCl absorption. In both tissues, the ability to control volume in hypertonic solutions also is enhanced.

ACKNOWLEDGMENT

This work is supported by NIH grant DK 32753 and by a Grant-In-Aid from the American Heart Association, with funds contributed in part by the American Heart Association, Maryland Affiliate, Inc.

REFERENCES

1. Bagnasco, S., Balaban, R., Fales, H. M., Yang, Y-M., and Burg, M. (1986): Predominant osmotically active organic solutes in rat and rabbit renal medullas. *J. Biol. Chem.*, 261:5872–5877.
2. Cala, P. M. (1980): Volume regulation by *Amphiuma* red blood cells: The membrane potential and its implication regarding the nature of ion-flux pathways. *J. Gen. Physiol.*, 76:683–708.
3. Ericson, A.-C., and Spring, K. R. (1982): Volume regulation by *Necturus* gallbladder: Apical Na^+, H^+ and Cl^-,HCO_3^- exchange. *Am. J. Physiol.*, 243:C146–C150.

4. Fisher, R. S., Persson, B.-E., and Spring, K. R. (1981): Epithelial cell volume regulation: Bicarbonate dependence. *Science*, 214:1357–1359.
5. Grantham, J. J. (1987): Cell volume regulation in renal tubule cells. In: *Modern Techniques Of Ion Transport*, edited by B. M. Brenner and J. H. Stein, Vol. 15, pp. 19–45. Churchill Livingstone, New York.
6. Grantham, J., Linshaw, M., and Welling, L. (1981): Volume regulation in isotonic and hypotonic media in isolated rabbit renal proximal tubules. In: *Epithelial Ion and Water Transport*, edited by A. D. C. MacKnight and J. P. Leader, pp. 339–347. Raven Press, New York.
7. Grinstein, S., Clarke, A., Dupre, A., and Rothstein, A. (1982): Volume-induced increase of anion permeability in human lymphocytes. *J. Gen. Physiol.*, 80:801–823.
8. Hebert, S. C. (1986): Hypertonic cell volume regulation in mouse thick limbs. I. ADH dependency and nephron heterogeneity. *Am. J. Physiol.*, 250:C907–C919.
9. Hebert, S. C. (1986): Hypertonic cell volume regulation in mouse thick limbs. II. Na^+, H^+ and Cl^-, HCO_3^- exchange in basolateral membranes. *Am. J. Physiol.*, 250:C920–C931.
10. Hebert, S. C., Schafer, J. A., and Andreoli, T. E. (1981): Principles of membrane transport. In: *The Kidney*, 2nd ed., edited by B. Brenner and F. Rector, Vol. 1, pp. 116–143. Saunders, Philadelphia.
11. Hoffmann, E. K., Sjoholm, C., and Simonsen, L. O. (1983): Na^+, Cl^- cotransport in Erlich ascites tumor cells activated during volume regulation. *J. Membr. Biol.*, 76:269–280.
12. Hoffmann, E. K., Simonsen, L., and Lambert, I. H. (1984): Volume-induced increase of K^+ and Cl^- permeabilities in Ehrlich ascites tumor cells. Role of internal Ca^{2+}. *J. Membr. Biol.*, 78:211–222.
13. House, C. R. (1974): *Water Transport in Cells and Tissues*. No. 24. Monographs of the Physiological Society, edited by H. Dawson, A. D. M. Greenfield, R. Whittam, and G. S. Brindley. Edward Arnold, Ltd., London.
14. Kregenow, F. M. (1981): Osmoregulatory salt transporting mechanisms: Control of cell volume in anisotonic media. *Annu. Rev. Physiol.*, 43:493–505.
15. Lau, K. R., Hudson, R. L., and Schultz, S. G. (1984): Cell swelling increases a barium-inhibited potassium conductance in the basolateral cell membrane of *Necturus* small intestine. *Proc. Natl. Acad. Sci. USA*, 81:3591–3594.
16. Law, R. (1985): Volume regulation by mammalian renal cells exposed to anisosmotic media. *Mol. Physiol.*, 8:143–160.
17. Lopes, A., and Guggino, W. B. (1987): Volume regulation in the early proximal tubule of the *Necturus* kidney. *J. Membr. Biol.*, 97:117–125.
18. MacKnight, A. D. C., and Leaf, A. (1980): Regulation of cellular volume. In: *Membrane Physiology*, edited by T. E. Andreoli, J. F. Hoffman, and D. D. Fanestil, pp. 315–334. Plenum, New York.
19. MacKnight, A. D. C., and Leaf, A. (1985): Cellular responses to extracellular osmolality. In: *The Kidney: Physiology and Pathophysiology*, edited by D. W. Seldin and G. Giebisch, Vol. 1, pp. 117–132. Raven Press, New York.
20. Richards, N. W., and Dawson, D. C. (1986): Single potassium channels blocked by lidocaine and quinidine in isolated turtle colon epithelial cells. *Am. J. Physiol.*, 251:C85–C89.
21. Sachs, F. (1986): Mechanotransducing ion channels. In: *Ionic Channels in Cells and Model Systems*, edited by R. Latorre, pp. 181–205. Plenum Press, New York.
22. Sansom, S., Muto, S., and Giebisch, G. (1987): Na-dependent effects of DOCA on cellular transport properties of cortical collecting ducts from adrenalectomized rabbits. *Am. J. Physiol. (in press)*
23. Schultz, S. (1981): Homocellular regulatory mechanisms in sodium transporting epithelia: Avoidance of extinction by "flush through." *Am. J. Physiol.*, 241:F579–F590.
24. Siebens, A. W. (1985): Cellular volume control. In: *The Kidney: Physiology and Pathophysiology*, edited by D. W. Seldin and G. Giebisch, pp. 91–115. Raven Press, New York.
25. Welling, P. A., Linshaw, M. A., and Sullivan, L. P. (1985): Effect of barium on cell volume regulation in rabbit proximal straight tubules. *Am. J. Physiol.*, 249:F20–F27.
26. Wong, S. M. E., and Chase, H. S., Jr. (1986): Role of intracellular calcium in cellular volume regulation. *Am. J. Physiol.*, 250:C841–C852.

The Regulation of Potassium Balance, edited
by Donald W. Seldin and Gerhard Giebisch,
Raven Press, Ltd., New York © 1989.

6

Mechanisms of Segmental Potassium Reabsorption and Secretion

Michael J. Field and *Gerhard Giebisch

University of Sydney, Concord Hospital 2139, Australia, and *Department of
Cellular and Molecular Physiology, Yale University School of Medicine,
New Haven, Connecticut 06510

The aim of this chapter is to describe the cell mechanisms involved in the transport of potassium along the nephron. It is necessary to explain how, in principle, an epithelium may achieve net transepithelial movement of potassium. In this analysis, we focus on potassium transport in the kidney and consider the characterization of potassium transport properties of individual cell membranes (apical and basolateral) of the tubule cell and further outline the role of each tubule segment in the process of potassium transport. This provides the information necessary for analysing overall handling of potassium and its renal regulation.

BASIC CONCEPTS

As outlined in detail in Chapter 4, potassium ions may cross individual cell membranes in two fundamentally different ways, via channels or carriers.

Channels are specific water-filled membrane structures through which passive electrodiffusion of potassium occurs. Passage of potassium through channels does not require a conformational change in the structural proteins of the channel for each ion to cross the membrane during the period in which the channel is in its open configuration. The driving force for potassium movement through channels is the electrochemical potential difference. Accordingly, both concentration differences and the electrical potential differences move potassium ions through channels.

Carrier-mediated transport of potassium, on the other hand, involves binding to a specific membrane carrier protein, followed by a conformational change in that protein for transport across a cell barrier, and release of potassium from the carrier once it has crossed the membrane. This form of carrier-mediated transport may occur in two basic modes.

1. In cotransport or countertransport mechanisms, movement of potassium is linked tightly via the carrier to movement of another ionic species without direct coupling to ATP hydrolysis. Here potassium may move downhill (down its electrochemical gradient) and, at the same time, drive the uphill movement of another ion species. Alternatively, potassium may itself be driven uphill by linkage with movement of another species down its electrochemical gradient. Such a transport modality is secondary active transport of potassium because the energy-yielding process (ATP hydrolysis) is not coupled directly to the movement of potassium. Rather, it is the transmembrane gradient of another ion species (most frequently that of Na^+) that provides the energy for an apparent active potassium translocation, i.e., its movement uphill against an electrochemical potential difference. Examples of secondary active potassium transport are given in the subsequent discussion of potassium transport across the renal tubule.

2. A special case of active, carrier-mediated transport occurs when potassium is moved against its electrochemical gradient by direct linkage with the source of metabolic energy, namely, hydrolysis of ATP. This constitutes primary active transport of potassium and is best exemplified by Na,K-ATPase, which is ubiquitous in cell membranes. This Na,K pump, for which a stoichiometry of $3Na^+:2K^+$ has been established, is responsible for generating and maintaining the high level of intracellular potassium activity that is central to the analysis of potassium movements across tubular epithelia. In addition, the $3Na^+:2K^+$ exchange ratio of active pump activity contributes directly to the cell-negative potential because of the extrusion of one net positive charge during the pump cycle; the Na,K pump is thus electrogenic.

Transepithelial Potassium Transport (20,22–24)

With this background, it is now possible to give a conceptual framework for understanding the mechanisms by which potassium may move across an epithelial barrier.

Figure 1 (top) shows the principles involved in reabsorption of potassium in

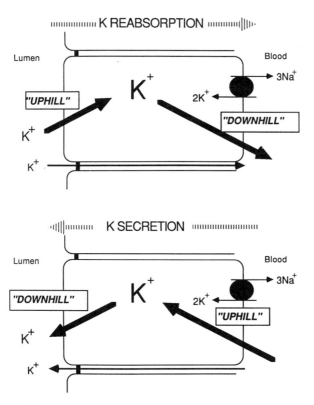

FIG. 1. Schematic diagrams to show the principles involved in transepithelial transport of potassium. **Top**: Reabsorption of potassium from the luminal to the blood-facing side of the epithelium. The large arrows indicate the direction of net potassium movement. Potassium movement is against an electrochemical potential gradient (uphill) across the apical cell membrane but along a favorable electrochemical potential gradient (downhill) across the basolateral cell membrane. In addition, a favorable concentration gradient (high potassium in the lumen) or a lumen-positive electrical potential will, in addition to the movement of potassium via the transcellular route, drive reabsorptive potassium movement along the intercellular (shunt) pathway. **Bottom**: Secretion of potassium from blood to tubule fluid. Potassium movement across the basolateral cell membrane is usually against an electrochemical potential gradient (uphill via the active, ATP-driven K^+ pump) but downhill across the apical cell membrane. Secretory movement of potassium through the intercellular pathway is favored by a lumen-negative electrical potential difference. Black circle (●) indicates primary active transport (e.g., Na,K pump). Adjacent cells are linked by tight junctions, shown toward the luminal end of the intercellular cleft.

a renal tubule, that is, movement of potassium ions from the lumen to the blood. A key starting point for the model is the operation of Na,K-ATPase in the basolateral membrane. This pump activity extrudes sodium from the cell into the interstitial fluid compartment and leads to accumulation of potassium within the cell. This results in the buildup of a high intracellular potassium activity, of the order of 120 mM,[1] a level of cell potassium activity that greatly exceeds that in the luminal or in the interstitial fluid. Both the apical and basolateral cell membranes are electrically polarized so that the cytoplasm is negatively charged with respect to the external environment. This charge is due largely to an outwardly directed potassium diffusion potential across both cell membranes and, in the case of the basolateral cell membrane, also to electrogenic Na^+, K^+ exchange. The net effect of these opposing electrical and chemical gradients is that the intracellular potassium is maintained above electrochemical equilibrium with respect to both the luminal and interstitial fluids. Ultimately, it is the active ATP-dependent Na,K pump that keeps the transmembrane potassium concentration difference above that to be expected from the electrical potential across the apical and basolateral cell membrane.

It follows that the first step in potassium reabsorption via a transcellular route must be its active (uphill) movement across the apical cell membrane from the luminal fluid into the cell. Theoretically, this may be achieved via secondary active transport, in which potassium entry is linked by a cotransporter to the downhill movement of sodium into the cell or by primary active transport, directly involving an ATPase. These possibilities are considered further in later discussions of individual nephron segments. An important prerequisite for effective K^+ reabsorption is the low (or virtually absent) potassium permeability of the apical cell membrane. This prevents potassium ions from leaking back into the lumen once they have been reabsorbed.

The second step in transepithelial reabsorption, potassium exit from the cell across the basolateral membrane, can occur passively down its chemical gradient, since the cell potassium concentration greatly exceeds that of the peritubular fluid and the cell negative electrical potential is insufficient to prevent potassium ions to leak out of the cell. Such passive downhill potassium exit across the basolateral membrane may be achieved either by electrodiffusion via specific potassium channels or by cotransport with another anion, such as chloride, or by both processes in parallel.

It should be noted that Fig. 1 (top) shows another possible route for transepithelial reabsorptive movement of potassium, that via the intercellular (shunt) pathway. Ionic passage through this route depends on the shunt pathway having an appreciable permeability to potassium and on the chemical as well as the transepithelial electrical potential difference. To drive outward movement of K^+, the lumen would have to be electrically positive with respect to the peritubular fluid or the potassium concentration in the lumen would have to exceed that in the peritubular fluid.

Figure 1 (bottom) shows the situation governing transepithelial secretion of potassium. On the basolateral membrane, Na,K-ATPase is again shown as the major driving force for active uptake of potassium into the cell. If potassium

---

[1]If the activity coefficient of cell fluid is taken to be similar to that of extracellular fluid, the cytosolic activity (measured with special ion-sensitive microelectrodes), divided by 0.76 (the activity coefficient of potassium), would yield the cell potassium concentration.

ions are kept above electrochemical equilibrium by the Na,K pump, a portion of potassium ions taken up via the Na,K pump will leak back passively into the peritubular fluid. Exit from the cell into the lumen also will be a downhill process, occurring largely by electrodiffusion along a favorable electrochemical potential gradient. A high potassium conductance in the apical membrane favors potassium secretion. Alternatively, downhill potassium movement at this site may be linked to chloride by cotransport in the same direction. Intercellular potassium movement must again be considered a possible mechanism of secretion, depending on shunt permeability for potassium and an appropriate transepithelial potential difference. In this case, the lumen must be negative with respect to the interstitium in order to induce passive intercellular potassium secretion.

NEPHRON HANDLING OF POTASSIUM

Overview of Potassium Transport in Successive Tubule Segments (14,18,20,22–24)

Micropuncture studies over the past 25 years have given rise to the model for nephron potassium handling shown schematically in Fig. 2. Note that some recent refinements of this model are discussed at the end of this chapter.

After free filtration at the glomerulus, most (60–65%) of potassium in the tubule fluid is reabsorbed along the length of the proximal convoluted tubule. A further fraction (25%) of potassium is reabsorbed by the loop of Henle

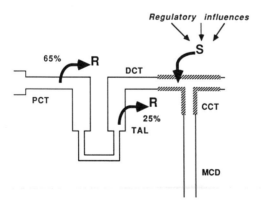

FIG. 2. Schematic diagram of a nephron located in the superficial part of the mammalian renal cortex, showing major sites of net transport of potassium. Percentage figures refer to estimates of the fraction of the filtered potassium load reabsorbed at the sites shown. (PCT) proximal convoluted tubule; (R) reabsorption; (TAL) thick ascending limb of the loop of Henle; (DCT) distal convoluted tubule (the early part of the distal tubule);(S) secretion; (CCT) cortical collecting tubule; (MCD) medullary collecting duct.

(considered as a whole) such that the fraction of filtered potassium present in the tubular fluid at the earliest part of the distal tubule is about 10%. These two reabsorptive steps operate continuously without great alterations despite wide fluctuations in the prevailing metabolic conditions. It is along the distal tubule and in the cortical collecting duct that major alterations in tubular transport of potassium occur.

On a normal potassium intake (Fig. 2), potassium is secreted into the late segments of the distal tubule and into the cortical collecting tubule.[2] The excreted fraction of filtered potassium under such conditions is about 10% to 20% of the filtered load. After dietary potassium loading, this secretory activity is markedly enhanced so that urinary potassium can approach or even exceed the filtered load. Conversely, during potassium depletion, the distal secretion of potassium is completely suppressed, and potassium reabsorption may now occur along the distal tubule and collecting duct system. Details of the factors regulating these transport processes are given in Chapter 7.

With this simplified overview of the net transport properties of successive nephron segments, it is now appropriate to consider what is known of the specific cellular mechanism(s) of potassium transport along the nephron.

Proximal Convoluted Tubule (1,12,14,20,22–24)

Reabsorption of potassium by the epithelium of the proximal tubule is a complex process that has not been fully elucidated to date. Two aspects of this process must be considered in any analysis: (a) to what extent does transepithelial reabsorption proceed via a transcellular as distinct from an intercellular route, and (b) are there important differences in the reabsorptive mechanism along the length of this nephron segment?

The proximal tubule acts as a classically leaky, low-resistance epithelium. It carries out extensive reabsorption of fluid as well as that of sodium, potassium, and other ions, generating only small transepithelial concentration gradients and a low transepithelial electrical potential difference. Experimental evidence suggests that in addition to transport through the cell transfer of solutes and water occurs, to a significant extent, via an intercellular shunt pathway (Fig. 3).

Two passive forces may act on an ion, such as potassium, to promote its transepithelial movement via this route. First, bulk movement of fluid through

---

[2]The nomenclature of the distal tubule (distal convolution) has undergone some changes. The distal tubule includes several segments: the distal convoluted tubule (made up of distal convoluted tubule cells), the connecting tubule (made up of both connecting tubule cells and intercalated cells), and the beginning portion of the cortical collecting duct (made up of principal and intercalated cells). This latter segment is also known as the "initial collecting tubule." In micropuncture terminology the early distal tubule corresponds to the distal convoluted tubule, and the late distal tubule includes the connecting tubule and beginning portion of the cortical collecting tubule.

EARLY PROXIMAL

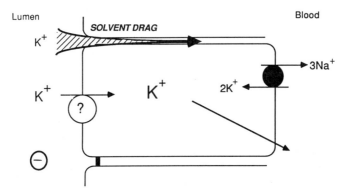

LATE PROXIMAL

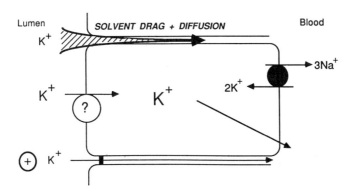

FIG. 3. Mechanisms involved in reabsorption of potassium in the early (**top**) and late (**bottom**) segments of the proximal tubule. (●) primary active transport; (○) some form of carrier--mediated transport; ⊕ or ⊖ polarity of the transepithelial electrical potential difference in that segment of the nephron (lumen with respect to interstitium); (obliquely sloping arrows) passive movement down an electrochemical gradient.

intercellular junctions may entrain large amounts of potassium by the process of solvent drag. The extent of this mode of potassium transfer will be proportional to the degree of volume reabsorption in a given segment of the proximal convolution and, hence, would normally be expected to be greater in the earlier than the later portions of the proximal tubule.

Second, the electrochemical driving force acting on potassium, in conjunction with an appreciable intercellular shunt permeability, leads to significant passive reabsorptive flux by electrodiffusion. Since there is only a small transepithelial chemical concentration difference for potassium along the proximal tubule—TF/P potassium ratios above and below unity have been reported—this transport will depend strongly on the prevailing electrical potential gradient. As shown in Fig. 3, this potential difference reverses along the proximal tubule; the potential is slightly lumen negative in the earliest parts of the proximal convolution but becomes lumen positive in the later portions.[3] One would, therefore, predict that any intercellular diffusional potassium flux across the proximal tubule would be significant only in these later proximal tubule segments.

In addition to the passive forces acting on potassium across the proximal tubular wall, there is some evidence that there exists, in addition, an active, transcellular route of potassium reabsorption. This conclusion follows from the observation that potassium reabsorption continues under certain experimental conditions in which sodium and fluid reabsorption are markedly reduced. As predicted in the earlier discussion of basic concepts (Fig. 1 top), such transcellular movement must involve an active uptake step in the apical membrane. In support of this assertion, direct potassium activity measurements by cell impalements in amphibian kidneys have confirmed that potassium is distributed above electrochemical equilibrium across both the luminal and basolateral membranes. However, the exact nature of the active uptake mechanism in the apical membrane has not been elucidated. In contrast to the situation in the thick ascending limb, there is no evidence that apical potassium transport involves cotransport with sodium and chloride. Transcellular potassium transport has not yet been studied extensively in the mammalian proximal tubule.

The exit step for potassium transfer from the proximal cell into the peritubular fluid appears to occur almost exclusively by passive diffusion. This conclusion follows from the demonstration of a downhill electrochemical gradient for potassium across this cell barrier, together with a high potassium permeability of the basolateral cell membrane. Some evidence favoring electrically neutral KCl exit has become available, but its physiologic role is not clear at present.

Thick Ascending Limb of Henle's Loop (4–6,15,22–24).

More precise information is available concerning the mechanism of potassium reabsorption across this nephron segment than for the proximal tubule. It is now well established that the uptake of potassium against its electrochemical gradient across the luminal membrane into the cells of the thick ascending limb (TAL) occurs by means of a cotransport mechanism such that one sodium, one potassium, and two chloride ions are translocated simultane-

---

[3]The reversal of the transepithelial potential from lumen negative to lumen positive is due to the generation of a chloride diffusion potential. With bicarbonate reabsorption taking place in the early proximal tubule, the chloride concentration rises to levels that exceed the chloride concentration in the peritubular interstitial fluid. Given the high chloride permeability of the intercellular shunt pathway, the preferential diffusion of chloride, in excess of the positively charged sodium ion, out of the tubule renders the lumen electrically positive.

THICK ASCENDING LIMB

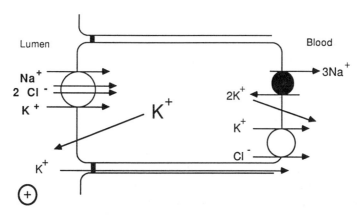

FIG. 4. Cell model indicating mechanisms involved in potassium transport across the thick ascending limb of Henle's loop. (●) primary active transport; (○) some form of carrier-mediated transport; ⊕ polarity; (obliquely sloping arrows) passive movement down an electrochemical gradient.

ously (Fig. 4). This electrically neutral process constitutes secondary active transport of potassium, the driving force being provided by the active extrusion of sodium across the basolateral membrane of the cell.

As shown in Fig. 4, some of the potassium entering the cell across the apical cell membrane by cotransport is recycled across the apical membrane through specific potassium channels that confer to this membrane a significant potassium permeability. The functional significance of this recycling process is that it replenishes the supply of luminal potassium ions necessary to permit continued operation of the cotransporter by which sodium chloride reabsorption proceeds in this nephron segment.

The existence of a specialized $Na^+,K^+,2\ Cl^-$ cotransport carrier in the cells of the TAL also provides a rationale for the specificity of action of the potent loop diuretics, of which furosemide is the prototype. These drugs appear to bind to the chloride site of the cotransport complex, thereby blocking its operation. Of interest in relation to potassium transport is the observation that in the presence of furosemide and related drugs, potassium uptake into the cell is blocked, whereas potassium exit into the lumen by electrodiffusion continues unopposed. This may even result in conversion of net potassium reabsorption in this segment to a small but significant net secretory flux. These effects—inhibition of potassium reabsorption and potassium secretion—contribute to the increase in urinary excretion of potassium observed during administration of loop diuretics.

During normal operation of the TAL, the second step in transcellular potassium reabsorption is the exit of potassium from the cell across the basolateral membrane. This is again a downhill transport step. It may involve potassium diffusion through specific potassium channels or, according to some evidence, coupled exit with chloride ions via a KCl cotransporter (Fig. 4).

Discussion of reabsorption in this segment must again include the possibility of intercellular movement of potassium between adjacent TAL cells. This process is favored by the lumen-positive electrical potential difference usually present in the TAL.

Distal Nephron (2,3,9,10,11,13,14,16–20,22–24)

The portion of the distal nephron responsible for the process of potassium secretion appears, from a variety of morphologic and transport studies, to be restricted to the late part of the segment between the macula densa and the confluence of two distal tubules (the late distal tubule referred to in the micropuncture literature), as well as the cortical collecting tubule. It is of interest that the distal convoluted tubule (or early distal tubule) has not been shown to carry out functionally significant net transport of potassium in either a reabsorptive or secretory direction, though it reabsorbs appreciable amounts of NaCl.

This heterogeneity of tubule function along the distal nephron is complicated further by the recent definition of cell heterogeneity within those tubule segments capable of potassium secretion. Two cell types are present in this region (Fig. 5). The principal (or light) cell is more numerous and is responsible for sodium reabsorption and for potassium secretion, whereas the intercalated (or dark) cell is thought to mediate potassium reabsorption and hydrogen ion secretion. These conclusions are the result of a number of studies using morphometric, electrical, and optical techniques to establish structure-function relationships for these cell types.

The principal cell achieves secretion of potassium as the result of sequential transport across the basolateral and luminal membranes, as discussed earlier in this chapter under *Basic Concepts*. As shown in Fig. 5, potassium is transported into the cell across the basolateral membrane by the activity of the Na,K-ATPase, as in other tubule segments. Both the apical and the basolateral membranes possess a finite potassium permeability, and, accordingly, potassium ions may leave the cell down an electrochemical gradient across either cell membrane. However, preferential movement of potassium occurs generally into the lumen and not into the peritubular fluid because the apical membrane is depolarized (i.e., the cytosol side is made less negative) by electrodiffusion of sodium in an inward direction from the lumen into the cell through an apical membrane sodium conductance. Thus, as illustrated further in Fig. 6, the presence of an entry channel for sodium in the apical but not the basolateral cell membrane sets up an electrical asymmetry that results in a lumen-negative transepithelial potential that favors the movement of potassium from the cell toward the lumen.

PRINCIPAL CELL

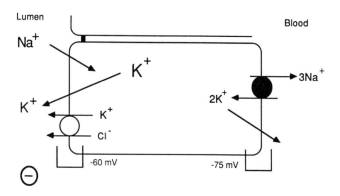

INTERCALATED CELL

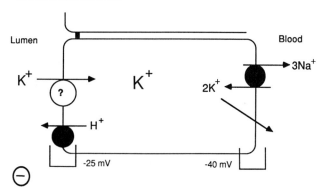

FIG. 5. Mechanisms involved in the transport of potassium across the two cell types constituting the distal tubule (late part) or cortical collecting tubule in the mammalian nephron. The principal (or light) cell is the more common cell type in these segments and carries out potassium secretion and sodium reabsorption, whereas the intercalated (or dark) cell appears to be involved both in potassium reabsorption and in hydrogen ion secretion. Electrical potential differences shown are typical of those measured (inside of cell relative to outside) across each individual cell membrane. (●) primary active transport; (○) some form of carrier-mediated transport; ⊖ polarity; (obliquely sloping arrows) passive movement down an electrochemical gradient.

Although the preceding description of potassium secretion is consistent with the great bulk of experimental evidence and certainly accounts for most of the secretory potassium movement in distal nephron segments, it should be noted that other mechanisms for potassium entry into the luminal fluid from the cell also are possible. Indeed, recent microperfusion experiments in the rat suggest that lowering the concentration of chloride in the lumen acti-

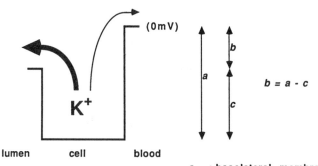

a : basolateral membrane pd
b : transepithelial pd
c : apical membrane pd

FIG. 6. Schematic diagram to show electrical potential difference profile across a single potassium-secreting (principal) cell of the distal nephron under normal conditions. Typical values for a = -80 mV, c = -50 mV (both inside cell relative to outside), b = -30 mV (lumen relative to interstitium).

vates a component of electroneutral potassium transfer across the apical membrane by cotransport with chloride.

Returning to the basic model for potassium secretion shown in Fig. 5, it is now possible to speculate on how alterations in key components of the overall transport mechanism may be involved in regulation and control of potassium secretion. This is illustrated in Fig. 7.

Clearly, any increase in activity of the basolateral membrane pump will have a profound effect on secretion by enhancing potassium uptake into the cell, hence increasing cellular potassium activity and the electrochemical gradient for secretion across the apical cell membrane. Stimulation of the basolateral Na,K pump is involved in the stimulation of potassium secretion after exposure to high levels of mineralocorticoids, such as aldosterone and desoxycorticosterone acetate, during adaptation to a high dietary potassium content, during hyperkalemia and in metabolic alkalosis.

Alterations in the potassium permeability of the apical cell membrane are another means for achieving control of potassium secretion.[1] An increase in

---

[1]The terms "ion permeability" and "ion conductance" are not interchangeable, although they are closely related (see ref. 21). The potassium permeability is the relationship between flux of a solute and the driving force; i.e., it is the coefficient relating the flux to a concentration difference or to an electrical potential difference. The conductance of potassium depends, in a complex way, on the permeability, the concentration of the ion on both sides of the membrane, and the electrical potential difference. Importantly, the conductance is affected by the availability of ions to carry current across a membrane. A high ion permeability *per se* does not provide for a high ion conductance if there is not an adequate amount of ions available to carry the current through the membrane. Current flow and ion conductance are further affected by the distribution of potassium across the membrane. For a given potassium concentration and electrical potential difference across a membrane, current carried by potassium ions is larger when current flows from the side of the membrane where the potassium concentration is high. When the potassium concentration is low, the conductance from that side of the membrane will also be less, since fewer ions are available to carry current.

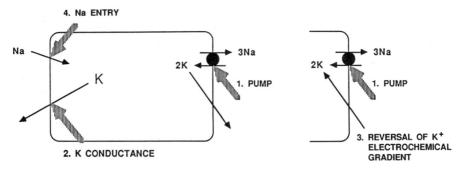

FIG. 7. Regulation of secretion. Diagram illustrates the three key sites within a principal cell of the distal nephron at which the process of potassium secretion may be regulated.

apical potassium permeability follows treatment with mineralocorticoids, further contributing to their stimulatory action on potassium secretion. Vasopressin (antidiuretic hormone) also has been shown to have this effect. On the other hand, acidification of the luminal fluid reduces the apical potassium permeability and contributes to the inhibitory influence of this maneuver on potassium secretion. In experimental settings, barium ions are used as effective blockers of the apical potassium channel, resulting in inhibition of potassium secretion.

Changes in passive potassium movement across the basolateral membrane may also play a significant role in the regulation of transepithelial potassium transport. Maximal stimulation of electrogenic Na,K exchange, for instance, following mineralocorticoid treatment, hyperpolarizes the basolateral membrane to such an extent that the membrane potential now exceeds the potassium equilibrium potential (Fig. 7, right). Under such conditions, the direction of passive potassium movement would change from passive loss of potassium ions from the cell to uptake of potassium into the cell. This increases the overall efficiency of potassium secretion because movement of potassium from peritubular fluid into the cytoplasm of principal cells would occur not only by active, pump-driven Na,K exchange but also by passive diffusion in the same direction.

Secretion of potassium may be powerfully influenced by anything acting to alter the entry of sodium ions into the cell across the apical membrane. Physiologically, mineralocorticoid action is once again the most important factor here. Aldosterone increases the sodium conductance of the apical membrane, resulting in depolarization of this membrane as sodium flux into the cell increases, with secondary enhancement of secretory potassium exit. Similar effects may result from fluctuations in sodium availability in the luminal fluid, although apical Na conductance is not greatly altered in this case. Thus, when luminal sodium delivery is very depressed (tubular fluid Na concentrations below 35 mM), the apical membrane potential difference rises; i.e., the membrane hyperpolarizes. This results in suppression of potassium secretion (Fig.

6 depicts the effect of unequal cell polarization upon potassium transport). Pharmacologically, an equivalent effect is produced by the drug amiloride, which blocks the apical Na conductance, brings the transepithelial potential difference to zero, and secondarily blocks the secretion of potassium.

The intercalated cells, scattered among the principal cells of the late distal tubule–cortical collecting tubule epithelium, are thought to contribute to potassium reabsorption rather than secretion. This conclusion is based largely on the morphologic observation of selective amplification of the apical membrane of only these cells in the medullary collecting duct of rats during potassium depletion. Since potassium uptake from the luminal fluid into the cell must take place against an electrochemical gradient, it can be surmised that an active transport process is involved. It is not clear if this involves direct linkage to an energy source (K,H-ATPase ?). Once inside the cell, exit across the basolateral membrane may occur by passive diffusion or perhaps KCl cotransport (not shown in Fig. 5). It is of interest that the density of Na,K-ATPase units along the basolateral membrane of this cell type is markedly less than that of the adjacent principal cells, consistent with a role for only the latter in transepithelial sodium reabsorption and potassium secretion.

A second type of potassium reabsorption may reside within the medullary collecting ducts. This nephron segment generates a lumen-positive potential that is due to electrogenic hydrogen ion secretion. This process is achieved by the action of an H-ATPase located in the apical cell membrane of these cells (Fig. 5). The medullary collecting duct also has a significant potassium permeability, which resides in the intercellular transport pathway. It is likely that the transport rates of potassium and hydrogen are linked at this nephron site. Stimulation of hydrogen ion secretion increases the lumen-positive potential, an event that augments passive potassium reabsorption. Conversely, with a fall in acid secretion, such passive potassium reabsorption would be attenuated and more potassium would appear in the final urine. This mechanism of pH-dependent, passive potassium transport may contribute to the frequently observed parallel relationship between urine pH and potassium excretion.

Medullary Recycling of Potassium (7,8)

Recent evidence supports the view that significant differences occur between the pattern of potassium transport in superficial—cortical—nephrons and that in nephrons more deeply placed within the cortex— juxtamedullary nephrons. The key observations that led to this view are micropuncture experiments performed on the exposed renal papilla. Fluid sampled from the hairpin bend of the loop of Henle (at which only the long loops of juxtamedullary nephrons are available) contains a greater amount of potassium than is present in the glomerular filtrate, even in animals on a normal diet. Assuming that the proximal convoluted tubule of these juxtamedullary nephrons reab-

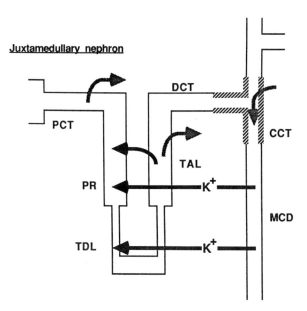

FIG. 8. Schematic diagram of a juxtamedullary, long-looped nephron (glomerulus deeply placed within the renal cortex) to illustrate the process of medullary recycling of potassium. Arrows indicate direction of net potassium movement at each site. Shaded arrows correspond to transport steps shared with superficial nephrons (see Fig. 2), whereas black arrows show potassium transfers typically observed in deep nephrons. (CCT) cortical collecting tubule; (DCT) distal convoluted tubule; (MCD) medullary collecting duct; (PCT) proximal convoluted tubule; (PR) pars recta of the proximal tubule; (TAL) thick ascending limb of Henle's loop; (TDL), thin descending limb of Henle's loop.

sorbed potassium at a similar rate as their cortical counterparts, it was clear that appreciable potassium entry into the tubular fluid must have occurred in the pars recta (end-proximal segment) and/or thin descending limb of Henle.

Several lines of evidence suggest that the principal origin of potassium added to the loop of Henle is from the medullary collecting duct, though the TAL may also contribute (Fig. 8). Potassium can thus undergo recycling within the renal medulla, where it is trapped in a manner reminiscent of that proposed for urea. The resulting high medullary interstitial concentrations of potassium provide a gradient favoring passive secretion of potassium into the pars recta and thin descending limb. The whole process of potassium recycling has been shown to be accentuated during both chronic and acute potassium loading but is suppressed by dietary potassium deprivation or amiloride therapy. It is functionally more important in those nephrons whose loops penetrate into the papilla than in short, cortical nephrons.

Medullary recycling of potassium does not contribute net extra potassium to the tubular fluid for excretion beyond that secreted along the late distal tubule and cortical collecting tubule. However, potassium recycling provides optimal conditions for the distal nephron to excrete potassium. Thus, when distal nephron potassium secretion is stimulated during exposure to an acute or chronic increase in potassium intake, it is important that the collecting duct system be able to maintain the resulting high urinary concentration of potassium during passage through the medulla. The effective trapping and high potassium concentration in the medulla achieved by the recycling process, which is also stimulated under these conditions, means that the high collecting duct potassium concentrations will not be significantly dissipated into the medullary interstitium, thereby maximizing the efficiency of potassium excretion.

ACKNOWLEDGMENT

We thank Amabel Shih for assistance in preparing the manuscript.

REFERENCES

1. Beck, L. H., Senesky, D., and Goldberg, M. (1973): Sodium-independent active potassium reabsorption in proximal tubule of the dog. *J. Clin. Invest.*, 52:2641–2645.
2. Boudry, J., Stoner, L., and Burg, M. (1976): The effect of lumen pH on potassium transport in renal cortical collecting tubules. *Am. J. Physiol.*, 230:239–244.
3. Ellison, D. H., Velazquez, H., and Wright, F. S. (1985): Stimulation of distal potassium secretion by low lumen chloride in the presence of barium. *Am. J. Physiol.*, 248:F638–F649.
4. Greger, R., and Schlatter, E. (1983): Properties of the lumen membrane of the cortical thick ascending limb of Henle's loop of rabbit kidney. *Pflügers Arch.*, 396:315–324.
5. Greger, R., and Schlatter, E. (1983): Properties of the basolateral membrane of the cortical thick ascending limb of Henle's loop of rabbit kidney. A model for secondary active chloride transport. *Pflügers Arch.*, 396:325–334.
6. Guggino, S. E., Suarez-Isla, B. A., Guggino, W. B., and Sacktor, B. (1985): Forskolin and antidiuretic hormone stimulate a Ca^{2+}-activated K^+ channel in cultured kidney cells. *Am. J. Physiol.*, 249:F448–F455.
7. Jamison, R. L. (1987): Potassium recycling. *Kidney Int.*, 31:695–703.
8. Jamison, R. L., Work, J., and Schafer, J. A. (1982): New pathways for potassium transport in the kidney. *Am. J. Physiol.* 242:F297–F312.
9. Kashgarian, M., Biemesderfer, D., Caplan, M., and Forbush, B. (1985): Monoclonal antibody to Na,K-ATPase: Immunocytochemical localization along nephron segments. *Kidney Int.*, 28:899–913.
10. Koeppen, B. M., Biagi, B. A., and Giebisch, G. (1983): Intracellular microelectrode characterization of the rabbit cortical collecting duct. *Am. J. Physiol.*, 244:F34–F47.
11. Koeppen, B. M., and Giebisch, G. (1985): Mineralocorticoid regulation of sodium and potassium transport by the cortical collecting duct. In: *Regulation and Development of Membrane Transport Processes*, edited by J. S. Graves, pp. 89–104. Wiley, New York.
12. Kubota, T., Biagi, B. A., and Giebisch, G. (1983): Intracellular potassium activity measurements in single proximal tubules of *Necturus* kidney. *J. Membr. Biol.*, 73:51–60.
13. Madsen, K. M., and Tisher, C. C. (1986): Structural–functional relationships along the distal nephron. *Am. J. Physiol.*, 250:F1–F15.
14. Malnic, G., Klose, R., and Giebisch, G. (1964): Micropuncture study of renal potassium excretion in the rat. *Am. J. Physiol.*, 206:674–686.
15. Morgan, T., Tadokoro, M., Martin, D., and Berliner, R. W. (1970): Effect of furosemide on Na and K transport studies by microperfusion of the rat nephron. *Am. J. Physiol.*, 218:292–297.

16. Stanton, B. A., Biemesderfer, D., Wade, J. B., and Giebisch, G. (1981): Structural and functional study of the rat distal nephron: Effects of potassium adaptation and depletion. *Kidney Int.*, 19:36–48.
17. Stetson, D., Wade, J., and Giebisch, G. (1980): Morphological alterations in the rat medullary collecting duct following K^+ depletion. *Kidney Int.*, 17:45–56.
18. Stokes, J. B. (1983): Ion transport by the cortical and outer medullary collecting tubule. *Kidney Int.*, 22:473–484.

General Review Articles

19. Field, M. J., and Giebisch, G. (1985): Hormonal control of renal potassium excretion (Editorial Review). *Kidney Int.*, 27:237–387.
20. Giebisch, G. (1978): Renal potassium transport. In: *Membrane Transport in Biology*, edited by G. Giebisch, D. C. Tosteson, and H. H. Ussing, Vol. 4A, pp. 215–298. Springer-Verlag, Berlin, Heidelberg, New York.
21. Katz, B. (1966): *Nerve, Muscle and Synapse*. McGraw-Hill, New York.
22. Stanton, B. A., and Giebisch, G. (1982): Regulation of potassium homesotasis. In: *Functional Regulation at the Cellular and Molecular Levels*, edited by R. Corradino, pp. 259–283. Elsevier North Holland, Amsterdam.
23. Wright, F. S., and Giebisch, G. (1978): Renal potassium transport: Contribution of individual nephron segments and populations. *Am. J. Physiol.*, 235:F515–F527.
24. Wright, F. S., and Giebisch, G. (1985): Regulation of potassium excretion. In: *The Kidney: Physiology and Pathophysiology*, edited by D. W. Seldin and G. Giebisch, pp. 1223–1249. Raven Press, New York.

The Regulation of Potassium Balance, edited
by Donald W. Seldin and Gerhard Giebisch,
Raven Press, Ltd., New York © 1989.

7

Renal and Extrarenal Excretion of Potassium

Jeffrey S. Berns and John P. Hayslett

*Section of Nephrology, Yale University School of Medicine,
New Haven, Connecticut 06510*

POTASSIUM BALANCE (1)

Body Stores and Distribution of Potassium

Maintenance of external potassium balance and distribution of potassium across cell membranes are vital for cell function. After a brief review of total body potassium balance, we discuss the factors that influence renal and extrarenal potassium excretion and serve to maintain potassium homeostasis.

The average daily dietary intake of potassium is approximately 75 to 100 mEq (Fig. 1). Absorption of dietary potassium occurs in the small intestine by passive mechanisms for which there are no important regulatory mechanisms.

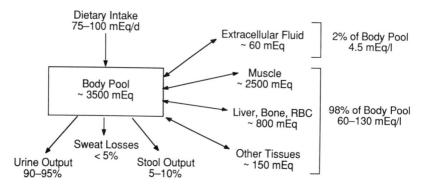

FIG. 1. Distribution of potassium within body fluid compartments and routes of potassium excretion.

Ninety to ninety-five percent of dietary potassium is normally excreted in urine each day, and 5 to 10% is excreted in stool (75 mEq/liter in approximately 100 ml of stool water). When stool water volume increases in diarrheal states, the concentration of potassium decreases, limiting fecal potassium loss. Since potassium concentration in sweat is only 5 to 10 mEq/liter, basal cutaneous losses of potassium are negligible. Normal dietary habits result in episodic meal-related increases in potassium ingestion with intervening periods of little or no potassium intake. These variations in potassium intake are followed promptly by appropriate changes in cellular uptake of potassium by nonrenal tissues and urinary excretion of potassium, which maintain total body stores and the extracellular concentration of potassium relatively constant within narrow limits.

Based on chemical analysis of cadavers, isotopic dilution studies, and total-body counting of the naturally occurring isotope ^{40}K, total body potassium content is approximately 50 to 55 mEq/kg. Only about 2% of total body potassium is present in the extracellular compartment, at a concentration of 3.5 to 4.5 mEq/liter. Approximately 60 to 85% of total body potassium is located in muscle cells, with lesser amounts in red blood cells, liver, bone, and skin. The average intracellular potassium activity is in the range of 60 to 130 mEq/liter. This critical distribution of potassium and the ability to effectively handle excesses or deficits of potassium are influenced by the activity of the enzyme Na,K-ATPase, acid-base status, hormonal factors (e.g., insulin, catecholamines, corticosteroids), prior dietary history, and body fluid tonicity.

POTASSIUM EXCRETION (3,4,16,19,20)

Renal Potassium Excretion

Potassium is freely filtered at the renal glomerulus. Fifty to seventy percent of the filtered potassium is absorbed in the proximal tubule (Fig. 2). Proximal

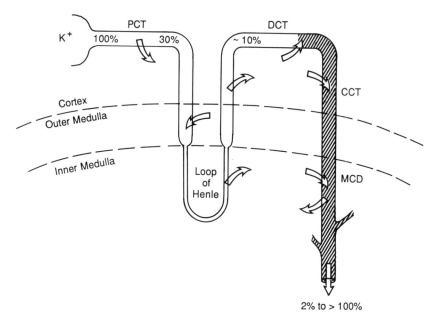

FIG. 2. Summary of potassium handling in various portions of the nephron. Arrows demonstrate direction of net movement of potassium. The medullary collecting duct (MCD) is capable of bidirectional net transport. The percentages of the filtered load of potassium remaining at specific sites and in the final urine are shown. The collecting duct system is depicted by the shaded area. PCT, proximal convoluted tubule; DCT, distal convoluted tubule; CCT, cortical collecting tubule.

tubule potassium absorption occurs primarily by bulk flow related to sodium and water reabsorption. The loop of Henle serves as a countercurrent exchanger for potassium, since potassium is absorbed from the ascending limb and secreted into the tubular fluid of the descending limb; this process results in a high potassium concentration in medullary interstitial fluid. Ten to fifteen percent of the filtered load of potassium reaches the early distal tubule in most physiologic conditions. Although a relatively constant fraction of the filtered load of potassium reaches the distal tubule, urinary excretion may range from a few percent of the filtered load to greater than 100 percent. Thus, addition or removal of potassium from tubular fluid in the collecting duct system determines the final urinary potassium excretion rate. Principal cells lining the initial collecting tubule, the cortical collecting tubule, and the medullary collecting duct are able to secrete potassium. The medullary collecting duct has been shown to be capable of net potassium absorption, as well as secretion, and absorption in this segment is critical for minimizing urinary potassium losses under conditions of potassium deprivation.

A variety of factors influence renal potassium excretion (Fig. 3). Increases in potassium intake tend to raise plasma potassium concentration, which directly enhances potassium excretion, presumably by increasing renal cell up-

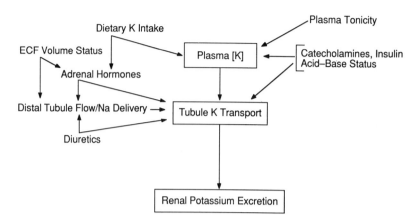

FIG. 3. Illustration of the major factors that affect the urinary excretion of potassium. (ECF) extracellular fluid.

take of potassium, and stimulates aldosterone production in a manner independent of renin-angiotensin. The role of aldosterone in increasing potassium excretion will be reviewed subsequently. Expansion of the extracellular fluid volume, in addition to suppressing aldosterone secretion, increases flow rate in the distal nephron, which stimulates secretion of potassium, since in this nephron segment secretion is flow dependent. Conversely, diminished tubular flow rate and sodium delivery to the distal nephron in volume depletion impair potassium excretion by the kidney. At constant plasma potassium concentrations, acidemia tends to decrease renal potassium excretion, whereas alkalemia has the opposite effect. Diuretics, such as the thiazides, furosemide, and bumetanide, increase urinary potassium excretion by enhancing flow rate in early portions of the collecting duct system, whereas amiloride, triamterene, and spironolactone are potassium-sparing diuretics and impair renal potassium excretion, apparently because of a reduction in transepithelial potential difference that decreases luminal negativity.

Intestinal Potassium Excretion

In humans, approximately 10% of the daily intake of potassium is excreted via the intestinal tract. The bulk of dietary potassium is absorbed in the small intestine. Secretion or absorption of potassium in the colon, analogous to the collecting duct system in the kidney, determines the rate of net excretion by the gastrointestinal tract. Studies of potassium transport in humans have demonstrated net secretion in the rectum.

Experimental studies in laboratory animals have demonstrated the presence of both active and passive transport processes for potassium transport in the colon, and, as in the nephron, a heterogeneity of colonic potassium transport has been apparent. In the proximal colon, potassium secretion occurs via an active transcellular mechanism as well as through the paracellular pathway by passive mechanisms. The active component is ouabain sensitive, indicating that potassium is pumped into the cell from the interstitial fluid by the Na,K-ATPase pump in the basolateral cell membrane. Secretion into the intestinal lumen occurs when potassium exits the cell across apical membrane potassium channels. There is no active absorptive transport of potassium in the proximal colon.

In the distal colon, both active secretory and absorptive mechanisms for potassium transport, which presumably serve to regulate the rate of net potassium movement *in vivo* in different physiologic states, have been demonstrated under *in vitro* conditions in which the transepithelial potential difference is eliminated. In the basal state and during potassium depletion, for example, the active absorptive mechanism predominates *in vitro*. In contrast, chronic potassium loading and aldosterone activate the secretory process. Since potassium movement results from active and passive mechanisms, net potassium secretion is found *in vivo* owing to the strong effect of the lumen negative potential difference on passive transport. The apical membrane uptake of potassium, accounting for the active absorptive transport, has been ascribed to a K-ATPase pump in the rabbit, and in the rat a K,H antiporter has been described.

Potassium Excretion by Sweat Glands

The potassium concentration in human eccrine sweat is approximately 5 to 10 mEq/liter and thus exceeds the plasma concentration. As sweat flow rate increases, the concentration of potassium decreases but remains above 4.5 to 5 mEq/liter. Assuming evaporative skin losses of 500 ml/day under basal conditions, sweat losses of potassium are negligible. However, with intense physical exertion in a hot climate, sweat volume may approach 10 liters/day. Under these conditions cutaneous potassium losses can amount to 10 to 40 mEq/day and contribute, along with sustained urinary losses, to the development of a deficit in total body potassium.

Potassium Excretion by Salivary Glands

Like surface sweat, human saliva is hypotonic but has a potassium concentration greater than that of plasma. Although the actual concentration varies depending on the particular gland, mode of salivary stimulation, and salivary flow rate, it is usually in the range of 10 to 25 mEq/liter. Since the daily output of saliva is approximately 750 ml, the total amount of potassium excreted in the saliva in 24 hr is less than 15 to 20 mEq, which, obviously, does not contribute to substantial external losses.

The composition of sweat and saliva results from modification by the ducts of the glands of a primary fluid secreted by the acinar portions of the glands. The primary fluid is approximately isotonic and resembles an ultrafiltrate of plasma. Potassium is secreted in the salivary duct by an apical membrane K, H antiporter, whereas sodium is reabsorbed to produce a hypotonic saliva.

RESPONSES TO CHANGES IN BODY STORES OF POTASSIUM AND RENAL INSUFFICIENCY (6–12,15,17)

Decreased Body Stores of Potassium

Renal Response

In addition to inadequate dietary intake, potassium deficiency may develop in a variety of clinical circumstances. Vomiting may result in potassium deficits due to losses in gastric contents (which are usually small, since the potassium concentration is only 10 mEq/liter in gastric juices) and in urine, which probably result from vomiting-induced metabolic alkalosis. Diarrhea, particularly when it results from a villous adenoma of the colon or a noninsulin-secreting pancreatic islet cell adenoma, may result in large losses of potassium from the gastrointestinal tract, since potassium secretion is, at least in part, flow dependent. Toxins produced by microorganisms also may stimulate potassium secretion. Laxative abuse may result in clinically important potassium deficiency. Diuretics are a common cause of renal potassium loss, which may result in significant potassium deficits and hypokalemia in some people. Other causes of urinary potassium loss include states of mineralocorticoid excess (primary hyperaldosteronism, Cushing's syndrome, renovascular and malignant hypertension, and Bartter's syndrome), renal tubular acidosis (particularly distal RTA) diabetic ketoacidosis, and the administration of drugs, such as amphotericin B, gentamicin, and carbenicillin. The causes of increased urinary potassium excretion in these conditions are not established, but in RTA and diabetic ketoacidosis, they are thought to correlate with hyperaldosteronism due to volume depletion and increased tubular flow rate and sodium chloride delivery to distal nephron sites. During carbenicillin administration, the delivery of negatively charged, nonabsorbable organic molecules to the distal nephron is thought to stimulate potassium secretion.

In humans, potassium conservation by the kidney, in conditions characterized by nonrenal causes of potassium deficiency, can reduce urinary potassium excretion to 5 to 10 mEq/day. Since this adaptive response may take several days to be maximally expressed, potassium deficits of 200 to 250 mEq may develop before a new balance is achieved. When dietary intake of potassium is below 10 mEq/day, obligatory renal and fecal losses cause progressive potassium deficits. Studies in the rat, a species that is capable of marked reductions in urinary potassium within 24 to 72 hr after the initiation of a potassium-deficient diet, demonstrated that urinary potassium conservation is associated with reduced plasma aldosterone levels and reduced potassium content in muscle and kidney tissues.

As noted previously, potassium delivery out of the loop of Henle to the distal tubule is similar in control and potassium-deficient animals, indicating that reduction in urinary potassium excretion is a function of more distal nephron segments. The initial connecting tubule and the cortical collecting tubule, which normally secrete potassium, can reduce net potassium transport to zero in potassium-deficient animals. The inner medullary collecting duct, which also secretes potassium under control conditions, is capable of net potassium absorption in potassium-restricted animals.

Intestinal Response

Although quantitatively less important than the kidney in terms of overall contribution to potassium homeostasis, the colon also plays a role in potassium conservation. Insights into colonic function are derived primarily from experimental studies in animals. In the rat, during luminal perfusion *in vivo*, net potassium secretion is markedly reduced in potassium-deficient animals compared to controls, and under some conditions net absorption can be demonstrated. Under *in vitro* conditions where the transepithelial potential difference is eliminated, net potassium movement (and hence active transport) in control animals is in a secretory direction in proximal colon and absorptive in distal colon. Chronic potassium deprivation causes proximal secretion to fall to zero and stimulates the rate of distal absorption. Recent studies indicate that active potassium absorption in distal rat colon involves an absorptive pump in the apical cell membrane, characterized by an electroneutral K,H antiporter, which facilitates cell uptake of potassium from luminal fluid and subsequent passive diffusion across the basolateral membrane.

Increased Potassium Intake

Homeostatic Responses to Transient Increases in Potassium Intake

The response to transient changes in potassium intake is a function of renal (and possibly colonic) excretion and cellular uptake of potassium, by nonrenal tissues, from the extracellular compartment. The kidney has the capacity to alter rapidly the rate of potassium secretion in response to acute variations in excretory load. During the first 4 to 6 hr after the administration of an acute potassium load, approximately one-half the potassium load is excreted in the urine; the remaining portion is taken up by nonrenal tissues, primarily muscle, fat, and liver. Studies in experimental animals have shown that potassium excretion responds rapidly to increases in the plasma potassium concentration with a rise in potassium secretion in distal portions of the nephron. Similarly, net potassium secretion increases in both proximal and distal portions of the colon. The change in the rate of potassium secretion appears to be induced directly by the increase in plasma potassium concentration and is not associated with alterations in transepithelial potential difference or luminal flow rate.

Several factors are known to regulate extrarenal potassium homeostasis. Basal levels of insulin secretion are important in maintaining plasma potassium concentration within the normal range, whereas increased secretion of insulin following an acute potassium load stimulates extrarenal potassium uptake. In normal individuals with intact renal function, epinephrine causes a decline in plasma potassium concentration because of extrarenal potassium uptake. This response is mediated specifically by the beta$_2$-adrenergic receptor and is simulated when other beta$_2$ agonists (or nonspecific beta agonists) are administered. Beta-blocking drugs, such as propranolol (beta$_1$ and beta$_2$ effect) or butoxamine (specific beta$_2$ antagonist), tend to increase the plasma potassium concentration and impair potassium homeostatic responses to acute infusions of potassium salts and exercise. In some uremic patients, epinephrine does not cause a decrease in plasma potassium concentration, probably because of tissue resistance to the effects of beta agonists. Aldosterone also may play a role in the regulation of extrarenal potassium homeostasis, although its role is less well defined than that of insulin and catecholamines. Other factors that are involved include plasma tonicity (hypertonicity induces a shift of potassium-rich intracellular water into the extracellular space) and acid-base status. It seems likely that complex interactions among these various factors may occur in clinical conditions.

Adaptation to Chronic Increases in Potassium Intake

After administration of a potassium-enriched diet for several days or more, potassium-secreting cells in the collecting duct system of the kidney increase their capacity for potassium secretion, which serves to protect against lethal hyperkalemia. This process, termed "potassium adaptation," involves principal cells in all portions of the collecting duct system, including the initial collecting tubule, cortical collecting tubule, and medullary collecting duct, and results in increased potassium excretion per nephron.

The cellular mechanism for potassium adaptation is shown in Fig. 4. An increase in the number of potassium pumps (Na,K-ATPase) in the basolateral membrane increases the uptake of potassium from interstitial fluid into the

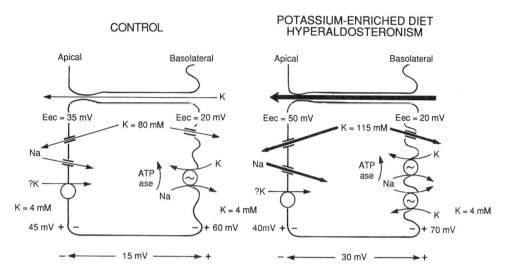

FIG. 4. Illustration of a principal cell of the collecting duct system of the kidney or surface epithelial cell of the large intestine under control conditions (**left**) and with hyperaldosteronism or during administration of a potassium-enriched diet (**right**). The model includes illustrative values for intracellular potassium activity, and potential differences (PD) across individual cell membranes and the epithelium as a whole. The symbol ⊖ indicates a carrier protein engaged in active transport, and the symbol // indicates a conductive channel protein. The electrochemical potential (Eec) acting on passive potassium movement across the cell membranes is calculated as: $Eec = PD + RT/zF(\ln K_i/K_o)$. Due to the effect of a high potassium diet or increased plasma levels of aldosterone to increase the number of potassium pumps (Na,K-ATPase), more potassium enters the cell across the basolateral membrane compared to controls. The transepithelial PD rises from 15 to 30 mV (lumen negative) because of hyperpolarization of the basolateral membrane and depolarization of the apical membrane. Transcellular potassium secretion increases because of the rise in Eec across the apical membrane and an increase in apical membrane potassium conductance. Intercellular movement of potassium also increases because of the rise in lumen negativity.

cell, with a rise in intracellular potassium activity. Driven by an increase in the electrochemical gradient across the apical membrane (caused by the rise in the chemical concentration gradient and an increase in the lumen negative potential difference), potassium diffusion from the cell into the luminal fluid is enhanced. Increased potassium ion movement through the paracellular pathway also occurs as a result of the increase in lumen negativity. Extensive amplification of the basolateral membrane area of potassium-secreting cells in the late distal tubule and the collecting duct system accompany these functional changes.

The stimulus for potassium adaptation involves the action of aldosterone as well as an increase in excretory load of potassium. Experimental studies in which plasma aldosterone levels and potassium intake were regulated independently show that both factors affect adaptation but that the full adaptive response requires the combination of increased aldosterone levels and excretory load.

It is of interest, since uptake of potassium by nonrenal tissues plays an important role in potassium homeostasis in people on a normal potassium diet, that the adaptive response to a high potassium diet also involves nonrenal tissues. In potassium-loaded animals that have had both kidneys removed or ligated, the rise in plasma potassium concentration is significantly less after acute infusion of potassium salts than in controls. The mechanism of this response is not established.

Similar changes in cellular adaptation and transepithelial potential difference have been observed in the large intestine of experimental animals during chronic potassium loading. Net potassium secretion increases in proximal colon, and net potassium absorption in distal colon, as determined under *in vitro* conditions, is converted to net secretion. As in the collecting duct system of the kidney, the intestinal adaptive changes are induced by both hyperaldosteronism and hyperkalemia and are accompanied by increases in basolateral membrane area and Na, K-ATPase activity in potassium-secreting cells.

Potassium Adaptation in Renal Insufficiency

Potassium balance is generally well maintained in patients with renal insufficiency until the glomerular filtration rate is reduced to less than 25% of normal. This adaptive response, which increases potassium excretion per remaining nephron, is proportional to the rise in excretory load per nephron, similar to the situation that occurs when potassium intake is increased in subjects with normal renal function. Since approximately 90% of filtered potassium is reabsorbed prior to the distal tubule in experimental animals with renal insufficiency, it seems likely that adaptive cellular changes occur in the collecting duct system. Furthermore, experimental studies have demonstrated that renal potassium adaptation is demonstrable within 24 hr after partial renal ablation.

The cortical collecting tubule, as well as medullary and papillary nephron segments, are important sites of potassium adaptation in the setting of renal insufficiency. *In vitro* studies have shown that potassium flux into luminal fluid of the isolated rabbit cortical collecting tubule increases twofold to threefold in uremic animals compared to controls. If dietary potassium is reduced in proportion to the reduction in nephron mass, the change in potassium transport is ameliorated, suggesting that the potassium excretory load per nephron plays a major role in inducing potassium adaptation.

The mechanism of potassium adaptation in renal insufficiency appears to be similar to the process demonstrated in subjects with intact renal function administered a high-potassium diet. For example, the activity of Na, K-ATPase is increased above control levels in renal cortex and medulla of animals with renal insufficiency, and there is amplification of the basolateral cell membrane of principal cells of the collecting duct system.

Studies in rats following unilateral nephrectomy and papillectomy in the remaining kidney provide experimental evidence for the importance of medullary structures to maintain potassium balance in renal insufficiency. Animals achieved potassium balance only in the presence of hyperkalemia and exhibited impaired maximal capacity for potassium excretion compared to animals with a similar degree of renal impairment but with intact papillae. The role of medullary nephron segments in potassium adaptation is further suggested by clinical renal disorders with medullary damage that are associated with impaired concentrating ability, urinary acidification defects, and impaired urinary potassium excretion following potassium loads. These alterations in renal transport function have been demonstrated in lupus nephropathy, Sjögren's syndrome, sickle cell disorders, obstructive nephropathy, and drug-related interstitial nephritis. In response to acute intravenous infusion of potassium, patients with sickle cell disease, for example, excrete only half as much potassium as normal controls. The kaliuretic response to furosemide also is blunted. These abnormalities presumably result from ischemic damage to medullary and papillary structures, which cause scarring and atrophy of distal tubule segments.

The gastrointestinal tract also undergoes adaptive changes to preserve potassium homeostasis in chronic renal insufficiency. Early studies in humans demonstrated that after severe reduction in renal function (glomerular filtration rate less than 10 ml/min), the fraction of dietary potassium intake excreted in stool increased from a control value of about 10% to approximately 35%. Recent studies have demonstrated that this increase in intestinal potassium excretion is due to adaptive changes in potassium secretion in large intestine. In a recent study, net potassium secretion in the rectum of patients with chronic renal insufficiency increased 2.5-fold compared to normal individuals.

EFFECTS OF ACID-BASE DISTURBANCES ON POTASSIUM EXCRETION (5)

Metabolic Acidosis

Acid-base balance affects both extrarenal and renal potassium homeostasis. The relationship between pH and plasma potassium concentration is complex and is influenced by the cause of the acid-base disturbance, status of body potassium stores, the time course of the development of the acid-base disturbance, and other factors. In general, plasma potassium concentration increases with acute metabolic acidosis of mineral acid origin (hydrochloric acid, ammonium chloride) because of a shift of potassium out of cells in exchange for extracellular hydrogen ions. Organic acidosis, such as lactic acidosis or ketoacidosis, does not directly result in significant changes in plasma potassium concentration, although associated volume depletion or hypotension with diminished glomerular filtration rate and urinary flow rate may decrease potassium excretion and result in hyperkalemia.

The renal response to acid-base disturbances has been well characterized. Despite an increase in plasma potassium concentration, acute metabolic acidosis initially inhibits absolute and fractional urinary potassium excretion. This response most likely results from a decrease in the potassium concentration gradient across the apical membrane of potassium-secreting renal epithelial cells due to a decrease in intracellular potassium activity. Within several hours after the onset of the acute metabolic acidosis, urinary potassium excretion begins to increase, and within 24 to 48 hr, a signficant kaliuresis develops. A substantial deficit in body potassium stores may develop, at which time potassium excretion gradually will return to normal.

Micropuncture studies in the rat have shown that at comparable rates of urine flow and sodium excretion, acute metabolic acidosis directly inhibits potassium secretion in the distal nephron. However, metabolic acidosis also results in increased urinary flow rate and delivery of sodium chloride to the distal nephron, which stimulate distal nephron potassium secretion. As a result, net potassium excretion may be increased, particularly with chronic acidemia. This phenomenon is partly responsible for the development of urinary potassium wasting and hypokalemia in people with renal tubular acidosis.

Little is known about the effects of acid-base disturbances on potassium excretion by the gastrointestinal tract. Acute metabolic acidosis changes net potassium absorption to net potassium secretion in the *in vivo* perfused jejunum of the rat and markedly stimulates potassium secretion by the ileum and colon. Since respiratory acidosis has no influence on gastrointestinal potassium excretion, factors other than systemic pH, such as bicarbonate ion concentration and hormonal and hemodynamic changes, may be important in the response to metabolic acidosis.

Metabolic Alkalosis

Metabolic alkalosis causes potassium ions to shift into cells from the extracellular fluid, decreasing the plasma potassium concentration. Urinary potassium excretion is stimulated, in part as a result of increased intracellular potassium activity, but probably also because of increased bicarbonate delivery to the distal nephron and increased aldosterone levels. Large deficits in body potassium stores and profound hypokalemia frequently develop in people with sustained metabolic alkalosis caused by protracted vomiting or nasogastric suction. Clinical disorders with increased production of adrenal hormones, such as primary hyperaldosteronism, Cushing's syndrome, and Bartter's syndrome, also are characterized by the presence of both metabolic alkalosis and hypokalemia.

Acute metabolic alkalosis stimulates potassium absorption in the jejunum and ileum of the rat but has little effect on colonic potassium transport.

Respiratory Acid-Base Disorders

Respiratory alkalosis decreases plasma potassium concentration to about the same extent as a comparable metabolic alkalosis, whereas the change resulting from respiratory acidosis is generally much less than occurs with a comparable mineral acidosis. The renal response to respiratory acidosis is similar to that following a metabolic acidosis. With acute respiratory alkalosis, renal potassium excretion increases initially, but in contrast to metabolic alkalosis, it returns to base-line levels within about 24 hr, and large deficits in potassium stores do not develop.

Neither respiratory alkalosis nor respiratory acidosis has any notable effects on potassium transport in the jejunum, ileum, or colon.

HORMONAL CONTROL OF POTASSIUM EXCRETION (2,13,14)

Adrenal Steroids

The action of aldosterone to stimulate the secretion of potassium has been known for over 30 years. Hyperkalemia is a hallmark of Addison's disease, providing clinical evidence for a role of adrenal hormones in the regulation of potassium balance. In adrenal insufficiency, the absence of glucocorticoids, as well as aldosterone, plays a role in altered potassium homeostasis. In experimental animals, adrenalectomy results in decreased blood pressure and renal blood flow, decreased glomerular filtration rate, increased urinary flow rate and urinary sodium excretion, hyperkalemia, and impaired potassium tolerance. Replacement of glucocorticoids in amounts sufficient to restore glomerular filtration rate and renal blood flow to normal results in increased rates of renal potassium excretion. Replacement of aldosterone by itself, however, has no effect on glomerular filtration rate but markedly reduces urinary volume and can normalize the plasma potassium concentration. Urinary potassium excretion and impaired potassium tolerance, however, are not corrected unless both glucocorticoid and aldosterone replacement is provided.

Since glomerular filtration rate and distal tubule sodium delivery and urinary flow rate—major determinants of renal potassium excretion—are influenced by aldosterone and glucocorticoids, it has been difficult to determine the separate direct effects these hormones have on potassium excretion. Although both glucocorticoids and mineralocorticoids stimulate urinary potassium excretion, they do so by different mechanisms. Mineralocorticoids directly stimulate distal tubule potassium secretion. This response may be masked, however, since the simultaneous reduction of distal tubule sodium excretion and urinary flow rate will tend to inhibit distal nephron potassium secretion. The relationship between distal delivery of sodium and flow rate and the action of aldosterone to increase potassium excretion is observed clinically in conditions of excess production of aldosterone, such as primary hyperaldosteronism or administration of mineralocorticoids, in subjects with intact renal function. In individuals with a moderate sodium chloride intake, urinary potassium excretion increases and may cause severe potassium deficiency. In conditions characterized by secondary hyperaldosteronism, such as nephrotic syndrome and congestive heart failure, in which there is a strong stimulus for proximal tubule sodium reabsorption and, as a consequence, a reduced delivery of sodium to distal nephron segments, potassium excretion rates are not increased, and hypokalemia does not develop. Glucocorticoids, rather than directly influencing renal epithelial cell potassium transport, cause the glomerular filtration rate and distal tubule sodium delivery and urinary flow rate to increase. Enhanced potassium excretion occurs, therefore, as a secondary phenomenon. It should be noted, however, that the administration of synthetic glucocorticoids to patients or experimental animals in pharmacologic doses generally does not cause urinary potassium wasting and hypokalemia.

Adrenalectomy also results in decreased potassium secretion from the gastrointestinal tract. Glucocorticoids appear to be more important than mineralocorticoids for the maintenance of normal basal potassium transport in the colon. Hyperaldosteronism, however, stimulates potassium secretion to increase above normal levels in the colon.

Aldosterone has been shown to participate in the adaptive changes that maintain potassium balance in renal insufficiency and chronic potassium loading. In chronic renal insufficiency, for example, plasma aldosterone levels are modestly elevated and, since administration of the aldosterone antagonist spironolactone results in hyperkalemia, may help to maintain high fractional excretion rates of potassium. Moreover, some patients with diabetic nephropathy and chronic interstitial nephritis develop hyperkalemia in the presence of mild renal insufficiency because the aldosterone production rate is impaired (hyporeninemic hypoaldosteronism). Adrenalectomized animals with intact renal function are able to increase urinary potassium excretion substantially with dietary potassium loading. However, the ability to excrete normally an acute potassium load in these animals requires the replacement of aldosterone, and both dietary and hormonal factors are required for the full adaptive response.

It has been recognized for some time that adrenal hormones induce ion transport in specific types of epithelia. These target sites respond to adrenal hormones because they possess specific, high-affinity receptor proteins in the cytosol for the individual classes of hormone. The lipophilic adrenal hormones, aldosterone and corticosterone, enter the cell across the basolateral membrane and activate the cytosolic receptor by binding to form a complex as shown in Fig. 5. The complex is then translocated to the cell nucleus, where the synthesis of mRNA, and then specific proteins, is induced. These hormone-induced proteins interact with specific portions of the cell membrane to effect phenotypic changes in cell function. Specific, high-affinity

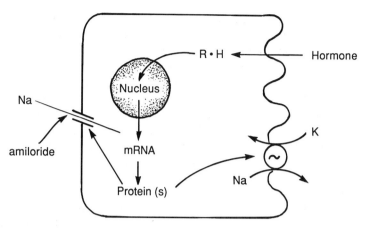

FIG. 5. Mechanism by which aldosterone induces phenotypic changes in target epithelial cells. As with other adrenal hormones, after entering the cell, a complex is formed with specific cytosolic receptor proteins. The activated complex is translocated to the nucleus and interacts with the cellular genome, resulting in the synthesis of mRNA and, subsequently, new proteins, which produce alterations in cellular function.

cytosolic receptors for glucocorticoids have been identified in the mammalian colon and throughout the nephron. Mineralocorticoid receptors, also present in the colon, are localized in the kidney to the late distal tubule and collecting duct system but are not found in the more proximal portions of the nephron.

Numerous techniques have been employed to determine the specific sites of action of aldosterone in the nephron, including estimates of ion movement, determination of Na,K-ATPase activity, and analysis of changes in cell membrane morphology. These studies suggest that aldosterone stimulates ion transport throughout the collecting duct system. Similar approaches have demonstrated that all portions of the large intestine are responsive to the action of aldosterone.

Recent studies involving techniques that permit impalement of individual cells with microelectrodes to estimate intracellular ion activities and cell membrane conductance have provided insights into the mechanism of action of aldosterone to increase net sodium absorption and potassium secretion. The initial effect of aldosterone is activation of amiloride-sensitive sodium channels in the apical cell membrane, which increases the rate of entry of sodium ions from luminal fluid into the cell. Since the Na,K-ATPase pump in the basolateral cell membrane is normally unsaturated, sodium is extruded from the cell at a rate equal to its entry into the cell, and net sodium absorp tion is increased. When the action of aldosterone is chronically maintained, the number of pump sites in the basolateral membrane is increased, and there is expansion of the basolateral membrane area.

As shown in Fig. 4, potassium ions enter the cell across the basolateral membrane via the Na,K-ATPase pump, and the intracellular potassium activity rises. In the steady state, potassium exits the cell at the same rate it enters, either by recycling across the basolateral membrane or by diffusing across the apical membrane into the luminal fluid. The rate of diffusion across the apical membrane is dependent on the electrochemical driving force and the conductance of the membrane for potassium. Aldosterone increases both the driving force for passive ion movement and the apical membrane potassium conductance, so that transepithelial movement of potassium, in a secretory direction, is stimulated. *In vitro* flux studies have demonstrated active potassium secretion. In addition, potassium ion transport through the paracellular pathway increases owing to a hyperpolarization of the transepithelial potential difference.

Aldosterone has been reported to increase the potassium concentration in sweat, presumably because of an effect on sweat duct epithelial cells. This has not been a consistent finding, however, and little is known about the cellular processes involved or the physiologic significance of hormonal regulation of potassium excretion by sweat glands.

The potassium concentration of salvia increases slightly when humans are placed on a sodium-restricted diet, an effect ascribed to increases in adrenal hormone activity. The Na/K ratio in saliva, an index of adrenal hormone effect, tends to be increased in patients with adrenal insufficiency and decreased in Cushing's syndrome, congestive heart failure, and primary hyperaldosteronism. The potassium concentration of saliva is decreased in rats by adrenalectomy. Administration of aldosterone to humans decreases salivary sodium excretion (without escape, as occurs in the kidney) and increases salivary potassium excretion.

Catecholamines

Catecholamines play an important role in the regulation of plasma potassium concentration by enhancing nonrenal cellular uptake of potassium from the extracellular compartment. Catecholamines also have a direct effect on the kidney, demonstrated initially in the isolated perfused rat kidney. Epinephrine produced a prompt decrease in fractional and net urinary potassium excretion, without a change in glomerular filtration rate, urine flow rate, or sodium excretion. Of interest was the finding that this response was mediated by the $beta_1$-adrenergic receptor, whereas the extrarenal homeostatic mechanism is $beta_2$ mediated. Microperfusion studies of individual nephron segments *in vivo* suggest that the site of action of epinephrine probably lies in the collecting duct system. Isoproterenol, a nonspecific beta agonist, decreases potassium secretion in the isolated cortical collecting tubule perfused *in vitro*. Since specific receptors for isoproterenol are present in this segment, it is likely that the cortical collecting tubule is the primary site at which catecholamines exert direct action on renal potassium secretion.

The precise physiologic significance and cellular processes involved remain to be clarified.

The addition of epinephrine to a solution bathing the serosal surface of distal colon segments *in vitro* increases net potassium secretion. This effect is blocked by the addition of propranolol and simulated by isoproterenol and the specific beta$_1$ agonist, dobutamine. The increase in potassium secretion may result from increased basolateral membrane Na,K-ATPase activity, which stimulates cellular uptake of potassium from the interstitial space, together with increased apical membrane potassium conductance.

Insulin and Glucagon

The administration of insulin to human subjects produces hypokalemia and a decrease in urinary excretion of potassium to approximately 30% of control levels, suggesting that insulin increases potassium uptake by nonrenal tissues. However, when somatostatin, a potent inhibitor of insulin and glucagon production, is infused into human subjects, there is no change in urinary potassium excretion despite the development of hyperkalemia. Two separate studies using the isolated perfused kidney preparation to examine the effect of insulin on renal potassium excretion have produced results in disagreement. In one study, very high concentrations of insulin decreased potassium excretion, whereas a recent study, using a more physiologic concentration of insulin, failed to show any effect on potassium excretion. In further studies, when hypokalemia, which usually accompanies insulin infusion, was prevented with a simultaneous potassium infusion, fractional as well as net urinary excretion of potassium increased nearly 2.5-fold. Alterations in urinary flow rate and sodium excretion did not appear to be responsible for the kaliuretic response, suggesting that insulin actually may stimulate urinary potassium excretion by a direct action. Studies in cultured cells have suggested a synergistic interaction between insulin and aldosterone on potassium transport.

A kaliuretic effect of intravenous, as well as intrarenal, glucagon has been demonstrated, which may be due, at least in part, to renal vasodilation. Coadministration of insulin blunts this effect. However, a more recent study, in which physiologic hyperglucagonemia was produced in five diabetic patients, failed to demonstrate any notable effects on either potassium or sodium excretion.

Clearly, further studies are needed to clarify the roles of catecholamines, insulin, and glucagon in the physiologic regulation of potassium excretion.

REFERENCES

1. Bia, M., and DeFronzo, R. A. (1981): Extrarenal potassium homeostasis. *Am. J. Physiol.*, 240:F257–F268.

2. DeFronzo, R. A. (1980): Hyperkalemia and hyporeninemic hypoaldosteronism. *Kidney Int.*, 17:118–134.
3. Field, M. J., and Giebisch, G. H. (1985): Hormonal control of renal potassium excretion. *Kidney Int.*, 27:379–387.
4. Foster, E. S., Sandle, G. I., Hayslett, J. P., and Binder, H. J. (1986): Dietary potassium modulates active potassium absorption and secretion in rat distal colon. *Am. J. Physiol.*, 251:G619–G626.
5. Gennari, F. J., and Cohen, J. J. (1975): Role of the kidney in potassium homeostasis: Lessons from acid-base disturbances. *Kidney Int.*, 8:1–5.
6. Hayslett, J. P. (1979): Functional adaptation to reduction in renal mass. *Physiol. Rev.*, 59:137–164.
7. Hayslett, J. P., and Binder, H. J. (1982): Mechanism of potassium adaptation. *Am. J. Physiol.*, 243:F103–F112.
8. Kashgarian, M., Taylor, C. R., Binder, H. J., and Hayslett, J. P. (1980): Amplification of cell membrane surface in potassium adaptation. *Lab. Invest.*, 42:581–588.
9. Knochel, J. P., Dotin, L. N., and Hamburger, R. J. (1972): Pathophysiology of intense physical conditioning in a hot climate. I. Mechanisms of potassium depletion. *J. Clin. Invest.*, 51:242–255.
10. Linas, S. L., Peterson, L. N., Anderson, R. J., Aisenbrey, G. A., Simon, F. R., and Berl, T. (1979): Mechanism of renal potassium conservation in the rat. *Kidney Int.*, 15:601–611.
11. Martin, R. S., and Hayslett, J. P. (1986): Role of aldosterone in the mechanism of renal potassium adaptation. *Pflügers Arch.*, 407:76–81.
12. Martin, R. S., Panese, S., Virginillo, M., et al. (1986): Increased secretion of potassium in the rectum of humans with chronic renal failure. *Am. J. Kidney Dis.*, 8:105–110.
13. Marver, M., and Kokko, J. P. (1983): Renal target sites and the mechanism of action of aldosterone. *Miner. Electrolyte Metab.*, 9:1–18.
14. Rabinowitz, L. (1979–1980): Aldosterone and renal potassium excretion. *Renal Physiol.*, 2:229–243.
15. Sandle, G. I., Foster, E. S., Lewis, S. A., Binder, H. J., and Hayslett, J. P. (1985): The electrical basis for enhanced potassium secretion in rat distal colon during dietary potassium loading. *Pflügers Arch.*, 403:433–439.
16. Sato, K. (1977): The physiology, pharmacology, and biochemistry of the eccrine sweat gland. *Rev. Physiol. Biochem. Pharmacol.*, 79:52–131.
17. Smith, P. L., and McCabe, R. D. (1984): Mechanism and regulation of transcellular potassium transport by the colon. *Am. J. Physiol.*, 247:G445–G456.
18. Sterns, R. H., Cox, M., Feig, P. U., and Singer, I. (1981): Internal potassium balance and the control of the plasma potassium concentration. *Medicine*, 60:339–354.
19. Wright, F. S., and Giebisch, G. (1985): Regulation of potassium excretion. In: *The Kidney, Physiology and Pathophysiology*, edited by D. W. Seldin and G. Giebisch, pp. 1223–1249. Raven Press, New York.
20. Young, J. A., and vanLennep, E. W. (1979): Transport in salivary and salt glands, In: *Membrane Transport in Biology*, edited by G. Giebisch, D. C. Tosteson, and H. H. Ussing, Vol. 4B, pp. 563–692. Springer-Verlag, Berlin.

Abnormal Potassium Metabolism

The Regulation of Potassium Balance, edited
by Donald W. Seldin and Gerhard Giebisch,
Raven Press, Ltd., New York © 1989.

8

Clinical Diagnosis of Abnormal Potassium Balance

Stuart L. Linas and *Tomas Berl

*Renal Division, Denver General Hospital, Denver, Colorado 80204-4507, and
*Division of Renal Diseases, University of Colorado School of Medicine,
Denver, Colorado 80262*

TOTAL BODY AND SERUM POTASSIUM (1,3,6,12)

The diagnosis of abnormalities in either the internal or external balance of K is made by the deviation of the cation's concentration from the normal range (3.5–5.0 mM/liter) as measured in serum. Nonetheless, approximately 90% of body exchangeable K is intracellular, and in contrast to the ease with which extracellular K concentration is measured, a measurement of intracellular concentration is not readily obtainable. Isotopic and chemical measurements estimate that the average K content in humans reaches a peak by age 20 of 55 to 60 mEq/kg in men and 40 to 45 mEq/kg in women. Most of this K is in muscle (3,000–3,500 mEq). The measurement of exchangeable K, however, does not directly provide a value of intracellular K concentration, since this would require a measurement of total body water and extracellular fluid space. None of these are readily available or clinically practical. Attempts to

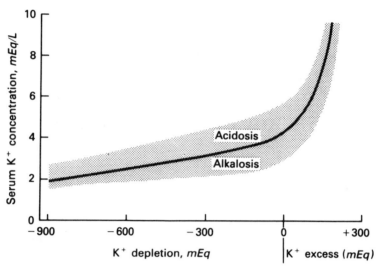

FIG. 1. Relationship between changes in total body and serum K in adults. The graph shows that acidosis raises and alkalosis lowers serum potassium concentration. (From ref. 16.)

relate changes in serum K to total body K have not been well quantitated. It is known, however, that substantial deficits of over 200 mEq occur before significant hypokalemia is evident. However, increments in serum K occur more promptly in K excess states (Fig. 1). Since external K balance is achieved primarily by the renal excretion of ingested K (approximately 1 mEq/kg/day), the rate of urinary K excretion serves as an important tool in the clinical assessment of abnormal K balance. We, therefore, describe in this chapter a diagnostic approach to states of K deficit and excess that relies heavily on the interpretation of urinary findings.

HYPOKALEMIA: AN OVERVIEW (5,10,11,13,15,17)

A decrease in serum K (Fig. 2) can result from either the transcellular shift of K from extracellular to intracellular compartments or from a decrease in total body K. In patients with transcellular shifts of K, there is no reduction in total body K, and replacement therapy generally is not required except in emergent conditions, such as periodic paralysis or in the setting of myocardial infarction. When there is a decrease in total body K, its stores cannot be corrected without the administration of K.

Internal K balance refers to K distribution across cell membranes and (*as reviewed in* Chapter 1) is influenced by a number of factors, including insulin and catecholamines. Thus, increases in the levels of these hormones cause a reduction in serum but not total body K. External K balance reflects the dif-

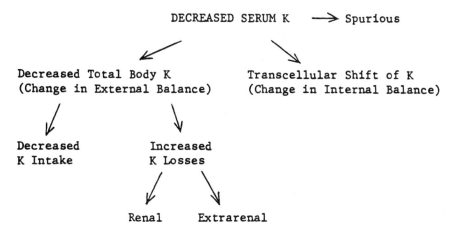

FIG. 2.   Mechanisms of decrease in serum potassium.

ference between K intake and excretion. Total body K depletion results from either a decreased K intake or increased K losses from renal or extrarenal sources. Reductions in dietary K intake generally lead to modest reductions in total body K. Although the kidney is able to reduce urinary K losses to very low values in response to a reduction in dietary K, there are obligatory, albeit small, continued K losses in the urine and stool. Over extended periods, cumulative negative K balance can be substantial. The major stimuli for renal K excretion are reviewed in Chapter 7 and include mineralocorticoids, distal nephron sodium and tubular fluid flow rates, systemic acid-base parameters, and the anion composition of tubular fluid. Extrarenal K excretion occurs mainly in the intestine, although, on occasion, significant K losses can occur in sweat.

Diagnostic Approach to Hypokalemia

The first step in evaluating the patient with hypokalemia is to exclude spurious causes. Most laboratories determine serum K by automated methods that are infrequently in error. Extreme leukocytosis (WBC >100,000) is the only known cause of spurious hypokalemia. If blood specimens from leukemic patients are allowed to stand at room temperature, the leukocytes can extract K from serum and cause hypokalemia. Spurious hypokalemia can be differentiated from true hypokalemia by comparing K levels in serum separated from cells in freshly drawn blood to serum separated from cells after permitting the specimens to stand at room temperature for 1 hr. There is little difference between these values in normal people, whereas there is a significant decrease in patients with spurious hypokalemia.

True hypokalemia can be approached initially on the basis of urinary K, systemic acid-base data, and urinary chloride. The strategy for using these parameters in the approach to the patient with a decrease in total body K is outlined in Fig. 3.

Determination of urinary K concentration is the initial discriminating factor in elucidating the etiology of hypokalemia. In interpretating the urinary K concentration, a number of assumptions must be considered.

1. Random spot urinary K concentrations accurately reflect 24 hr K excretion. It is apparent that a urinary K of 10 mEq/liter would represent renal K retention if 24 hr urine volume were less than 1 liter per day. In contrast, if urinary volume were 5 liter per day, a random determination of 10 mEq/liter would not be indicative of K conservation. Compared to other urinary electrolytes, spot urinary K concentrations are often misinterpreted because K depletion *per se* can cause primary polydipsia as well as a defect in renal concentrating ability. Both of these defects in water metabolism can result in underestimation of 24 hr K excretion on the basis of spot urinary K concentration determinations.

2. The appropriate response to a reduction in serum K is renal K conservation and a reduction in urinary K excretion. It follows from this assumption that the finding of a low urinary K in the hypokalemic patient reflects nonrenal K losses, whereas a high urinary K reflects a renal source of K loss. It is important to recognize, however, that there are a number of situations in which urinary K may not discriminate readily between renal and nonrenal causes of hypokalemia. Perhaps the best example of the dissociation between serum and urinary K occurs in patients with so-called stress hypokalemia. In

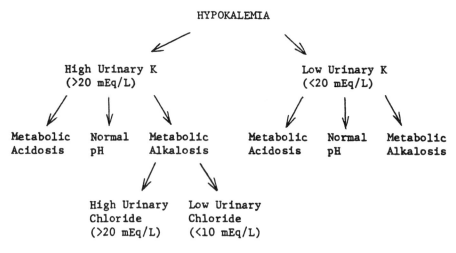

FIG. 3.   Diagnostic approach to the hypokalemic patient.

this circumstance, there is a surge in endogenous catecholamines (e.g., in association with chest pain or a myocardial infarction) or exogenous catecholamines (e.g., beta-adrenergic agonists in asthma). Catecholamines activate the $beta_2$-adrenergic receptor and result in a shift of K from the extracellular to the intracellular space. Since there is no reduction in total body K and since the catecholamine effect is relatively acute, there is no reduction in urinary K excretion. In this clinical situation, the finding of a high urinary K does not reflect renal K loss. Conversely, there are also situations in which a low urinary K is found despite the fact that the kidney had been the source of K losses. For example, diuretic-induced hypokalemia and total body K depletion are clearly mediated by diuretic-induced renal K excretion. If urinary K is determined while the patient is consuming diuretics, urinary K will be high. However, if urinary K is obtained after the pharmacologic half-life of the drug has been exceeded, urinary K may not be elevated despite the obvious fact that the kidney was the source of K loss.

Hypokalemia in Association with a Reduction in Urinary Potassium Concentration

In response to extrarenal K losses, urinary K excretion is reduced to very low levels (Fig. 4). Although the kidney is able to reduce Na excretion rapidly, the time course of renal K conservation has not been studied carefully. However, on the basis of animal studies, it seems likely that renal K conservation in humans is more efficient than has been recognized previously. Although very early in K deficiency urinary K may not reflect maximal conservation, reduction in urinary K in association with hypokalemia is strong evidence in support of a nonrenal source of K loss. The major causes of hypokalemia in this circumstance are K losses from the gastrointestinal tract or skin and poor dietary intake of K. Systemic pH is used to distinguish among these possibilities.

Metabolic Acidosis and Metabolic Alkalosis

Hypokalemia from diarrhea is usually readily apparent because symptoms of diarrhea are elicited easily. On occasion, however, it may be difficult to determine if diarrhea quantities are sufficient to result in hypokalemia. In this circumstance, arterial blood gases are used to distinguish gastrointestinal losses of K from other extrarenal causes of K depletion. The finding of hyperchloremic metabolic acidosis supports the diagnosis of gastrointestinal K losses, since reduction in K intake and excess K loss through sweat are not usually associated with hyperchloremic metabolic acidosis.

There are three circumstances in which hypokalemia from diarrhea may be

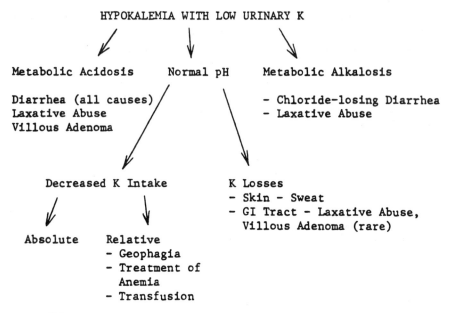

FIG. 4.   Approach to the hypokalemic patient with low urinary potassium.

associated with normal or increased systemic pH: laxative abuse, chloride-losing diarrhea, and villous adenoma (Fig. 4). The systemic pH in patients who consume laxatives is variable. In most circumstances, hypokalemia and reduction in total body K are more severe than changes in serum pH. Moreover, laxative abuse can be associated with metabolic alkalosis and renal K wasting. The mechanism of alkalosis in these patients is unclear. Chloride-losing diarrhea is a rare congenital disease manifested by severe diarrhea, hypokalemia, K depletion, and metabolic alkalosis. Villous adenomas are large, bulky rectal tumors that produce a mucous secretion containing high concentrations of chloride and K. Although most patients with adenomas develop metabolic acidosis from bicarbonate loss, rare patients have been reported with metabolic alkalosis.

Normal Serum pH

Hypokalemia in patients with a normal serum pH can be caused by a reduction in K intake or excess K loss from intestine or skin (Fig. 4). Absolute reduction in K intake occurs in people who do not eat (e.g., alcoholics) or in those consuming diets depleted in K (e.g., anorexia nervosa or "tea and toast diets"). In addition, clay ingestion (geophagia) can lead to a reduction in gastrointestinal K absorption because clay binds K in the gut. In circumstances in which absolute K intake is reduced, there is intense renal K conservation, small deficits in total body K, and slight increases in serum HCO_3. Relative reductions in K intake have been described in association with abrupt changes in cell mass. For example, hypokalemia can occur during therapy of both megaloblastic and iron deficiency anemia. The reduction in serum K usually occurs at the time of reticulocytosis and can be quite profound in patients with marginal K intake before therapy. Although urinary K excretion is usually low, urinary K may not be reduced in the presence of high K intake. Hypokalemia has been described after transfusion of frozen, thawed, deglycerolized erythrocytes. These cells tend to have low K content and reaccumulate K on exposure to normal body temperature.

Hypokalemia in Association with Increased Urinary Potassium Excretion

There are many causes of hypokalemia with increased urinary K excretion. As with hypokalemia and reduced urinary K, systemic pH is used to distinguish among these possibilities.

Metabolic Acidosis

Hypokalemia in association with metabolic acidosis occurs with both hyperchloremic and increased anion gap types of metabolic acidosis (Fig. 5). In type I (distal) and type II (proximal) renal tubular acidosis, there is an increase in urinary K excretion. Although there are multiple causes of renal tubular acidosis, hypokalemia and K depletion are prominent laboratory abnormalities in patients who inhale toluene by sniffing paint or glue vapors. There are three clinical syndromes associated with toluene inhalation: neuromuscular (muscle weakness), gastrointestinal (abdominal pain, diarrhea, vomiting), and neuropsychiatric (altered mental status or cerebellar symptoms). Toluene inhalation should be suspected in patients with one or more of these clinical syndromes who also have hypokalemia, hypophosphatemia, and hyperchloremic acidosis. Although renal K wasting occurs in some patients, it is not inevitable. Type I can be distinguished from type II renal tubular acidosis on the basis of urine pH after NH_4Cl (usually >5.4 in type I and <5.5 in type II) and fractional excretion of HCO_3 (<5% in type I and >15% in type II).

K depletion can be a complication of ureterosigmoidostomy. K loss and hyperchloremic acidosis result from K and bicarbonate secretion in the sigmoid colon. In these individuals, it is occasionally difficult to distinguish K loss from the sigmoid colonic segment from K loss from renal tubular acidosis. This can be accomplished by ureteral catheterization and determination of urinary K. Urinary K will be high in patients with hypokalemia and renal tu-

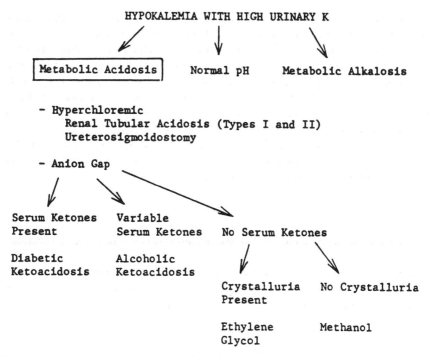

FIG. 5. Approach to the hypokalemic patient with high urinary potassium and metabolic acidosis.

bular acidosis. In contrast, urinary K conservation will occur in patients with extrarenal K loss from the sigmoid colonic segment.

In both diabetic and alcoholic ketoacidosis, there is an increase in urinary K excretion with an increased anion gap metabolic acidosis. The distinction between renal tubular acidosis and diabetic ketoacidosis is usually apparent on the basis of anion gap, urine and serum glucose, and ketones. The distinction between diabetic and alcoholic ketoacidosis occasionaly can be difficult, but the diagnosis of alcoholic ketoacidosis is made on the basis of normal to mild increases in serum glucose and a disproportionately increased serum anion gap relative to either serum or urine ketone bodies. Compared to diabetic ketoacidosis in which there are increased levels of acetoacetate and beta-hydroxybutyrate, in alcoholic ketoacidosis the predominant ketoacid is beta-hydroxybutyric acid. Since the tests used to measure ketoacids do not measure beta-hydroxybutyric acid, the finding of metabolic acidosis with an increased anion gap and negative or marginally positive qualitative test for ketones is highly suggestive of alcoholic ketoacidosis. However, there are other causes of metabolic acidosis with increased anion gap negative ketones. These include exogenous (e.g., ethylene glycol, methanol) as well as endogenous (e.g., lactate) acids. Although hypokalemia can occur with exogenous ingestions, it is unusual in lactic acidosis.

Both methanol and ethylene glycol ingestion should be considered in the hypokalemic acidemic patient with an increased anion gap but no urinary or serum ketones. The diagnosis of methanol intoxication is suggested further in patients who smell of alcohol and complain of visual disturbances, although this is a late finding. Methanol intoxication is confirmed by demonstrating methanol in the serum. Ethylene glycol intoxication is suggested in patients who smell of alcohol and have crystalluria. The crystals can be either hippurate or calcium oxalate. The diagnosis is confirmed by demonstrating ethylene glycol in the blood. Since ethylene glycol is nephrotoxic, the finding of hypokalemia in the setting of azotemia and an anion gap type acidosis should raise the question of this ingestion.

Normal pH

Hypokalemia with an increase in urinary K in association with normal acid-base parameters can result from shifts of K from the serum to cells or from renal K losses (Fig. 6). It is important to reemphasize that hypokalemia from transcellular shifts of K does not result in K depletion. In contrast, hypokalemia from renal K loss results in a decrease in total body K.

Transcellular K shifts can result from increases in insulin or catecholamines.

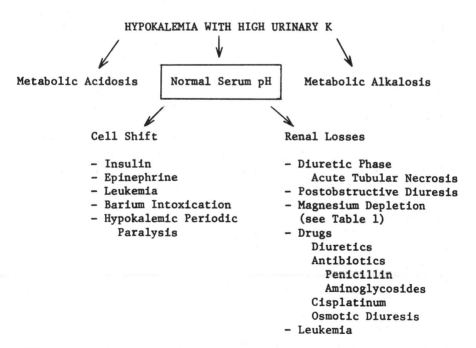

FIG. 6. Approach to the hypokalemic patient with high urinary potassium and normal serum pH.

Although the role of insulin in the regulation of internal K balance has long been known, the pivotal role of epinephrine in extrarenal K homeostasis has been recognized only recently. Physiologically attainable levels of epinephrine cause cellular shifts of K that are mediated by the beta$_2$-adrenergic receptor. This mechanism of hypokalemia may occur in settings in which catecholamines are elevated: myocardial infarction, acute bronchial asthma, and alcohol withdrawal syndromes (in this setting, there may also be total body K depletion). Since total body K is normal and since the reduction in serum K is acute, renal K conservation does not occur, and urinary K remains elevated.

Hypokalemia is found frequently in patients with myelocytic or monomyelocytic leukemia. In acute leukemia, hypokalemia may result from rapid cellular proliferation. Although urinary K usually is elevated, on occasion leukemic cellular proliferation results in reduction in serum and muscle K, and renal K conservation ensues. In both acute and chronic leukemia, total body K depletion can occur as a result of renal K losses caused by leukemia-induced increases in the excretion of lysozyme.

Barium intoxication results in severe hypokalemia. Barium blocks the K channels from which K exits cells. Hypokalemic periodic paralysis is a rare autosomal dominant hereditary disorder characterized by recurrent attacks of flaccid paralysis and hypokalemia. The mechanisms that account for transcellular shifts of K are not known.

Hypokalemia with high urinary K and a normal serum pH can be the result of renal K wasting. In the diuretic phase of acute tubular necrosis (ATN) and in patients recovering from obstructive uropathy, renal K wasting can be profound. Both of these conditions are usually readily apparent.

Three classes of drugs can cause K depletion without altering serum pH. These include antibiotics (penicillins and aminoglycosides), cisplatin, and the osmotic diuretics. Penicillins, especially carbenicillin and its congeners, in large quantities can result in renal K wasting. These agents are large nonreabsorbable anions that, like sulfate, trap secreted K in the distal nephron. The mechanisms of K wasting with aminoglycosides and cisplatin are not known, but hypokalemia (in association with hypomagnesemia) is not infrequent in patients treated with large doses of aminoglycosides even in the setting of azotemia. The use of osmotically active agents, such as mannitol, to prevent brain swelling in the setting of intracranial hemorrhage frequently results in renal K wasting and hypokalemia.

The syndrome of hypomagnesemic hypokalemia has been described in the clinical settings listed in Table 1. Although the mechanism of K wasting in magnesium depletion states in unclear, often it is not possible to replete total body K without concomitant replacement of total body magnesium. This syndrome is often not recognized at the time of diagnosis of hypokalemia and only becomes apparent after attempts at K repletion therapy have failed. Thus, magnesium levels should be obtained in all hypokalemic patients with renal K wasting in whom normal levels of serum K cannot be maintained despite adequate repletion therapy.

TABLE 1. *Magnesium depletion in association with renal potassium wasting*

Drugs
    Antibiotics: Aminoglycosides
    Antineoplastic: Cisplatin
    Diuretics: Non-K-sparing
Leukemia
Postobstructive diuresis
Isolated magnesium depletion
Primary and secondary hyperaldosteronism
Chronic alcoholism

Metabolic Alkalosis

Hypokalemia and a reduction in total body K occur most frequently in the setting of metabolic alkalosis (Fig. 7). Determination of urinary chloride concentration is the initial test used to distinguish among the various causes of hypokalemia in this setting.

A reduction in urinary chloride to below 10 mEq/liter occurs in association with diuretic-induced K depletion. It is critically important to recognize, however, that urinary chloride will only be reduced after the renal effect of diuretics has dissipated. In this regard, most of the non-K-sparing diuretics

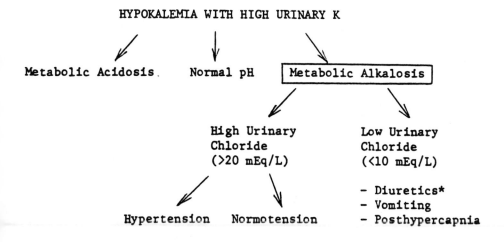

* After effects of drugs have dissipated.

FIG. 7. Approach to the hypokalemic patient with high urinary potassium and metabolic alkalosis.

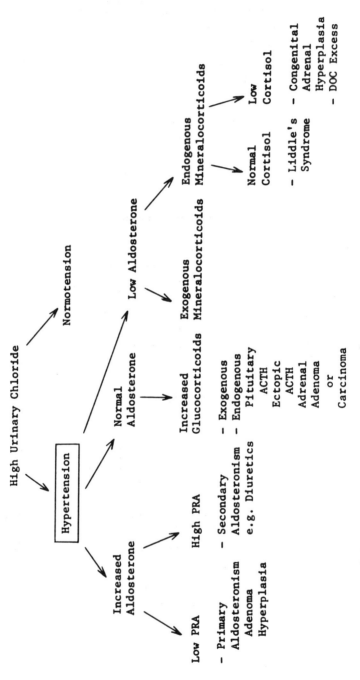

HYPOKALEMIA: HIGH URINARY K AND METABOLIC ALKALOSIS

High Urinary Chloride

Normotension

Hypertension

Increased Aldosterone

Low PRA

- Primary
  Aldosteronism
  Adenoma
  Hyperplasia

High PRA

- Secondary
  Aldosteronism
  e.g. Diuretics

Normal Aldosterone

Increased Glucocorticoids

- Exogenous
- Endogenous
  Pituitary
  ACTH
  Ectopic
  ACTH
  Adrenal
  Adenoma
  or
  Carcinoma

Low Aldosterone

Exogenous Mineralocorticoids

Endogenous Mineralocorticoids

Normal Cortisol

- Liddle's Syndrome

Low Cortisol

- Congenital Adrenal Hyperplasia
- DOC Excess

FIG. 8. Approach to the hypertensive, hypokalemic patient with high urinary potassium and chloride. (PRA) plasma renin activity.

(furosemide, thiazides, bumetanide) enhance renal excretion of chloride as well as sodium and K. Thus, in the presence of these agents, diuretic-induced K depletion will be associated with increased urinary chloride excretion. Vomiting also results in K depletion, which is mediated by the kidney. Vomiting-induced chloride depletion results in a bicarbonate-rich, chloride-free tubular fluid that favors K excretion. Although it is not difficult to diagnose the cause of K depletion in patients who admit to vomiting, the etiology of hypokalemia can be exceedingly difficult to elucidate in the patient with surreptitious vomiting.

There are a number of causes of K depletion, metabolic alkalosis, increased urinary K, and increased urinary chloride (Figs. 8 and 9). In the initial evaluation of hypokalemia in this setting, the presence or absence of hypertension is used to guide further evaluation. In hypertensive patients both mineralocorticoid and glucocorticoid excess can result in hypokalemia, K wasting, and high urinary chloride (Fig. 8).

Hyperaldosteronism can be primary or secondary. Primary hyperaldosteronism is accompanied by suppression of renal renin release and hyporeninemia. Secondary hyperaldosteronism is the consequence of an increase in renal renin secretion. Although hypokalemia and K depletion are the most common electrolyte abnormalities in patients with primary aldosteronism, the syndrome can occur in the setting of normokalemia. Primary aldosteronism is caused by adrenal hyperplasia, adrenal adenoma, or, very rarely, adrenal carcinoma. Hypokalemia, renal K wasting, metabolic alkalosis, and high urinary chloride occur in hypertensive patients taking diuretics as well as in primary aldosteronism. Urinary K is a relatively good laboratory test to distinguish diuretic-induced from primary aldosterone-induced hypokalemia. Since diuretic-induced K depletion is a manifestation of diuretic-induced kaliuresis,

HYPOKALEMIA: HIGH URINARY K AND METABOLIC ALKALOSIS

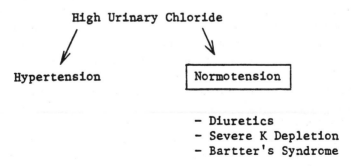

FIG. 9. Approach to the normotensive hypokalemic patient with high urinary potassium and metabolic alkalosis.

urinary K is determined 48 to 72 hr after discontinuation of diuretics. In diuretic-induced hypokalemia, the cause of K wasting is withdrawn, and urinary K decreases to low levels. Conversely, in aldosteronism, even in the absence of diuretics, aldosterone excess causes continued renal K wasting.

It is necessary to exclude secondary causes of hyperaldosteronism in patients with suspected primary aldosteronism. Two types of studies are used to make this distinction. In the first study, stimulated renin levels are determined. Patients are placed on an Na-restricted diet for 3 days. Plasma renin activity (PRA) is measured 4 hr after administration of 40 mg furosemide and ambulation. In primary aldosteronism, PRA is low and nonresponsive, whereas in secondary aldosteronism, PRA can be stimulated by volume-depleting maneuvers. Since diuretic and antihypertensive drugs influence renal renin production, renin studies should be performed at least 7 to 10 days after these agents have been discontinued. After establishing that PRA is suppressed, it is necessary to demonstrate that aldosterone levels are increased and not suppressible by physiologic tests. This can be accomplished by one of a number of maneuvers. We prefer the determination of plasma aldosterone after the administration of NaCl. For this study, plasma aldosterone is determined after 2 liters of normal NaCl are administered between 8 and 10 A.M. while the patient is supine. In normals and in secondary aldosteronism, plasma aldosterone levels are suppressed by volume expansion. Conversely, aldosterone is not suppressed in patients with primary aldosteronism, and values above 13 ng/dl are diagnostic of this disease.

The distinction between adrenal hyperplasia and adenoma can be difficult. A number of noninvasive radiologic and biochemical tests have been purported to be useful. The choice of study often depends on its availability and the expertise of those performing the test. Adrenal ultrasound and computed axial tomography (CAT) scanning are used for detection of adenoma. Although many authors advocate these tests, the diagnostic accuracy has been reported to be less than 50%. Adrenal imaging with iodocholesterol is used to give a functional assessment of the zona glomerulosa. Adrenal scanning is performed after 5 days of dexamethasone pretreatment to reduce ACTH steroidogenesis and reduce nonadenomatosis uptake of the isotope. Asymmetrical uptake on the ipsilateral side is seen in patients with adenoma. No lateralization is noted in patients with hyperplasia. Although imaging with iodocholesterol is reported to be accurate in over 80% of patients, the radionuclide is not readily available, and interpretation of imaging results is difficult.

18-Hydroxycorticosterone and postural responses of aldosterone are the biochemical tests used to distinguish adenoma from hyperplasia. Patients with adenoma and those with hyperplasia secrete 18-hydroxycorticosterone, but the plasma levels are much higher in adenoma than in hyperplasia. The postural response of aldosterone is abnormal in 75% of patients with adenoma. For this study, aldosterone is determined supine at 8:00 A.M. and again at 12:00 noon after 4 hr of ambulation. In normal individuals and in patients with hyperplasia, assumption of the upright posture results in an increase in aldosterone. In contrast, in adenoma, there is a postural decrease in aldosterone. In adenoma, ACTH rather than angiotensin II has a major modulating effect on plasma aldosterone. Thus, the increase in PRA that occurs after assumption of the upright posture does not result in an increase in aldosterone in adenoma. Since ACTH levels decrease between 8:00 A.M. and 12:00 noon, aldosterone levels tend to decrease in patients with adrenal adenoma.

Bilateral adrenal venous sampling for measurement of aldosterone is the test of choice in distinguishing adenoma from hyperplasia. In adenoma, adrenal vein aldosterone levels are increased from the side of the lesion compared to the contralateral side by 5 to 20 times, whereas in hyperplasia, there is less than a fivefold differential between the two sides. Although this test has an accuracy of greater than 90%, several problems have been encountered that can decrease accuracy. These problems include (1) a small risk of trauma coincidental with adrenal venography, (2) it is often technically difficult to enter the right adrenal vein, and samples from the left adrenal vein often can be diluted by blood from nonrenal sources, and (3) there may be episodic secretion of aldosterone in primary aldosteronism so that if there is a time differential, values obtained from one adrenal gland may be at the peak of secretion and those obtained from the other adrenal gland may be at the trough.

To minimize these potential artifacts, adrenal vein catheterization should be performed by an investigator experienced in the technique, and adrenal venography should not be attempted when obtaining specimens for aldosterone measurement, since the excess volume of contrast required for venography is associated with a high incidence (>10% in some centers) of adrenal hemorrhage. To avoid the episodic nature of aldosterone secretion, patients are pretreated with ACTH (intravenous Cortrosyn, 5 IU/hr in 500 ml of dextrose). The accuracy of catheter placement and the problem of nonadrenal dilution of adrenal venous blood are overcome by measuring simultaneous adrenal venous cortisol levels.

In a subset of patients with adrenal hyperplasia, the excessive aldosterone secretion is suppressible with the administration of glucocorticoids. These patients are distinguishable from other patients with hyperplasia by demonstrating that hyperaldosteronism is suppressible after administration of dexamethasone (0.75 mg/day).

In contrast to primary hyperaldosteronism, hypokalemia is not invariably associated with secondary hyperaldosteronism. Since the kaliuretic effect of aldosterone is dependent on distal nephron tubular flow rate and sodium delivery, conditions that reduce distal nephron sodium and water delivery cause less K loss than conditions that are associated with normal or enhanced distal sodium and water delivery. In primary aldosteronism, sodium delivery is normal or even increased, and kaliuresis ensues. In secondary aldosteronism, distal sodium delivery is often decreased. For example, secondary hyperaldosteronism often occurs in patients with heart failure. It is unusual to see severe hypokalemia in this condition before institution of diuretic therapy. Since heart failure results in a reduction in distal nephron sodium and water delivery, profound kaliuresis is rare. In contrast, when loop diuretic agents are used to treat heart failure, distal nephron sodium delivery is enhanced, and a profound kaliuresis ensues. Secondary hyperaldosteronism can occur also in the setting of normal distal sodium delivery. A variety of renin-producing tumors has been reported. Most frequently, these are renal in origin, but nonrenal malignancies also have been described. Although renin produced in these circumstances (especially in nonrenal malignancies) may be of the inactive type, hypokalemia as the result of hyperreninemic hyperaldosteronism can occur.

Hypokalemia also can occur in patients with secondary aldosteronism from malignant hypertension, renovascular hypertension, or renal vasculitidies. In these conditions, hyperreninemia is caused by renal ischemia.

Hypokalemia and metabolic alkalosis can occur in the setting of hypertension and low aldosterone levels (Fig. 8). Most often this situation is the result of exogenous steroid administration. Hypokalemia has been described after the use of steroid nasal spray as well as oral steroids. There are other drugs and foods that have been associated with hypokalemia, including carbenoxolone, a derivative of glycyrrhetinic used in the United Kingdom for therapy of peptic ulcer disease, and glycyrrhizic acid, a compound found in unprocessed (i.e., European but not American) licorice.

In addition to exogenous mineralocorticoids, there are several hereditary illnesses that result in reduced aldosterone and hypokalemia. These include Liddle's syndrome and congenital adrenal hyperplasia with excess desoxycortisone production. Liddle's syndrome is a familial illness characterized by hypokalemia, metabolic alkalosis, high urinary chloride, hypertension, and extremely low aldosterone production. High levels of a nonaldosterone mineralocorticoid have been identified. Interestingly, hypokalemia is not responsive to inhibitors of aldosterone action but is responsive to triamterene or amiloride.

In congenital adrenal hyperplasia, there is defective production of cortisol and of sex hormones. In patients with 17 α-hydroxylase deficiency, reduction in cortisol leads to increased ACTH and secretion and production of large quantities of corticosterone and desoxycorticosterone. In patients with 11 β-hydroxylase deficiency, reduction in cortisol also leads to an increase in secretion of ACTH and desoxycorticosterone. Since the enzymatic deficiency prevents conversion of desoxycorticosterone to corticosterone and aldosterone, hypokalemia occurs only in approximately 25% of patients.

Hypokalemia also occurs with normal aldosterone (Fig. 8). In this setting, hypokalemia in association with metabolic alkalosis, and hypertension is the result of glucocorticoid excess states. Cushing's syndrome can result from exogenous steroid administration, adrenocortical hyperplasia due to excessive production of cortisol by adrenal adenoma, or ectopic production of ACTH or corticotropin-releasing hormone by neoplasms. The incidence of hypokalemia is much higher in the ectopic ACTH syndrome. Diagnosis of hypercortisolism depends on showing high cortisol production rates that fail to subside with varying doses of dexamethasone. Cushing's disease is diagnosed if urinary cortisol levels are suppressed to less than 50% of basal levels after high dose (2 mg every 6 hr for 2 days) dexamethasone. In patients with nonsuppressible cortisol after high dose dexamethasone, ACTH levels are elevated in ectopic states and low when adrenal tumor is present.

Metabolic Alkalosis and Normotension

Perhaps the greatest challenge in evaluating hypokalemia is the distinction between Bartter's syndrome and so-called pseudo-Bartter's syndrome caused by surreptitious vomiting or diuretic abuse. In both conditions, there are urinary K and chloride wasting, metabolic alkalosis, and normotension (Fig. 9). The key to distinguishing between these diagnostic possibilities is in obtaining multiple urine samples for diuretic testing, K, and chloride. In patients with suspected surreptitious diuretic abuse, urine diuretic tests may be positive. If the test is performed when the patient has withheld diuretics, the test may be negative. However, in the absence of diuretics, urinary chloride excretion frequently is appropriately reduced. Thus, a positive diuretic screen or a negative diuretic screen in association with a reduction in chloride excretion is very strong presumptive evidence for surreptitious diuretic abuse. In contrast, urinary chloride excretion is persistently elevated in patients with Bartter's syndrome. Therefore, in Bartter's syndrome, urine tests for diuretics are negative, and urinary chloride excretion is elevated on all occasions.

Surreptitious vomiting can mimic Bartter's syndrome on the basis of urinary chloride. Vomiting is associated with chloride loss, and urinary chloride excretion is reduced to low levels when the patient reaches a new steady state. Thus, the finding of a low urine chloride value should raise the possibility of surreptitious vomiting.

The distinction between Bartter's syndrome and pseudo-Bartter's syndrome may be very difficult in patients with prolonged total body K depletion. Severe total body K depletion results in renal K and chloride wasting as well as metabolic alkalosis. Therefore, with very severe K deficits (e.g., a serum K less than 2.0 mEq/liter and a total body deficit of over 500–1000 mEq), the presence of K or chloride in the urine is not a helpful factor in excluding pseudo-Bartter's syndrome. In patients with severe deficits in K, partial correction of the K deficit is undertaken before a definitive evaluation of the underlying cause.

HYPERKALEMIA: AN OVERVIEW (2,4,7–9,14)

Hyperkalemia is defined as a serum K above 5.0 mEq/liter. In contrast to hypokalemia where reductions in serum K can result from transcellular shifts of K with normal cellular K or from frank cellular K depletion, hyperkalemia rarely is associated with measurable increases in cellular K. Rather, increases in serum K reflect increases in extracellular K and normal cellular K stores.

Since small increases in K can result in life-threatening hyperkalemia, a tightly controlled, complex K regulatory mechanism exists for the maintenance of normal serum K and total body K. For example, if one assumes that extracellular water contains 2% of total body K, that total body K is 50 mEq/kg of water, and that total body water is 70% of total body weight, extracellular K would be approximately 70 mEq in a 70 kg man. Thus, if one consumed as little as 30 mEq of K, serum K would increase by almost 50% (i.e., from 4 to 6 mEq/liter) in the absence of rapidly acting regulatory processes. The mechanisms that exist to maintain a normal serum K in response to a K load are reviewed in Chapter 1 and include insulin, beta$_2$-adrenergic receptors, and, possibly, aldosterone.

Although transcellular shifting of K is a rapid, efficient mechanism to reduce serum K, K must be excreted by the kidney to maintain external balance. The factors that control renal K excretion are reviewed in Chapter 7. Filtered K is largely reabsorbed before reaching the distal convoluted tubule. Distal nephron K delivery is approximately 10% of filtered K regardless of the glomerular filtration rate (GFR). Thus, renal K regulation is for the most part dependent on those factors that influence tubular secretion and reabsorption of K along the distal convoluted tubule and collecting ducts. The most important factors influencing K excretion by the distal nephron are prior K exposure, body K content, acid-base balance, mineralocorticoids such as aldosterone, the rate of fluid–sodium delivery to the distal nephron, and impermeant anions.

Hyperkalemia occurs when the input of K into the vascular compartment exceeds removal of K from the vascular compartment (Fig. 10). K input is determined by the K content of the diet (almost 100% of dietary K is absorbed from the intestine) as well as by K input from cells. K removal occurs when K is transferred across cellular membranes from the extracellular to the intracellular space. Ultimately, however, renal K excretion must occur to maintain total body K balance.

As in the hypokalemic patient, the determination of urinary K excretion is the initial laboratory test used to distinguish extrarenal from renal causes of hyperkalemia. In the setting of hyperkalemia, a normal to increased value of K excretion is highly suggestive of an extrarenal cause. Extrarenal causes of hyperkalemia include increases in exogenous or endogenous K intake or decreases in K removal from the vascular to cellular space. A reduction in urinary K is suggestive of a renal cause of hyperkalemia.

It is important to recognize that hyperkalemia is the end result of a K regulatory system that has failed. In most patients, there are frank abnormalities in either extrarenal or renal systems that regulate K balance. However, on occasion, there may not be gross changes in the determinants of serum K. Spe-

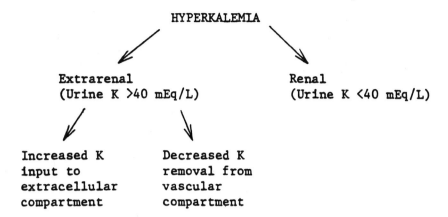

FIG. 10. Approach to the patient with hyperkalemia.

cifically, individuals with normal kidneys tolerate large increases in K without developing hyperkalemia. In contrast, even small increases in K intake can result in hyperkalemia in the setting of fixed urinary K excretion as might occur in patients with chronic renal failure.

Pseudohyperkalemia

Pseudohyperkalemia (spurious hyperkalemia) occurs in the conditions listed in Table 2. When blood is drawn after prolonged tourniquet application, K is released from muscles, and a high serum K is observed. In thrombocytosis or leukocytosis, release of K from cells during clotting can result in pseudohyperkalemia. In these situations, plasma K will be less than serum K. There is an additional mechanism by which leukocytosis can result in spurious hyperkalemia. When specimens with more than 500,000 leukocytes are left at room temperature for longer than 1 to 2 hr, there is leakage of cellular K into serum or plasma. In patients with extreme leukocytosis, K levels should be determined on plasma samples that have been separated rapidly from cellular ele-

TABLE 2. *Causes of pseudohyperkalemia*

Ischemic blood drawing
Thrombocytosis (platelet count > 1,000,000/mm³)
Leukocytosis (WBC count >500,000/mm³)
Infectious mononucleosis
Familial
Hemolysis

ments. In infectious mononucleosis and in some families, pseudohyperkalemia results from leaky leukocytes or erythrocytes at room temperature.

Since spurious hyperkalemia may be difficult to differentiate from real hyperkalemia and since the consequences of real hyperkalemia may be devastating, an electrocardiogram (ECG) should be performed in all patients with a serum K greater than 6 mEq/liter. The presence of ECG changes indicates true hyperkalemia and warrants immediate reduction in serum K.

Hyperkalemia with Normal Renal Potassium Excretion

Increased Potassium Input

Although food substances are the most common source of exogenous K, there are a number of other exogenous sources (Fig. 11), including K-containing salt substitutes (5–25 mEq/0.5 teaspoon) and such drugs as K citrate, K phosphate, K chloride, K gluconate, K salicylate, and K penicillin.

There are endogenous as well as exogenous sources of K. These can be subdivided on the basis of whether K is released from normal or from injured cells. In both circumstances, K is lost from cells into the extracellular compartment at a rate exceeding the rate at which K can be transported out of the extracellular compartment. K is released from normal cells in response to the stimuli noted in Fig. 11. Metabolic acidosis caused by mineral acids is associated with an increase in serum K. There is an approximate 0.6 mEq/liter increase in serum K for each 0.1 unit decrease in serum pH (infusion of arginine or lysine monohydrochloride also causes a shift of K from cells to the extracellular compartment). In contrast to mineral acidosis (e.g., NH_4Cl), organic acidosis and respiratory acidosis are not associated consistently with hyperkalemia. It is uncertain if this inconsistency indicates that organic acidosis does not cause hyperkalemia or if the absence of hyperkalemia reflects prior total body K depletion.

Succinylcholine is a depolarizing muscle relaxant that increases K permeability of muscle cells. Small increases in serum K occur in most people. However, profound increases in K have been described in patients receiving exogenous K, in those with increased K stores, and in those with underlying neuromuscular diseases.

Although insulin deficiency alone rarely results in hyperkalemia, when it is associated with hyperglycemia, moderate increases in serum K often are found. In the absence of insulin, glucose is unable to enter cells and serves as an osmotically active extracellular agent extracting water and K from cells. Hyperkalemia can occur after administration of other hypertonic small molecular weight compounds that do not access the intracellular space, such as mannitol or NaCl, but not after administration of compounds, such as urea, that do access the interior of cells.

HYPERKALEMIA WITH NORMAL URINARY K EXCRETION
(>40 mEq/day)

Increased K Input	Decreased K Removal
- Exogenous	- Insulin Deficiency
Food Substances	- Beta Blockers
Salt Substitutes	K Load
Drugs	Exercise
K Citrate	Nifedipine
K Phosphate	- Digitalis
K Chloride	- Hyperkalemic
K Gluconate	Periodic Paralysis
K Salicylate	
K Penicillin	

- Endogenous
  Normal Cells
    Metabolic Acidosis
      Mineral Acids
    Hyperglycemia
    Hypertonic Solutions
    Succinyl Choline
  Cellular Injury
    Erythrocytes
      Intravascular Hemolysis
      GI or Other Sources of Internal Bleeding
      Resolving Hematoma
  Other Cells
    Tumor Lysis
    Rhabdomyolosis
    Intense Catabolic State

FIG. 11. Approach to the hyperkalemic patient with normal urinary potassium excretion.

Since the cellular content of K is high, hyperkalemia can result from any condition associated with cellular death. Red blood cells are a common source of K. Hyperkalemia can result from intravascular hemolysis or from resorption of internal blood lost in third spaces, such as the gastrointestinal tract or retroperitoneal space.

The acute tumor lysis syndrome is produced by massive tumor lysis after chemotherapy of malignancies with rapid cellular proliferation and high drug sensitivity. It is seen most commonly after treatment of Burkitt's lymphoma and acute leukemias. In rare circumstances, severe catabolic states can result in hyperkalemia.

Rhabdomyolysis can be caused by trauma, congenital diseases, infectious diseases, and ingestion of drugs or toxins. Although the diagnosis is often obvious in the clinical setting of muscle pain and tenderness, in other settings it may only be suspected on the basis of urinalysis findings of hematest positivity without red blood cells. Rhabdomyolysis is confirmed by demonstrating an increase in muscle enzymes (creatinine phosphokinase). In addition to increases in serum K, there are increases in serum phosphorus, uric acid, and creatinine. Rhabdomyolysis generally results in mild to moderate increases in serum K, although it also may cause acute renal failure. The combination of increased K input to the extracellular space from muscle necrosis plus decreased K excretion can result in profound hyperkalemia.

Decreased Potassium Transport from Extracellular to Intracellular Space

When hyperkalemia with normal renal K excretion cannot be attributed to an increase in K input, it is necessary to consider situations in which K cannot be transported from the extracellular space into cells. Under physiologic conditions, K shifts are controlled by circulating levels of insulin and catecholamines. Although epinephrine causes shifts of K into cells by activating the beta$_2$-adrenergic receptor, nonselective beta blockade has been associated with significant hyperkalemia in only two conditions: (1) exogenous K loads and (2) moderate to severe exercise. Hyperkalemia also has been reported in patients receiving combinations of beta blockers and calcium channel blockers.

Hyperkalemia can be a manifestation of digitalis intoxication. Since digitalis impaires the Na,K pump, less K is able to be transported into cells in the presence of toxic levels of digitalis. This diagnosis is suspected clinically in the setting of ECG abnormalities suggestive of digitalis toxicity and is confirmed by measuring plasma digoxin levels.

Hyperkalemic periodic paralysis is a rare autosomal dominant hereditary disease in which transcellular shifts of K occur in the setting of rest, exercise, exposure to cold, or increased K intake. Hyperkalemia need not be present when the attacks occur.

It is important to reemphasize that hyperkalemia on the basis of transcellular shifts in K across cellular membranes generally causes mild or moderate transient increases in serum K. Redistribution increases in serum K are rarely the cause of sustained or severe hyperkalemia unless there is a concomitant decrease in renal K excretion. This does not mean, however, that moderate increases in K are not potentially dangerous, especially in patients with underlying heart disease.

Hyperkalemia with Decreased Renal Potassium Excretion

Hyperkalemia commonly is associated with acute reductions in GFR (Fig. 12). Although hyperkalemia occurs frequently in oliguric acute renal failure, renal K excretion is often compromised in nonoliguric renal failure as well. In acute renal failure, hyperkalemia is made worse when there is a concomitant increase in K input to the extracellular space (exogenous or endogenous).

Chronic decreases in GFR are rarely the sole cause of reductions in urinary K excretion until GFRs are less than 5 to 10 ml/min. The development of chronic renal insufficiency is associated with K adaptation so that the quantity of K excreted per nephron is enhanced and absolute K excretion remains normal even though GRF declines. K adaptation is mediated by an increased K secretion or decreased K reabsorption by the distal nephron. Eventually, in the course of development of chronic renal failure, the mechanism for K adaptation is saturated, and the absolute quantity of K excreted is less than K intake. With a normal K intake, this occurs at a GFR of 5 to 10 ml/min. How-

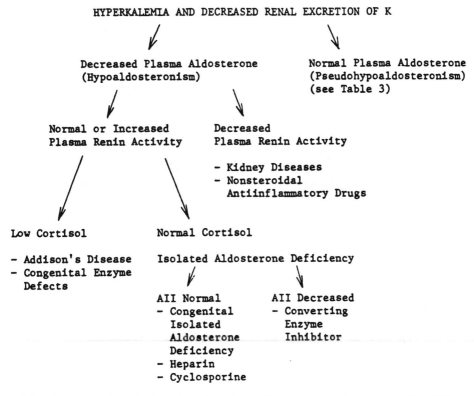

FIG. 12. Approach to the hyperkalemic patient with decreased potassium excretion. (AII) angiotensin II.

ever, as K intake is increased (especially acutely), hyperkalemia may ensue at higher levels of GFR.

Hyperkalemia with reduced urinary K is categorized initially on the basis of whether the disorder is primarily a manifestation of end-organ (renal) resistance to aldosterone or of aldosterone deficiency. Although this classification is arbitrary, it is useful clinically. The distinction between pseudohypoaldosteronism and hypoaldosteronism as causes of a reduction in urinary K is made on the basis of circulating levels of aldosterone and the kaliuretic response to the administration of mineralocorticoids, such as fludrocortisone or desoxycorticosterone acetate. End-organ resistance to aldosterone or pseudohypoaldosteronism is suggested by the finding of a normal to increased level of plasma aldosterone after volume-depleting maneuvers (such as administration of furosemide 40 mg orally at 8:00 A.M., followed by 4 hr of upright posture) and a diminished kaliuretic response after fludrocortisone (0.1 mg twice daily for 2 days) and a high salt (10 g for 2 days) diet. Hypoaldosteronism is suggested by the finding of a reduction in plasma aldosterone after volume-depleting maneuvers and a normal kaliuretic response after fludrocortisone and a high salt diet.

Hypoaldosteronism

Aldosterone is produced and secreted by the zona glomerulosa of the adrenal gland. The major factors controlling aldosterone biosynthesis are angiotensin II, K, and ACTH. Maximum levels of aldosterone are seen in the presence of all three aldosterone agonists. Reduction in circulating ACTH (e.g., in hypopituitarism or during the administration of pharmacologic quantities of glucocorticoids) does not result in hypoaldosteronism. However, reduction in angiotensin II blunts the maximum aldosterone response to K, and reduction in K blunts the maximum aldosterone response to angiotensin II. The approach to the patient with hypoaldosteronism is first to determine whether the decrease in circulating aldosterone is caused by an abnormal adrenal gland or by a reduction in circulating angiotensin II. Theoretically, this could be accomplished by determining plasma angiotensin II levels in response to volume-depleting maneuvers. However, measurement of angiotensin II is not readily available. In addition, although high angiotensin II values suggest an adrenal cause, low values do not exclude an adrenal as well as an extra-adrenal cause of hypoaldosteronism. Because of these caveats, measurement of stimulated PRA and stimulated cortisol are undertaken in patients with hypoaldosteronism (Fig. 12).

Hypoaldosteronism: Normal plasma renin activity

The finding of normal PRA in association with reduction in both stimulated aldosterone and cortisol occurs in primary adrenal insufficiency (Addison's disease) or in patients with congenital adrenal hyperplasia caused by C-21-hydroxylase deficiency or 3 β-OL-dehydrogenase deficiency. Hyperkalemia is more often associated with acute adrenal crisis than chronic adrenal insufficiency. In adrenal crisis, hyperkalemia is caused by marked decreases in distal nephron sodium and water delivery as well as by low levels of aldosterone. Although mineralocorticoid levels are low in chronic adrenal insufficiency, hyperkalemia does not occur if salt intake is high.

Hypoaldosteronism with normal renin and cortisol can be caused by failure of conversion of angiotensin I to angiotensin II or by processes that selectively interfere with aldosterone biosynthesis. Since aldosterone production is critically dependent on angiotensin II, use of such drugs as the angiotensin-converting enzyme inhibitors that interfere with angiotensin II generation can result in hypoaldosteronism. Not all patients taking converting enzyme inhibitors develop hypoaldosteronism or become frankly hyperkalemic. However, a subset of patients appears to be at risk. This group includes patients in whom converting enzyme inhibitors are used to treat heart failure rather than patients in whom converting enzyme inhibitors are used to treat mild to moderate hypertension. Approximately 25% of heart failure patients treated with converting enzyme inhibitors have been reported to develop hypoaldosteronism. These tend to be patients with class III and class IV functional disorders.

Selective biosynthetic defects in aldosterone production are also associated with normal angiotensin II and normal cortisol. These metabolic abnormalities can be congenital or acquired. Hereditary defects in the terminal enzymes required for aldosterone production, corticosterone methyl oxidase I or II, result in deficits in aldosterone but not in glucocorticoid production. Acquired defects in aldosterone secretion have been described in a small percentage of patients with underlying renal disease and in patients receiving large doses of heparin. In addition, hyperkalemia has been reported in heparin-induced hypoaldosteronism. Hyperkalemia has been reported in both renal and cardiac transplant recipients receiving cyclosporine. Although detailed evaluations are not yet available, cyclosporine appears to be associated with low renin and low to normal aldosterone levels. Since cyclosporine may have a direct toxic effect on renal tubules, it is also possible that the drug causes end-organ resistance to aldosterone.

Hypoaldosteronism: Low plasma renin activity

The syndrome of hyporeninemic hypoaldosteronism accounts for at least 30% of cases of unexplained hyperkalemia in patients with renal insufficiency in whom the level of reduction of GFR would not be expected to result in hyperkalemia. The diagnosis of this syndrome is based on the finding of hyperkalemia with a reduction in urinary K excretion in association with reduced levels of both PRA and aldosterone after volume-depleting maneuvers. It is often difficult to decide whether aldosterone levels are truly low. This may be especially problematic when interpretating basal aldosterone values.

As has been noted, aldosterone secretion is under control of both K and angiotensin II. Thus, under basal conditions, aldosterone levels may not be frankly reduced in hyperkalemia patients with hyporeninemic hypoaldosteronism. However, after volume depletion, the renin response is inadequate, and stimulated aldosterone is abnormally low in over 80% of patients with this syndrome.

Hyporeninemic hypoaldosteronism is associated with a number of disease entities and with the use of nonsteroidal anti-inflammatory drugs. The disease entities associated with the syndrome are noted in Chapter 1. Diabetes and interstitial renal disease are the most common renal causes of the syndrome, although the syndrome has been described in association with glomerular diseases, such as amyloidosis. Nonsteroidal anti-inflammatory agents have also been reported to cause hyperkalemia in association with low levels of renin and aldosterone. Nonsteroidal agent-induced hyperkalemia is more common in patients with underlying glomerular disease; however, it also occurs in patients with normal renal function.

Pseudohypoaldosteronism (renal resistance to aldosterone)

The most common cause of hyperkalemia in clinical practice is the use of K-sparing agents: spironolactone, amiloride, and triamterene. These agents inhibit aldosterone binding to cellular receptors (spironolactone) or nonaldosterone-mediated renal sodium reabsorption (amiloride, triamterene). Hyperkalemia is more likely to occur in patients with a reduced GFR or in patients with increased K intake.

After excluding K-sparing diuretic agents, the evaluation of patients with suspected renal resistance to aldosterone consists of demonstrating that aldosterone levels are normal or elevated and that there is renal resistance to pharmacologic levels of exogenous mineralocorticoid (e.g., fludrocortisone 0.1 mg twice daily). Patients are considered to have renal resistance to aldosterone if they are not able to increase urinary K excretion after the administration of mineralocorticoid. It should be recognized, however, that these patients may not in the true sense be resistant to the effects of aldosterone. The primary effect of aldosterone on renal K is to cause K secretion in the distal nephron (*see* Chapter 1). Part of the secreted K is then reabsorbed in more distal segments of the collecting tubule. Thus, K excretion represents the net difference between K escaping reabsorption before the distal convoluted tubule plus K secreted by the distal nephron minus K reabsorbed in the collecting tubule. Since the quantity of K escaping reabsorption before the distal tubule is small, it is generally not considered in the pathogenesis of hyperkalemia in clinical settings. Hyperkalemia, therefore, results from decreased K secretion and normal K reabsorption or from normal K secretion and enhanced K reabsorption. In either situation, the kaliuretic response to aldosterone will be reduced. For example, true aldosterone resistance results in a reduction in K secretory flux while K reabsorptive flux is normal. In other conditions, aldosterone-induced K secretory flux is normal while reabsorptive flux is enhanced.

Nonreabsorbable anions, such as bicarbonate or sulfate, are used to distinguish between these different pathways of hyperkalemia. These anions do not alter K secretion but serve to trap secreted K in tubular fluid, thereby reducing K reabsorption. In normal people, the administration of mineralocorticoid plus either acetazolamide and sodium bicarbonate or sodium sulfate results in marked increases in K excretion, presumably by reducing K reabsorption. In patients with reduced K secretion, the kaliuretic response to this maneuver is blunted because K secretion is low. In contrast, the kaliuretic response to this maneuver is preserved in patients with enhanced K reabsorption because the nonreabsorbable anion traps secreted K in the lumen, thereby normalizing net K excretion.

Tubular resistance to aldosterone occurs in a number of conditions shown in Table 3. Attempts to distinguish diseases characterized by decreased K secretion from those characterized by enhanced K reabsorption have not been undertaken in many cases. In addition, many of these clinical entities have been associated with hyporeninemic hypoaldosteronism. Although hyperkalemia occurs in the conditions depicted in Table 3, it is rarely the presenting abnormality in most of these situations. However, hyperkalemia can be a prominent feature of patients with unrecognized obstructive uropathy. Thus, urinary obstruction should be excluded in patients in whom the cause of hyperkalemia is not readily apparent.

TABLE 3. *End-organ resistance to aldosterone*

Decreased K secretion
Drugs
Spironolactone
Triamterene
Amiloride
Sickle cell disease[a]
Renal transplantation[a]
Amyloidosis[a]
Systemic lupus erythematosus[a]
Hyperglobulinemic states: Sjogren's syndrome
Obstruction[a]
Pseudohypoaldosteronism type I
Enhanced K reabsorption
Obstruction[a]
Pseudohypoaldosteronism type II

[a]Also associated with hyporeninemic hypoaldosteronism.

Idiopathic pseudohypoaldosteronism types I and II are extremely rare disorders in which the kaliuretic response to aldosterone is impaired in the absence of the disorders listed in Table 3. In type I disease, there is a reduction in K secretion in multiple aldosterone-responsive target organs, including the kidney, colon, salivary glands, and sweat glands. It is a disease of infants and is associated with failure to thrive, hyperkalemia, and renal salt wasting. In contrast, pseudohypoaldosteronism type II is seen in adults and has a different pathophysiologic basis than type I disease. These patients also are hyperkalemic and have an impaired kaliuretic response to aldosterone. However, in contrast to type I patients, they do not salt waste and are usually hypertensive. In type II patients, K retention is mediated by enhanced K reabsorption, since the kaliuretic response to bicarbonate or sulfate is normal. It has been postulated that K reabsorption is mediated by an increase in distal nephron chloride transport.

REFERENCES

1. Adrogue, H. J., and Madias, N. E. (1981): Changes in plasma potassium concentration during acute acid-base disturbances. *Am. J. Med.*, 71:456–467.
2. Batlle, D. C., Arruda, J. A. L., and Kurtzman, N. A. (1981): Hyperkalemic distal renal tubular acidosis associated with obstructive uropathy. *N. Engl. J. Med.*, 304:373–380.
3. Brown, M. J., Brown, D. C., and Murphy, M. B. (1983): Hypokalemia from Beta$_2$-receptor stimulation by circulating epinephrine. *N. Engl. J. Med.*, 309:1414–1419.
4. Brown, R. S. (1986): Extrarenal potassium homeostasis. *Kidney Int.*, 30:116–127.
5. Kassirer, J. P., and Harrington, J. T. (1977): Diuretics and potassium metabolism: A reassessment of the need, effectiveness and safety of potassium therapy. *Kidney Int.*, 11:505–515.
6. Patrick, J. (1977): Assessment of body potassium stores. *Kidney Int.*, 11:476-490.
7. Ponce, S. P., Jennings, A. E., Madias, N. E., and Harrington, J. T. (1985): Drug-induced hyperkalemia. *Medicine*, 64:357–370.
8. Schambelan, M., and Sebastian, A. (1979): Hyporeninemic hypoaldosteronism. *Annu. Rev. Med.*, 24:385–405.
9. Schambelan, M., Sebastian, A., and Rector, F. C., Jr. (1981): Mineralocorticoid-resistant renal hyperkalemia without salt wasting (type II pseudohypoaldosteronism): Role of increased renal chloride reabsorption. *Kidney Int.*, 19:716–727.
10. Schwartz, W. B., and Relman, A. S. (1953): Metabolic and renal studies in chronic potassium depletion resulting from overuse of laxatives. *J. Clin. Invest.*, 32:258–272.
11. Stein, J. H. (1985): The pathogenic spectrum of Bartter's syndrome. *Kidney Int.*, 28:85–93.
12. Sterns, R. H., Cox, M., Fieg, P. U., and Singer, I. (1981): Internal potassium balance and the control of the plasma potassium concentration. *Medicine*, 60:339–354.
13. Struthers, A. D., Whitesmith, R., and Reid, J. L. (1983): Prior thiazide diuretic treatment increases adrenaline-induced hypokalemia. *Lancet*, 1:1358–1360.
14. Tan, S. Y., Shapiro, R., Franco, R., Stockard, H., and Mulrow, P. J. (1979): Indomethacin-induced prostaglandin inhibition with hyperkalemia: A reversible cause of hyporeninemic hypoaldosteronism. *Ann. Intern. Med.*, 90:783–785.
15. Tannen, R. L. (1985): Diuretic-induced hypokalemia. *Kidney Int.*, 28:988–1000.
16. Valtin, H. (1979): *Renal Dysfunction Mechanism Involved in Fluid and Solutes Imbalance.* Little, Brown, Boston.
17. Weinberger, M. H., Grim, C. E., Hollifield, J. W., et al. (1979): Primary aldosteronism: Diagnosis, localization, and treatment. *Ann. Intern. Med.*, 90:386–395.

General Review Articles

18. DeFronzo, R. A., Bia, M., and Smith, D. (1982): Clinical disorders of hyperkalemia. *Annu. Rev. Med.*, 33:521–554.
19. Gabow, P. A., and Peterson, L. N. (1986): Disorders of potassium metabolism. In: *Renal and Electrolyte Disorders*, 3rd ed., edited by R. W. Schrier, pp. 207–250. Little, Brown, Boston.
20. Tannen, R. L. (1986): Potassium disorders. In: *Fluid and Electrolytes*, edited by J. Kokko and R. Tannen, pp. 150–228. Saunders, Philadelphia.

The Regulation of Potassium Balance, edited
by Donald W. Seldin and Gerhard Giebisch,
Raven Press, Ltd., New York © 1989.

9

Clinical Expression of Potassium Disturbances

James P. Knochel

*Department of Internal Medicine, The University of Texas Southwestern Medical
Center, and Presbyterian Hospital, Dallas, Texas 75231*

Hypokalemia
  Expression of Potassium Deficiency on Specific Organ Systems • Metabolic Disturbances in Potassium Deficiency • Carbohydrate Metabolism in Potassium Deficiency
Hyperkalemia
  Cardiovascular Effects of Hyperkalemia • Skeletal Muscle in Hyperkalemia
References

HYPOKALEMIA

Hypokalemia is defined as a serum potassium concentration below 3.5 mEq/liter. Mild hypokalemia, herein defined as a serum potassium concentration ranging from 3.0 mEq/liter to 3.5 mEq/liter, does not usually cause symptoms. Symptoms nearly always occur with levels below 2.5 mEq/liter. Similar to other disturbances of electrolyte balance, symptoms tend to be unnoticed or only moderate if hypokalemia develops very slowly, but, in contrast, may be prominent if it develops very quickly. The acute decline in serum potassium concentration from normal to a level of 2.5 to 3.0 mEq/liter that may occur as a result of redistribution of potassium into cells does not necessarily produce symptoms. Examples of the latter include hypokalemia that develops during the course of infusing glucose and insulin, that associated with acute respiratory alkalosis, or the mild transient hypokalemia that may occur after completion of strenuous exercise. However, it should be recognized that acute hypokalemia incident to infusions of glucose and insulin has been associated with electrocardiographic changes and ventricular premature contractions.

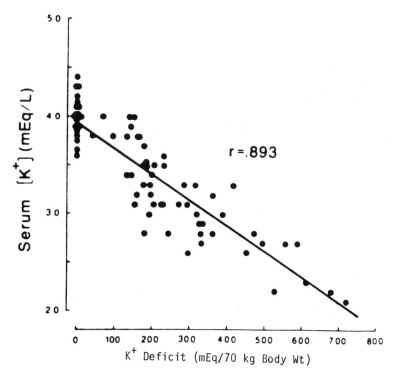

FIG. 1. Relationship of serum potassium concentration to body potassium deficit. The data are derived from seven metabolic balance studies carried out on 24 subjects depleted of potassium.

Serum potassium levels in potassium deficiency correlate in a very rough manner with the existing total body potassium deficit (Fig. 1). A number of factors may be responsible for normal serum concentrations in people who are frankly deficient. An important example of the latter is the patient with diabetic ketoacidosis with reduced renal function who is also volume depleted as a result of salt and water losses.

Expression of Potassium Deficiency on Specific Organ Systems (1–3,5–9,11,12,15,17–19,21,22,24,26,29–31)

Skeletal Muscle

Patients who have become hypokalemic as a result of potassium deficiency often complain of a vague sensation of simply not feeling well, which is best described as malaise. Although weakness is also a common subjective complaint, in early potassium deficiency, objective signs of muscular weakness may be difficult to identify. Myalgia is common and usually described by the patient as a poorly definable, troublesome discomfort in the extremities that is more aching than painful. It often is relieved by assuming a different posture or position. However, within a few moments the sensation reappears. This particular complex of symptoms resembles the restless leg syndrome that has been described in patients with peripheral vascular disease, diabetic neuropathy, gout, acute intermittent porphyria, or autonomic neuropathy.

If a person who has an important degree of potassium deficiency[1] exercises, there will occur a reduction in endurance, and it will be noted that a greater period of rest is required before exercise can be resumed. Cramps may be prominent. If exercise is continued to the point of physical exhaustion, the classic syndrome of exertional rhabdomyolysis may follow. The latter is characterized by frank muscle pain localized to those muscles used in exercise, muscle stiffness and swelling, and profound weakness or even paralysis. Dark urine characteristic of myoglobinuria and acute renal tubular necrosis may appear. Spontaneous rhabdomyolysis, defined as that form not precipitated by an immediate event, usually occurs only in individuals with extremely severe potassium deficiency. In such cases, preceding serum potassium concentrations commonly have been below 2.0 mEq/liter. Such levels generally correspond to total body potassium deficits in excess of 800 mEq (Fig. 1).

Electrical excitability

The precise cause of muscular weakness in potassium deficiency is unknown. Theoretically, abnormalities of electrical excitability of the muscle cell could be responsible. For example, in humans and experimental animals with early potassium deficiency, as predictable by the Nernst equation ($E_m = -61.5 \log [K_1/K_o]$), the resting transmembrane electrical potential difference (E_m) of skeletal muscle rises because the fractional reduction of extracellular potassium concentration K_o is substantially greater than that of intracellular potassium concentration K_1. Figure 2 shows a relationship between the strength of the electrical stimulus applied to a muscle cell and the all-or-none response in formation of an action potential. Unless a stimulus has sufficient strength to depolarize the muscle cell membrane from its normal resting potential of -90 mV to its activation potential of -60 mV, an action potential will not result, and accordingly, there can be no muscle cell contraction. The arithmetic difference between the resting membrane potential and the activation potential is defined as excitability. If the strength of the stimulus is sufficient to depolarize a cell to its activation threshold. i.e., -60 mV, the remainder of the action potential complex proceeds spontaneously and results in contraction of the muscle cell. In early hypokalemia, the resting membrane

---

[1]Total body potassium content in a normal person of ideal proportions is 50 mEq/kg in a man and 40 mEq/kg in a woman. A clinically important deficit is about 10% or more of the total.

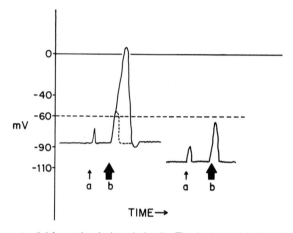

FIG. 2. Action potential formation in hypokalemia. The horizontal broken line represents the activation potential. In the left complex, the letter **a** represents a miniature end-plate or spike potential, which is of insufficient intensity to cause an action potential. The letter **b** represents a voluntary impulse that is sufficiently strong to reach the activation potential. Consequently, a normal action potential follows that causes contraction of the muscle cell. In hypokalemia, the membrane potential moves from -88 mV to about -106 mV. In this instance, even the voluntary impulse is inadequate to depolarize the cell to its activation potential. The lack of a contractile response is defined as inexcitability and perceived as weakness.

potential is hyperpolarized, but the activation threshold is unchanged. Thus, a proportionately greater electrical stimulus must be applied in order that an action potential will follow. By definition, the muscle cell under these conditions becomes relatively inexcitable and is said to be in a state of hyperpolarization block. It is belived that the electrical inexcitability is the bioelectrical phenomenon perceived as muscular weakness.

In cases of advanced potassium deficiency, the Nernst relationship disappears, and the cell becomes electrically depolarized. Presumably this occurs as a result of derangements in the muscle membrane itself, Na,K-ATPase (pump) failure, or possibly an effect of alpha-adrenergic stimuli, so that the resting membrane potential either approaches or even falls below the activation potential. Although the difference between the resting membrane potential and the activation potential becomes less, excitability becomes less and less as serum potassium values become severely depressed. In the presence of a serum potassium concentration between 1.4 and 1.8 mEq/liter, the muscle cell becomes essentially inexcitable (so-called depolarization block), and at that time paralysis supervenes. Hypokalemia of this degree is sufficiently severe to inhibit activity of Na,K-ATPase. It is noteworthy that in patients with familial hypokalemic paralysis (*see* Chapter 12), the muscle cell fiber may become electrically silent and inexcitable at higher serum potassium concentrations than the latter value. Figure 3 illustrates the relationships among the extent of total body potassium deficiency, the prevailing serum

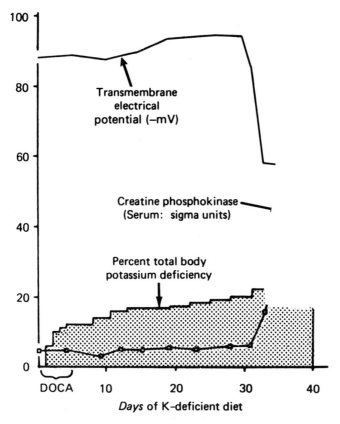

FIG. 3. A representative time sequence of transmembrane electrical potential of skeletal muscle cells (E_m) and serum creatine phosphokinase activity during advancing potassium deficiency in the dog.

potassium concentration, the resting membrane potential of muscle cells and the eventual elevation of serum creatine phosphokinase (CK) that generally appears in dogs during progressive potassium deficiency. It is noteworthy that the early muscle cell hyperpolarization falls to subnormal values as the total body potassium deficit approaches 20%.

Along with muscle cell depolarization, there appears to occur a spontaneous release of CK. Observations at this point in the course of progressive potassium deficiency show that the muscle cell depolarization approximately corresponds to the appearance of clinical weakness in the dog manifested by inability to maintain the head in an erect position and evident weakness in the legs. Although it is virtually certain that similar events occur in humans, data are not available to prove that muscle cell depolarization occurs in coincidence with spontaneous elevation of muscle enzyme activity in serum. Nevertheless, one can be fairly certain that this occurs, since histologically injured muscle cells, which are known to occur in severe potassium deficiency in humans, would hardly be expected to maintain a normal E_m. Such cells show nearly a 50% reduction in intracellular potassium concentration and abnormal elevations of sodium, chloride, and water.

Myoedema

An interesting hypothetical relationship exists between an injured muscle cell and a clinical observation known as "myoedema." If one forcibly strikes a resting muscle with a neurologic hammer, a localized contraction of the muscle will immediately appear as a lump, which will disappear over the course of a few seconds. Myoedema can be elicited in a normal person if a blow is delivered to a muscle, such as the triceps brachialis, that overlies a bony surface. This same response can be elicited much more easily in virtually any muscle in patients with myopathies, including those with advanced potassium deficiency. It is assumed that a local mechanical blow depolarizes the cell and causes local leakage of calcium ions into the myoplasm sufficient to induce a contracture. Electromyographic recordings in this phenomenon show an initial burst of depolarizations followed by a period of electrical silence, compatible with a contracture.

Tetany

Tetany has been described in association with hypokalemia. In many instances, patients were also hypocalcemic and hypomagnesemic consequent to steatorrhea. Serum potassium values were very low, and tetany did not appear until patients were given KCl. This response illustrates the opposing electrical effects of K^+ and Ca^{2+} on electrical stability of membranes. Such cases apparently represent true tetany secondary to hypocalcemia. It appears that hypokalemia probably helps to prevent tetany. Observations on tetany in other hypokalemic patients show that serum calcium may be normal or only slightly depressed, calcium excretion into the urine is normal, tetany is not relieved by calcium infusions, and it occurs in association with alkalosis.

Fourman observed tetany in two human subjects who were experimentally depleted of potassium by feeding a potassium-deficient diet in conjunction with a resin that exchanges ammonium for potassium in the intestine. Their respective potassium deficits were 540 mEq and 274 mEq. Symptoms did not appear until the resin had been stopped and the associated metabolic acidosis had spontaneously converted to metabolic alkalosis. The subjects demonstrated spasmodic contractions of the forearm in a manner identical to patients with hypocalcemic tetany (*main d'accoucheur*). The contractions were usually brought on by using the muscles voluntarily, for example, in an activity such as writing. Fascicular twitching was seen around the eyes and mouth. Paresthesias were prominent, and Chvostek's and Trousseau's signs could be elicited. In each of these subjects, serum calcium had fallen from control values ranging from 10.2 mg/dl to 10.9 mg/dl to 9.1 mg/dl to 9.6 mg/dl. Magnesium values also fell slightly. Measurements of ionized calcium were not obtained. In an additional hypokalemic patient who had undergone gastric bypass surgery for obesity, the only manifestation of tetany was a positive Trousseau sign. In this patient, serum potassium was 2.8 mEq/liter, calcium was 9.2 mg/dl, and magnesium was 1.8 mEq/liter. Serum ionized calcium was 2.43 mEq/liter (normal), and arterial blood showed a pH of 7.41 and a Pco_2 content of 31 torr. Of interest, the Trousseau sign persisted for 1 to 2 days after correction of hypokalemia. Although it is widely appreciated that either respiratory or metabolic alkalosis lowers the tetanic threshold, hypokalemic tetany may occur in the presence of a normal blood pH. The term "spasmophilia" has been used to describe tetany that occurs in the absence of hypocalcemia.

It is unfortunate that there are no electromyographic data available on patients who have tetany with hypokalemia whose serum calcium is normal. Hypocalcemic tetany, classically seen in hypoparathyroidism, is clearly the result of electrically mediated muscle contraction.

A decrease in ionized calcium concentration in extracellular fluid moves the activation potential toward the resting membrane potential, thereby increasing excitability. The resting membrane potential is unchanged. During electromyography in a normal person, repetitious spike potentials occur that are of such small amplitude that they fail to elicit depolarization. Although the amplitude of spike potentials does not change in hypocalcemia, they are sufficient in magnitude to depolarize the resting membrane potential to the activation potential threshold more easily and result in an action potential. Repeated and rapid firing of the muscle spike potentials results in tetanic contractions. Therefore, tetany is an electrically mediated muscle cell contraction, whereas a contracture is not. A contracture, or cramp, represents a sustained muscle contraction caused by local metabolic disturbances in the myoplasm that occur independently of electrical stimulation and are thus electrically silent. For this reason, if a hypokalemic normocalcemic patient demonstrates persistent muscle contraction, the clinician might carefully ascertain that electrical silence prevails, thus clearly differentiating the condition from tetany.

Portable electromyography is widely available and simple to perform. Although it will not yield information on membrane potential of an individual cell, it will differentiate clearly electrically mediated contractions from cramps that are electrically silent. Knowledgable electrolyte physiologists dispute the issue whether hypokalemia of itself or hypomagnesemia of itself can cause true tetany in the absence of hypocalcemia. If tetany is precisely defined as described previously as an electrical event, there should be no confusion. In contrast, advanced potassium deficiency and, independently, magnesium deficiency are both associated with sizable accumulations of calcium in the myoplasm of the muscle cell. If, under either set of circumstances, the calcium concentration becomes sufficiently high or if calcium transport into its mitochondrial or sarcoplasmic reticulum storage sites is suppressed because of associated disease, it is conceivable that a contracture mimicking clinical tetany could occur in the absence of hypocalcemia.

Rhabdomyolysis

Older medical literature contains sporadic reports of skeletal muscle necrosis or rhabdomyolysis in patients who were hypokalemic because of intestinal malabsorption or because of diarrhea associated with hyperthyroidism, alcoholism, or diabetic ketoacidosis. Fatal cases showed patchy myocardial necrosis. Clinicians well versed in skeletal muscle pathophysiology doubted that potassium deficiency alone was responsible for rhabdomyolysis as described in these reports because most of these patients had associated disturbances, including hyperthyroidism, alcoholism, malnutrition, hypomagnesemia, phosphorus deficiency, or other influences that could affect skeletal muscle integrity. However, in the early 1960s, when muscle enzyme measurements became available for clinical use, patients with uncomplicated hypokalemia associated with the use of diuretic drugs were noted to have slight or modest elevations of aldolase or CK activity. The symptoms of muscle weakness, pain, and cramps were described in hypokalemic patients with increased enzyme activity. The symptoms could be relieved and elevated CK activity could be returned to normal by correction of potassium deficiency.

More recently, a number of observers have reported frank rhabdomyolysis in patients with potassium deficiency. The majority of cases occurred in patients with severe potassium deficiency induced by diuretics, especially combinations of diuretics that act at different sites in the nephron, thus carrying a greater risk of hypokalemia. Rhabdomyolysis also has been observed in patients with primary aldosteronism or other conditions that cause potassium wasting independently when they were given diuretics. As noted in other causes of potassium deficiency, muscle cell necrosis is more likely to occur if a condition coexists that affects energy production in the cell. One of the single most important influences is metabolic acidosis, for example, in patients who develop hypokalemic, hyperchloremic, renal tubular acidosis as a result of therapy with amphotericin B or after inhalation of glue containing toluene. Although it is possible that the severity of the metabolic acidosis is sufficient to impair glycolysis as a result of reduced phosphofructokinase activity and, in turn, critically suppress energy production, this hypothesis would not explain the virtual absence of rhabdomyolysis in patients with diabetic ketoacidosis who are potassium deficient and have similar, if not worse, levels of metabolic acidosis. It also appears that rhabdomyolysis is exceptionally rare in patients with severe hypokalemia and metabolic alkalosis as a result of prolonged vomiting. Although one might postulate that alkalosis is protective, it should be kept in mind that hypokalemic alkalosis is associated with sufficient accumulation of hydrogen ions in the cell to cause a significant reduction in pH. Patients with mineralocorticoid excess who also receive potassium-wasting diuretics have developed severe rhabdomyolysis despite coexisting metabolic alkalosis.

Experimental rhabdomyolysis with potassium deficiency

Experimental studies suggest three possible explanations for rhabdomyolysis in potassium deficiency: ischemia, disordered carbohydrate metabolism, and a derangement of the sarcolemma. As described in more detail in Chapter 2, potassium release from contracting muscle cells may play an important role in regulation of muscle blood flow during exercise. When a muscle cell becomes depolarized in response to a normal electrical stimulus, potassium ions are released into the interstitial fluid of the muscle. The concentration of potassium ions as a result of this event approaches 15 mEq/liter to 18 mEq/liter. As potassium rises above its normal concentration in extracellular fluid, it becomes a potent vasodilator. Consequently, interstitial hyperkalemia is thought to act on muscle arterioles, where it induces vasodilatation and, in turn, permits increased muscle blood flow during exercise.

At rest, normal muscle blood flow averages only about 1 ml/100 g muscle weight per min. During intense physical work, muscle blood flow may increase to values approaching 40 ml/100 g/min. Normally, the rate of flow varies directly with the intensity of work performed, and this, in turn, varies directly with the quantity of potassium released from contracting muscle cells. Other factors, including adenine nucleotides, osmolality, hypoxia, release of vasodilatory peptides, or the drop in pH, also may play a role in sustaining muscle blood during exercise. Nevertheless, it can be shown clearly in the endogenously perfused isolated gracilis muscle preparation of the dog that under conditions of potassium deficiency, muscle cell contraction is not associated with release of potassium ions, and, in addition, muscle blood flow does not increase. Because the initial force of muscle contraction often is entirely normal in potassium-deficient muscle, the lack of adequate blood flow to deliver energy substrates or provide removal of heat and metabolites can lead to serious ischemic damage. On the other hand, if potassium is infused directly into the arterial blood supply of a working, potassium-deficient muscle, blood flow is restored toward normal. Although skeletal muscle sometimes may appear normal by light microscopy even in the presence of severe potassium deficiency, frank muscle cell necrosis can be produced easily by exercise. In contast, exercise of a normal skeletal muscle within a reasonable range of intensity and duration does not cause histologic abnormalities.

Disordered carbohydrate metabolism in skeletal muscle as a result of potassium deficiency appears to be limited to a reduction of glycogen synthesis. Potassium deficiency virtually eliminates glycogen synthesis in skeletal muscle. Thereby a situation is established in which muscle cell integrity will be jeopardized in the event of ischemic exercise. During sustained hard work, oxidation of fatty acids and glucose as a source of ATP production becomes limited in direct relationship to oxygen availability. Energy requirements during such work often exceed that which can be produced by oxidative metabolism. Thus, when oxygen cannot be supplied in sufficient amounts to meet energy demands, the required quantity of ATP can be produced only by glycolysis using glycogen as a substrate. It can be demonstrated readily that as glycogen stores become exhausted in skeletal muscle, fatigue rapidly supervenes. Since potassium deficiency practically eliminates glycogen synthesis in skeletal muscle, the experimental observation that exercise endurance is proportionately reduced appears to be explained. Similar to patients with McArdle's syndrome, who have plentiful muscle glycogen but cannot use it because of myophosphorylase deficiency, sustained exercise in potassium-deficient humans also may cause severe muscle cramping and the appearance of rhabdomyolysis and myoglobinuria. A more extensive discussion of the deranged carbohydrate metabolism in potassium deficient skeletal muscle is found later in this chapter.

Loss of sarcolemmal integrity also is a major complication of potassium deficiency. We noted that the muscle cell becomes electrically hyperpolarized in early potassium deficiency, in a sense behaving as a potassium electrode. This response is predictable in accordance with the Nernst relationship. However, as potassium deficiency becomes severe, changes appear that suggest a loss of sarcolemmal integrity. These include increased permeability to sodium and a sharp reduction of resting membrane potential of the muscle cell to values even below the activation potential and, almost simultaneously, an apparent leakage of intracellular myofibrillar enzymes (aldolase, CK) into the blood. Recent studies by Clausen et al. in both experimental animals and humans show that as potassium deficiency progresses, there is a proportional and progressive loss of ouabain-binding sites in skeletal muscle. Since ouabain-binding sites appear to quantitatively identify Na,K-ATPase pumps in skeletal muscle, it is believed that potassium deficiency causes a progressive reduction in the capacity of muscle cells to transport sodium and potassium ions by the Na,K pump. Such a complication has enormously important implications. Although a reduction in the number of pump sites possibly could maintain normal intracellular sodium concentration under resting conditions, it seems logical that if a cell is confronted with a situation in which sodium ions flood the myoplasm, for example, during exercise, removal of sodium ions from the cytoplasm by the pump would be reduced materially.

In accordance with our current understanding of sodium-calcium exchange across the sarcolemma, sodium retention would lead to a dangerous accumulation of calcium sufficient to activate potentially destructive enzymes, such as phospholipase or myofibrillar proteases. Unregulated release of such enzymes could be responsible for continued destruction of the cell and, thus, be responsible for rhabdomyolysis. The sodium pump depends on availability of oxygen and metabolites, such as fatty acids or glucose, for its energy requirements. Under conditions of ischemia that would exist during exercise in potassium deficiency, neither oxygen nor substrates to energize the pump could be delivered. Therefore, even if the density of pump units was not depressed, the pumps would nevertheless be functionally incapacitated. Although not examined in potassium deficiency *per se*, it has been shown recently that potentially destructive oxygen free radicals accumulate in ischemic muscle. These compounds would very likely contribute to ongoing cellular injury.

Potassium intolerance caused by potassium deficiency

Intolerance to therapeutically administered potassium salts is commonly seen in patients with underlying renal insufficiency. Potassium intolerance may be aggravated by simultaneous insulin deficiency, drugs that block beta-$_2$-adrenergic receptors (propranolol), drugs that suppress aldosterone formation (nonsteroidal anti-inflammatory agents, angiotensin-converting enzyme inhibitors), drugs that interfere with the action of aldosterone (spironolactone), drugs that interfere with sodium-potassium exchange (triamterene or amiloride), and even cyclosporin because of its action to reduce renin production. Occasionally, one encounters a severely hypokalemic patient who may become acutely hyperkalemic following administration of normal supplements of potassium salts. I have observed this under two sets of circumstances. The first was in a 45-year-old man with severe thyrotoxicosis complicated by thyrotoxic heart disease, modest congestive heart failure, thyrotoxic myopathy, and diarrhea. This patient's serum potassium concentration when first seen was 3.3 mEq/liter. He was given 40 mg of propranolol and, 1 hr later, a 40 mEq dose of potassium chloride solution by mouth. His serum potassium rose after several hours to 6.8 mEq/liter.

A second patient was a 62-year-old man with severe, refractory congestive heart failure who developed ventricular ectopy in association with hypokalemia. Because he had become refractory to furosemide, metolazone was added to his regimen. Although this combination of diuretics successfully mobilized edema fluid, the patient promptly became hypokalemic and showed frequent, multifocal premature ventricular contractions and short runs of ventricular tachycardia. Because his serum potassium was 2.2 mEq/liter, 80 mEq of potassium chloride was given orally over 6 hr. His serum potassium rose to 8.3 mEq/liter, and hyperkalemic toxicity was clearly evident electrocardiographically. As is nearly always the case, the patient had a modest degree of baseline renal insufficiency, probably as a result of decreased renal perfusion associated with congestive heart failure.

In both instances, it seems very likely that the normal capacity for potassium uptake by skeletal muscle cells was sharply reduced. Although administration of thyroid hormones may increase acutely the density of Na,K-ATPase binding sites in skeletal muscle, long-standing, severe hyperthyroidism in humans is associated with thyrotoxic myopathy, muscle atrophy, and in the case described, decreased muscle blood flow as a result of associated congestive heart failure. Published and our own unpublished observations on three additional patients with advanced thyrotoxicosis complicated by myopathy have shown cellular compositional changes in skeletal muscle compatible with the sick cell. These include a high content of sodium and chloride, a reduced content of potassium, an increased content of water, and a marked reduction in membrane potential as measured directly with intracellular, Ling-type microelectrodes.

In the second patient, severe potassium deficiency probably caused a major reduction in the number of Na,K-ATPase binding sites in skeletal muscle. This, in conjunction with renal insufficiency and decreased muscle blood flow and hypoxia because of congestive heart failure, almost certainly reduced muscle cell capacity to take up potassium ions.

If we assume that both of the foregoing patients had approximately 14 liters of extracellular fluid, if renal excretion of potassium were severely limited because of decreased renal blood flow and if the quantity of administered potassium were essentially confined to extracellular fluid, the sharp rise in serum potassium concentration in each patient can be explained. In the first patient, administration of 40 mEq resulted in a rise in serum potassium from 3.3 mEq/liter to 6.8 mEq/liter. This indicates that the administered potassium once absorbed was essentially confined to the patient's extracellular fluid. In the second patient, whose serum potassium rose from 2.3 mEq/liter to 8.3 mEq/liter, the 80 mEq administered also remained within the extracellular fluid space. In both cases, pump failure on a background of renal insufficiency and decreased muscle perfusion caused acute hyperkalemia.

Such events as those described make a critically important point in management of patients who are severely ill who also have severe potassium deficiency and severe associated disease. There is no predetermined dose of KCl that can be safely administered to such patients. The physician cannot anticipate how much of a given dose of potassium will be taken up by cells under such conditions. Finally, when one administers potassium salts to such people, which may be required as a lifesaving measure, it must be realized that acute hyperkalemia could supervene. Accordingly, administration of potassium salts even in nominal doses should best be done in conjunction with electrocardiographic monitoring to detect hyperkalemic cardiotoxicity before it becomes disastrous. A safe guideline would be to administer no more KCl initially than is required to correct the deficit in the extracellular space. For practical purposes, 60% of body weight is water. One third of this volume in an edema-free subject is extracellular. Thus, if a sick patient whose body weight is 70 kg has a serum potassium of 2.5 mEq/liter, the extracellular volume will be 12.6 liters. This value, multiplied by the difference between the observed serum potassium concentration and normal (4.0 mEq/liter), results in a KCl dose of about 20 mEq. This quantity could be given intravenously over 1 hr while obtaining another measurement and examining the electrocardiogram for appropriate changes.

Cardiovascular System

Cardiac arrhythmias, autonomic insufficiency, and myocardial necrosis are the major cardiovascular complications of potassium deficiency.

Both atrial and ventricular arrhythmias may occur as a consequence of hypokalemia. People with normal hearts usually do not display arrhythmias unless hypokalemia becomes moderately severe. If arrhythmias, especially of ventricular origin, occur in the presence of a serum potassium ranging from 3.0 mEq/liter and 3.5 mEq/liter in a patient not medicated with digitalis preparations, other factors that could increase the likelihood of arrhythmias should be considered. These include subclinical heart disease, coexistent hyperthyroidism, drug toxicity such as that related to ingestion of amphetamines, cocaine, or other arrhythmia-provoking drugs, or hypercalcemia. Although mild hypokalemia (serum K 3.0–3.5 mEq/liter) usually does not cause important clinical disturbances in normal people, there are important exceptions. One study examined 10 patients with life-threatening ventricular arrhythmias whose serum K was between 2.4 mEq/liter and 3.3 mEq/liter. The arrhythmias disappeared after simple correction of hypokalemia. The importance of this study lies in the fact that none of the patients was receiving digitalis. This indicates that even mild hypokalemia may cause polymorphic ventricular tachycardia or ventricular fibrillation, and such patients may show no clinical evidence of heart disease before the occurrence of hypokalemia.

It is important to realize that elevated concentrations of ionized calcium exaggerate the pathologic effects of hypokalemia, and low concentrations of ionized calcium tend to ameliorate the harmful consequences of hypokalemia. A young man with severe diabetic ketoacidosis came to our hospital in coma, with a serum potassium concentration of 1.5 mEq/liter. He was not paralyzed and showed no changes in his electrocardiogram compatible with hypokalemia. His simultaneous serum calcium concentration was 4.8 mg/dl. In contrast, patients with untreated uremia may show frank hyperkalemic cardiotoxicity, with only modest elevations of serum potassium concentration, because their ionized serum calcium concentration is abnormally low. If confronted with the rare patient who is hypokalemic and who displays cramps of the forearm muscles resembling tetany, one can visualize the potential disastrous consequences of infusing calcium salts for the mistaken diagnosis of hypocalcemia. Hypernatremia may aggravate the physiologic effects of hypokalemia. However, this relationship is not nearly so important as that seen with hypercalcemia.

Possible changes in the electrocardiogram as a result of uncomplicated hypokalemia include increased AV conduction time, diminished QRS voltage, depression of the S-T segment, widening, flattening, or inversion of the T waves, and, most characteristically, the appearance of U waves. The importance of Q-T prolongation has been emphasized as a factor underlying dangerous ventricular arrhythmias. Severe potassium depletion may increase the amplitude of the P wave, prolong the P-R interval, and widen the QRS complex. At least some of these electrocardiographic changes usually will be evident when serum potassium levels fall below 2.7 mEq/liter, and these are rapidly reversible by correction of hypokalemia. Atrial arrhythmias described in hypokalemia include sinus bradycardia, premature atrial contractions, paroxysmal atrial tachycardia, junctional tachycardia, atrioventricular block, and atrial fibrillation. Ventricular arrhythmias are more important and include simple or multifocal premature contractions, ventricular fibrillation, unifocal ventricular tachycardia, and polymorphous ventricular tachycardia (*torsade des pointes*).

It is of critical importance to keep in mind that simultaneous medication with digitalis preparations markedly increases the propensity toward development of arrhythmias in hypokalemic patients. The digitalis glycosides and potassium ions apparently both compete for the same binding site on the Na, K-ATPase pump at its external surface of the cell membrane. A number of studies conducted in humans show that resistance to the toxic effects of digitalis on the heart is provided by simultaneously infusing potassium salts, and, conversely, digitalis toxicity is increased by successively lowering serum concentration of potassium ions (Fig. 4). A number of important experimental studies, now confirmed in humans, show that when potassium deficiency occurs, virtually all of the potassium ions lost are from skeletal muscle. Potassium content in the heart, brain, and almost all vital organs with the exception of the kidney remain essentially normal.

Although the mechanism whereby muscle selectively gives up its potassium during potassium depletion was obscure for a good many years, recent important studies from Denmark have shown a progressive decline in the total number of Na, K-ATPase pump units per gram of muscle tissue during progressive potassium deficiency (Fig. 5). Using ^{14}C-ouabain binding as an index of pump density in experimental animals, these investigators showed that pump density in vital organs remains normal. The interpretation of these data is that a substantial portion of a normal dose of digoxin, for example, when administered to a normal person, becomes bound to pump receptor sites in skeletal muscle, and of the quantity administered, even less will become bound to receptors in the heart. However, in the face of potassium deficiency in which pump receptor density is decreased in skeletal muscle, more of the digoxin becomes available for binding in the heart, and consequently, digitalis toxicity is more apt to occur. An additional explanation for the increased likelihood of digitalis toxicity in hypokalemia could be the result of reduced Na, K-ATPase enzyme activity in the myocardial sarcolemma. Theoretically, partial suppression of pump activity by digitalis results in two

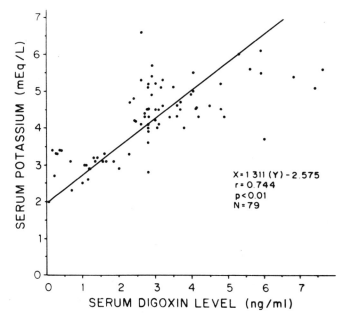

FIG. 4. Correlation of serum potassium and serum digoxin levels from 79 studies in 73 patients with arrhythmias associated with digitalis intoxication. The *r* value was significant ($p<0.01$). These data are consistent with a relation between these two factors affecting myocardial sensitivity to arrhythmia induction.

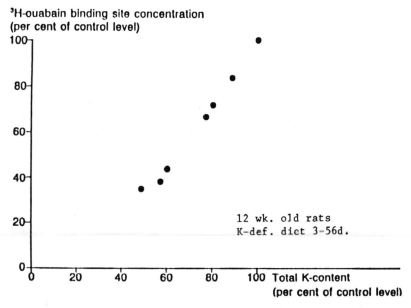

FIG. 5. A comparison of ^{3}H-ouabain binding sites (representing Na,K-ATPase pumps) in skeletal muscle of the rat and total body potassium content. (Modified from ref. 7.)

major effects that increase the concentration of calcium ions in the myoplasm, which, in turn, increases calcium binding to troponin and thus increases contractility. Maintenance of a high extracellular/intracellular sodium concentration by the pump increases the chemical potential for sodium ions to diffuse inwardly across the cell membrane. Once inside the cell, sodium ions activate the Na,K-ATPase. Since three sodium ions are pumped outwardly in exchange for two potassium ions entering the cell, the pump generates a negative intracellular voltage (which is the electrogenic effect of the pump). This electrical force also promotes passive diffusion of sodium ions from the outside toward the inside of the cell. The increased traffic of sodium ions incident to the chemical and electrical gradients tends to activate the Na,Ca exchanger and thereby maintain a very low concentration of calcium ions inside the cell. Interruption of the pump by digitalis not only reduces the chemical diffusion potential for sodium but also reduces the membrane potential and, consequently, reduces Na,Ca exchange. The result is a high intracellular calcium concentration.

Studies on skeletal muscle from potassium deficient dogs have shown that advanced potassium deficiency is associated with accumulation of calcium in the cell. This also occurs in magnesium deficiency. Potassium deficiency is associated also with an elevated intracellular sodium concentration, and, especially in the late stages of potassium deficiency, there occurs a reduced membrane potential across the cell. Thus, many of the changes induced by potassium deficiency *per se* resemble those produced independently by digitalis glycosides. It seems possible that the chemical and electrical alterations induced by potassium deficiency and digitalis therapy would become additive and help to explain, at least partially, the increased propensity for digitalis poisoning in hypokalemic patients.

An explanation for the observation that the site of potassium loss in potassium deficiency is selective for skeletal muscle is not available. Akaike is the only investigator thus far who has attempted to explain this observation. In unconfirmed studies, he showed that during the course of progressive potassium deficiency in the rat the level of hypokalemia reaches a plateau, and there occurs an increase in alpha-adrenergic catecholamine activity. The claim is made that norepinephrine interferes with uptake of potassium by potassium-deficient muscle sufficiently to prevent development of fatal hypokalemia. However, at the same time, muscle continues to release its potassium. If a substance, such as phentolamine, is administered, there is a major reduction in serum potassium concentration as it is taken up into skeletal muscle. This series of observations needs confirmation. Nevertheless, it is interesting that other investigators have shown elevated levels of norepinephrine in potassium-deficient rats. Infusion of norepinephrine into a potassium-deficient animal or human is met with resistance to the vasopressor effects of this hormone. Implications of this relationship may well apply to the next cardiovascular complication of hypokalemia, i.e., autonomic insufficiency.

Autonomic insufficiency in hypokalemia

The first description of postural hypotension and apparent autonomic insufficiency as a result of hypokalemia was published by Biglieri and McIlroy. In patients with primary aldosteronism and hypokalemia, assumption of the erect posture was associated with a marked reduction in blood pressure. Although their blood pressure fell in erect posture, their pulse rates remained slow, strongly suggesting autonomic insufficiency. The patients also showed an abnormal blood pressure response to the Valsalva maneuver and a marked resistance to the pressor effects of infused norepinephrine and angiotensin II. Other investigators have confirmed vasopressor resistance in the presence of clinical or experimental hypokalemia. Several cases of apparent hypokalemic autonomic insufficiency have been observed in patients with otherwise uncomplicated hypertension who became hypokalemic as a result of diuretic therapy. Although the precise cause and mechanism whereby autonomic insufficiency occurs in certain hypokalemic patients is unknown, it is interesting that rapid correction of hypokalemia, even over a period of hours, corrects the postural hypotension and bradycardia and restores pressor responsiveness to vasoconstrictors.

Gastrointestinal Effects

Gastrointestinal complaints are among the most common manifestations of hypokalemia. Although seldom appreciated, anorexia is one of the most important. When fed potassium-deficient diets, experimental animals quickly become anorexic. If they are young, growth either is retarded or ceases. Potassium-deficient children also grow poorly. Normal humans with mild potassium deficiency require an increased protein intake to maintain nitrogen balance. These characteristic features of potassium deficiency may represent a teleologic response to permit survival in the event that potassium becomes unavailable in the diet. Anorexia, by limiting intake of other important intracellular substances, such as phosphorus, magnesium, and protein, could permit an orderly shrinkage of cells as potassium is lost, especially from muscle, and thereby help forestall an important imbalance of intracellular constituents. Clearly, if one forcefeeds an animal a diet selectively deficient in potassium but replete in other components, potassium deficiency will appear more rapidly and be more severe. On the other hand, if an animal is allowed to consume a selectively potassium-deficient diet freely, there will occur not only losses of potassium but also net losses of phosphorus, magnesium, and nitrogen.

In patients with moderately severe potassium deficiency, symptoms of constipation are common and may progress to frank ileus with gaseous dilatation and abdominal distention. Such symptoms may occur in those who become potassium deficient as a result of diuretic therapy, vomiting, or losses mediated by renal disease. In patients who become hypokalemic as a result of acute or chronic diarrheal disorders, potassium deficiency and hypokalemia do not correct the diarrhea spontaneously.

Decreased gastrointestinal motility consequent to potassium deficiency probably reflects impaired smooth muscle function and reduced peristalsis. The entity of hypokalemic obstipation, which has received very little attention, disappears rapidly after correction of potassium deficiency.

Genitourinary Effects of Potassium Deficiency

Kaliopenic nephropathy encompasses both functional and structural abnormalities. Its most overt functional expression consists of classic findings of polydipsia, vasopressin-resistant polyuria, decreased ability to concentrate the urine, and retained ability to dilute the urine. In potassium-deficient animals, the polydipsia appears to be mediated in the central nervous system. Thus, the amount of water consumed far exceeds that necessary for excretion of solute as isotonic urine. Part of this may be explained by accumulation of dipsogenic substances in the brain, e.g., angiotensin II. One of the mechanisms to explain vasopressin resistance at the renal tubular site in potassium deficiency is overproduction of prostaglandins.

The increase in urine osmolality and decreased urine volume that would be anticipated during administration of vasopressin to a water-loaded normal subject or experimental animal can be reduced substantially or eliminated by a simultaneous infusion of PGE_2. Nevertheless, there is considerable disagreement about the role of PGE_2 in the polyuria of potassium deficiency. Thus, experimental studies have failed to show an increase of PGE excretion in humans with a potassium deficit of 225 mEq. Perhaps one would not anticipate endocrine changes of any importance or alterations of autocoid production in such mild potassium deficiency in humans. Although PGE_2 production has been reported to be increased in potassium-deficient dogs, increased production in potassium-deficient rats and rabbits has not been demonstrated. In studies conducted on rats and rabbits, potassium deficiency has been mild or modest. In our own experience with a large number of potassium-deficient dogs, polyuria disappears completely within 1 or 2 hr after administration of agents that impair PGE_2 production, such as acetylsalicylic acid or indomethacin. The possible relationship of enhanced PGE_2 production, impaired renal concentrating ability, and impairment of response to vasopressin deserves study in other animals with more severe potassium deficiency. The classic syndrome of nephrogenic diabetes insipidus with vasopressin-resistant polyuria as a result of hypokalemia has been observed in its overt form only on rare occasions in humans.

Vacuolar nephropathy, characterized by the appearance of vacuolar lesions in the proximal tubular epithelium, has been observed in patients with long-standing potassium deficiency and also in those in whom potassium depletion has occurred rapidly, e.g., in Asiatic cholera. Interstitial fibrosis and tubular atrophy also have been described. A reduction in glomerular filtration rate has been reported in human subjects experimentally depleted of potassium. Nevertheless, most of these abnormalities appear to be reversed after several weeks of potassium repletion. The fact that structural and permanent functional changes as a result of potassium deficiency appear to be inconsistent and rare events in patients with hypokalemia suggests that, when they occur, other factors may underly their occurrence. For example, recent evidence suggests that enhanced ammonium production as a result of potassium deficiency may play a role in experimental tubular injury. In addition, decreased ureteral peristalsis and ureteral dilatation have been reported in a potassium-deficient patient which were reversed by appropriate treatment. Since potassium deficiency appears to affect other smooth muscle structures in a similar fashion, it seems likely that ureteral dysfunction shares a similar mechanism.

Although never formally reported in the literature or submitted to experimental study, it has been observed that dilatation of the bladder and possibly impaired emptying of the bladder may occur as a result of potassium deficiency.

Pyelonephritis in potassium deficiency

It has been suggested that patients with chronic potassium deficiency are more susceptible to urinary tract infections. Beeson and Rowley showed that the ambient concentration of ammonia in the renal medulla from normal humans producing an acid urine was sufficient to inhibit complement. They postulated that this could be the mechanism permitting growth of bacteria in such medullary tissue *in vitro*, whereas growth of the same organisms was inhibited under conditions of a higher or alkaline pH. Recent evidence suggests that reduction of tissue NH_3 levels in potassium-deficient rats by administration of $NaHCO_3$ reduces the interstitial damage that otherwise occurs. Thereby, NH_3 toxicity has been cited as a factor producing anatomic damage in the potassium-deficient kidney. It is known that anatomic damage in the medulla of the rat predisposes to bacterial pyelonephritis. I have observed this putative relationship between hypokalemia and pyelonephritis in a 45-year-old man with malignant hypertension associated with secondary hyperaldosteronism. Each time this patient became hypokalemic, he developed acute symptomatic pyelonephritis as a result of *Escherichia coli* infection. As long as he was maintained normokalemic, he did not show evidence of urinary tract infection.

Central Nervous System Dysfunction in Hypokalemia

Confusion, disorientation, and memory loss have been described in patients with hypokalemia. Such observations were based mainly on clinical notation and did not examine the effect of potassium repletion. Patients with severe hypokalemia very commonly have associated severe disease. Disturbances of volume regulation, disturbances of glucose metabolism, or acid-base disorders could well contribute to disordered cerebral function. Thus, there is no proof that potassium deficiency *per se* alters cerebral function. Perhaps the best evidence that potassium deficiency does not influence cerebral function is the fact that it is seldom observed in people who become hypokalemic as the result of diuretic therapy.

Metabolic Disturbances in Potassium Deficiency (4,25,27,32)

Overproduction of Ammonia by the Kidney

Ammonia production by the kidney increases in response to potassium deficiency. In fact, ammonia production in potassium-deficient patients may approach levels seen in patients with diabetic ketoacidosis. One theoretical explanation is intracellular acidosis. During potassium depletion, potassium ions lost from the cytoplasm of the cell[2] are replaced partially by sodium and partially by hydrogen ions so that the pH falls. In turn, intracellular acidosis is thought to increase ammonia production. Ammonia is highly diffusible and distributes itself freely throughout the substance of the kidney. As sodium ions are reabsorbed from the tubular lumen in exchange for hydrogen ions from the cytoplasm of the renal tubular cell, ammonia interacts with H^+ and is converted to ammonium (NH_4^+). Since the ammonium ion is essentially nonreabsorbable from the tubular lumen, it will be excreted into the urine. Because some of the hydrogen ions secreted into the tubular lumen are incorporated into ammonium and are, therefore, no longer free, the pH of the urine rises in subjects made potassium deficient.

Ammonia Production and Increased Nitrogen Requirements

Although increased ammonia production by the kidney in potassium deficiency may, in a teleologic sense, be beneficial in that NH^+ may serve to conserve K^+ ions, the increased nitrogen requirements for ammonia production may at times become critically important. Walker et al. studied the effects of mild potassium deficiency on nitrogen balance in humans who were healthy except for essential hypertension. Human subjects in good health can maintain nitrogen balance if they ingest as little as 0.5 g of protein per kg

---

[2]Older studies on potassium-deficient rats claimed that total renal potassium content remained normal. More recent studies indicate that renal tubular cells do indeed become potassium deficient.

body weight per day. Employing balance techniques, it was shown that normal subjects consuming such a protein intake showed an initial net loss of nitrogen but came into balance on the fourth or fifth day. However, using the same diet after depleting subjects of approximately 250 mEq of potassium by administration of furosemide, nitrogen balance remained negative until potassium stores were repleted. It was shown that the entire deficit of nitrogen was explained by that quantity required for enhanced ammonia production. In the study by Walker et al., urinary losses of NH_4^+ fell from 200 mmol/day to 85 mmol/day after potassium deficiency was corrected. Clinical observations on children with hypokalemia due to renal tubular defects or ureterosigmoidostomy show that they do not grow normally but that their growth is restored to normal by correction of hypokalemia. The precise meaning of this information is twofold. If protein intake is marginal, a potassium-deficient subject will undergo muscle atrophy because skeletal muscle protein will be mobilized to provide precursors for ammonia synthesis by the kidney. Second, since a positive nitrogen balance is mandatory for normal growth, by stimulating losses of NH_4^+ into the urine, potassium deficiency increases the quantity of nitrogen required to permit growth or cellular repair. A host of other factors obviously could be involved under such conditions. For example, potassium deficiency sharply reduces insulin secretion. The anabolic effect of insulin has been well established. Thus, reduction of insulin supplies could contribute to the catabolic state.

Potassium Deficiency and Hepatic Encephalopathy

When effective diuretics became available for clinical use several decades ago, it was discovered that hypokalemia in patients with cirrhosis of the liver and ascites might bear some relationship to the complication of hepatic encephalopathy. Important studies on this issue were published by Shear and Gabuzda. They examined patients with alcoholic cirrhosis to determine if potassium deficiency induced by diuretics increased ammonia production by the kidney and if this were related to induction of hepatic coma. When hypokalemia was induced by administration of a mercurial diuretic, there followed a fourfold increase in the renal venous NH_3 level. Renal venous NH_3 fell promptly after administration of potassium. These changes were independent of arterial pH. Correlations were made among hypokalemia, hyperammonemia, and hepatic coma.

Continued observations since those studies show that several interesting conditions must exist in a hypokalemic patient with severe liver disease to permit accumulation of NH_3 in the blood and cause hepatic coma.

First, such patients almost always have severe liver disease and are forming edema and ascites and, as a result, receive a diuretic. Aldosterone production is increased because of volume contraction. Potassium deficiency occurs by means of enhanced tubular exchange of sodium and potassium ions. Although some of the edema fluid may be mobilized as an initial response to the diuretic, the drug's effect generally becomes negligible so that the urine becomes essentially sodium free. Because of volume contraction, Na^+ ions are reabsorbed almost completely in the proximal nephron. Since hydrogen ions entering the tubular urine depend on exchange for sodium, hydrogen secretion is virtually halted in distal tubular sites because the urine is sodium free. Therefore, in the absence of Na,H exchange, the urine pH does not become sufficiently acid to entrap NH_3 by converting it to NH_4^+. Thus, the urinary acidification defect in patients with cirrhosis and ascites becomes critically important as a factor allowing NH_3 to diffuse into the renal venous blood and enter the systemic circulation. The next critical prerequisite in the sequence of events leading to NH_3 poisoning is the sick liver itself. Normally, any NH_3 gaining access to the systemic circulation would be instantly metabolized to urea in the liver. Since the liver is seriously diseased, this does not occur, and the result is hyperammonemia and ammonia intoxication. Thus, the critical steps in this process are as follows:

1. Potassium deficiency causes increased NH_3 production by the kidney.
2. Lack of adequate Na^+ delivery to the distal tubular site prevents exchange for H^+.
3. Impaired conversion of NH_3 to NH_4.
4. Impaired excretion of NH_3 as NH_4.
5. Return of NH_3 to the circulation.
6. Inability of the liver to metabolize NH_3 to urea.
7. Ammonia intoxication.

Figure 6 shows pertinent observations made by Shear and Gabuzda on a 40-year-old woman with alcoholic cirrhosis. She had become hypokalemic as a result of diarrhea and a poor potassium intake. She demonstrated classic neurologic findings of hepatic coma. Her serum potassium was 2.7 mEq/liter. As her hypokalemia resolved with KCl, her NH_3 level fell and her neurologic status became normal. Thereupon, the KCl was stopped, thiazide treatment was initiated, and the patient once again became hypokalemic and comatose. The neurologic abnormalties again resolved on correction of hypokalemia. Fig. 7 shows the relationship between hypokalemia and blood ammonia levels.

The urine acidification defect in patients with cirrhosis and ascites has been well described. Indeed, it can be corrected quickly if a substance is infused that will enhance distal tubular delivery of Na^+ ions, e.g., mannitol, which in turn will permit exchange for H^+ and enhance excretion of NH_4^+.

Because of the reasons outlined, diuretics favoring K^+ retention are ideal for use in patients with liver disease and ascites. These include spironolactone, amiloride, and triamterene. Most cases of hepatic coma associated with diuretic therapy have occurred with the use of thiazide diuretics, chlorthali-

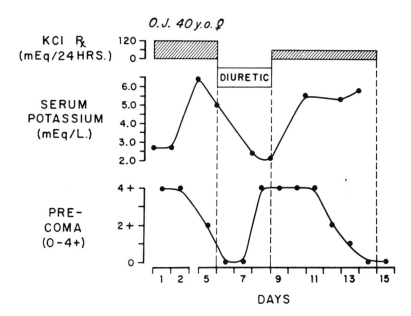

FIG. 6. Precipitation of hepatic coma by hypokalemia, which attended administration of diuretic agent. Potassium deficiency and coma on day 1 (time of hospitalization) appeared by history to have resulted from low dietary intake and enteric losses (diarrhea).

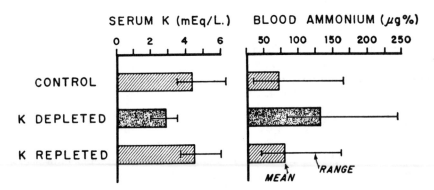

FIG. 7. Changes in serum potassium and blood ammonium concentrations with diuresis and subsequent repletion of potassium deficits. Overlap is apparent between control and potassium depletion values for the grouped data shown here. However, increments and decrements in values from five patients were statistically significant.

done and metolazone. Obviously, diuretic therapy in such patients should be conducted carefully with close monitoring for hypokalemia.

Carbohydrate Metabolism in Potassium Deficiency (10–14,16,18,20,23)

Glucose Intolerance and Kaliopenic Diabetes Mellitus

That potassium deficiency may be associated with glucose intolerance is well established. Although this is an old observation, this phenomenon did not stimulate widespread interest until thiazide diuretics became available for clinical use. It was discovered that some patients treated with thiazides for edema who had a positive family history of diabetes mellitus developed overt diabetes, and some patients who had established diabetes mellitus became worse. Although some evidence was obtained to suggest that thiazides themselves interfered with glucose utilization, it is important to note that only when large doses were employed or, especially, when the drug was injected as an intravenous bolus along with a glucose load was glucose intolerance noted. It was quickly appreciated that deterioration of glucose metabolism in the diabetic or the development of impaired glucose utilization in normal subjects associated with thiazide therapy was clearly related to potassium deficiency. Thus, it was shown that this phenomenon could be reversed by administration of potassium chloride supplements or that it did not occur if hypokalemia were prevented.

The mechanism underlying potassium deficiency-associated glucose intolerance appears to be a deficit of insulin release in response to hyperglycemia. Studies on patients with primary aldosteronism who also demonstrated glucose intolerance established that potassium deficiency reduced peak insulin levels following glucose infusions. If potassium levels in these patients were restored to normal, insulin release also became normal. Later studies by Gaynor et al. suggest that prostaglandins may be involved in suppressing insulin release that otherwise occurs in response to hyperglycemia. Based on studies showing that infusions of prostaglandins in conjunction with glucose markedly reduce insulin secretion by the beta cell, the possible role of overproduction of prostaglandins was examined in potassium-deficient dogs. Evidence suggests that in the presence of severe potassium deficiency, prostaglandin production becomes excessive and, as such, may be responsible for several events. One of these is polyuria that disappears very rapidly in a potassium-deficient dog after administration of either indomethacin or acetylsalicylic acid. Figure 8 illustrates studies on insulin and glucose responses during hyperglycemia in normal and potassium-deficient dogs. They show clearly that insulin release is impaired by potassium deficiency and is associated with a decreased rate of glucose disappearance from plasma following intravenous infusion. Figure 9 shows that after administration of acetylsalicylic

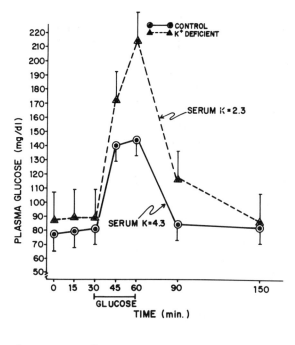

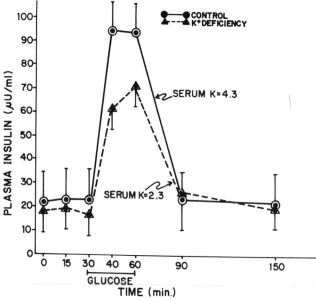

FIG. 8.   Top: Hypokalemia is associated with glucose intolerance. **Bottom:** Reduction of insulin levels in hyperglycemic, hypokalemic dogs.

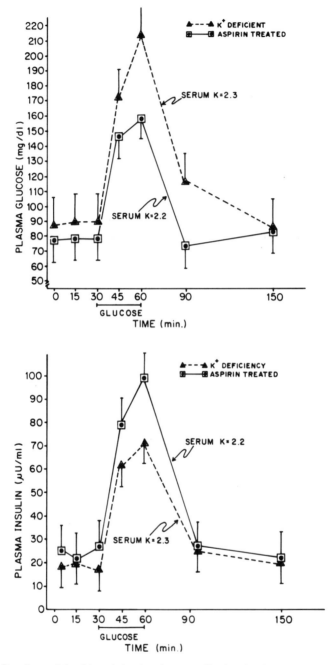

FIG. 9. Despite sustained hypokalemia, glucose utilization (**top**) and insulin release (**bottom**) are corrected by administration of acetysalicylic acid before the glucose infusion.

acid, although hypokalemia is unaffected, both insulin release and glucose utilization are restored to normal. (The controversy on whether or not increased prostaglandin production results from potassium deficiency is discussed in the section describing the genitourinary effects of hypokalemia.)

In potassium-deficient dogs, serum potassium levels averaged 2.2 mEq/ liter, which represents a total body potassium deficiency of at least 20% or more. It is interesting to note reports from the literature from the 1920s and 1930s describing an occasional patient whose diabetes mellitus was cured with acetylsalicylic acid. It was speculated that glucose utilization increased, since acetylsalicylic acid caused uncoupling of oxidative phosphorylation and, therefore, would explain increased glucose utilization rates. However, it is noteworthy that in those reports, the patients were usually young and had what we now know is insulin-deficiency type diabetes mellitus. It seems possible that they were also potassium deficient and were overproducing prostaglandins because of volume depletion and potassium deficiency and that suppression of prostaglandin overproduction by acetylsalicylic acid improved insulin release and thereby ameliorated their diabetes. Since we have no specific information from those patients described 50 years ago, this notion must be regarded as highly hypothetical. However, it coincides with data obtained on experimental animals. It is also of interest that glucose utilization by skeletal muscle under conditions of severe potassium deficiency appears to be within normal limits. In dogs with potassium deficiency ranging between 20% and 30% of body stores, using the isolated perfused gracilis muscle, it can be shown that basal glucose utilization rates are within normal limits and, during stimulated exercise, glucose utilization remains normal. Lactate production at rest and during exercise is also normal in terms of the amount produced from glucose.

Glycogen Metabolism in Potassium Deficiency

The major defect in carbohydrate metabolism by skeletal muscle in potassium deficiency is a reduced content of muscle glycogen. Older studies on several species of experimental animals establish clearly that potassium stores are necessary to maintain normal glycogen levels in skeletal muscle. Studies on potassium-deficient rats clearly showed that muscle glycogen content fell during potassium depletion. Nevertheless, this study was potentially flawed because of two problems. The first is that rats, like other animals, when fed a potassium-deficient diet, become anorectic and lose weight. Thus, partial starvation and weight loss could independently reduce muscle glycogen content. Second, the rat is not a good experimental model of potassium deficiency in humans; e.g., the rat, despite severe hypokalemia, neither becomes paralyzed nor develops rhabdomyolysis. Glycogen levels in normal rat muscle are only about one-tenth that which exists in dogs or humans. Thus, the dog is apparently the most representative experimental model to characterize the effects of potassium deficiency in humans. Studies by Blachley et al. have established that dogs fed a potassium-deficient diet by gavage to ensure normal intake of all other components show a marked fall in muscle glycogen content to levels that are barely measurable. Second, dogs, like humans, normally show a marked overproduction and accumulation of glycogen in skeletal muscle after a single bout of exhaustive exercise. Figure 10 shows that this phenomenon, known as "glycogen supercompensation," is eliminated by potassium deficiency. Finally, human subjects with diuretic-induced hypokalemia show a reduction of muscle glycogen content.

The precise mechanism whereby potassium deficiency reduces muscle glycogen content has not been clearly established. However, studies on rat liver from potassium-deficient animals suggest that sodium accumulation in cells increases the activity of phosphorylase phosphatase, which serves to increase glycogen turnover. Perhaps it is the sodium poisoning inside the muscle cell more than potassium deficiency itself that results in inability to store glycogen. Because these studies were conducted in rats, their relevance to potassium deficiency in humans or dogs remains unclear.

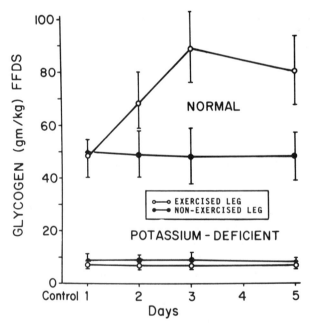

FIG. 10. Effect of potassium deficiency on muscle glycogen content at rest and after exercise. Muscle glycogen content rises (supercompensation) after a single bout of exhaustive exercise in the normal dog in the exercised but not the unexercised muscle. In potassium-deficient dogs, base-line values for muscle glycogen become very low and show no change after exercise.

The clinical implications of disordered carbohydrate metabolism in potassium-deficient humans are fairly clear. It seems obvious that one can induce overt diabetes mellitus in a patient with mild, otherwise controlled diabetes or induce a state of glucose intolerance in a normal subject by any mechanism that induces potassium deficiency. In both situations, glucose metabolism rapidly returns to normal by correction of potassium deficiency. That prostaglandin overproduction might be responsible for reduced insulin release under conditions of potassium deficiency is suggested by studies on dogs but remains to be proven in human beings with potassium deficiency and glucose intolerance.

Perhaps the most important correlation of potassium deficiency is the relationship of glycogen storage to increased susceptibility to rhabdomyolysis if exercise is performed by potassium-deficient subjects. Elimination of glycogen stores from skeletal muscle obviates one of the most important adaptations to physical conditioning. Muscle glycogen content in a trained subject increases from about 1% wet weight to as high as 5% wet weight. Since glycogen is the major fuel for anaerobic exercise during sustained work, it becomes evident why endurance is limited by potassium deficiency. Reduced endurance coupled with exhaustive exercise would lower the threshold level for development of muscle cell necrosis. In a sense, rhabdomyolysis in the glycogen-depleted potassium-deficient subject resembles rhabdomyolysis in the person with McArdle's syndrome. In McArdle's syndrome, although muscle glycogen content is abnormally high, the absence of muscle phosphorylase prevents its utilization so that during exercise, cramps and rhabdomyolysis are anticipated events.

Edema in Potassium Deficiency

If a normal human subject or an experimental animal is selectively deprived of potassium in the diet, there will follow a net retention of sodium ions that partially replace potassium losses from cell water. Keeping in mind that intracellular chloride concentration varies inversely with the negative charge inside the cell, it has been shown that as potassium deficiency becomes severe and muscle membrane potential falls, there occurs a net cellular uptake of chloride ions. Thus, there is a net retention of sodium chloride in a potassium-deficient subject. This is not necessarily associated with edema, however. Edema in potassium-deficient patients usually appears during the early period of treatment with potassium salts. It has been described for the most part in people who became hypokalemic as a result of vomiting or diarrhea. It is seen less seldom in those who have become potassium deficient as a result of diuretic therapy. The latter would appear to be the result of the saluretic effect of the diuretic. Nevertheless, if the diuretic is suddenly stopped, edema can occur in transient fashion and will disappear when potassium retention is sufficient to correct the deficit. This pattern of intermittent hypokalemia followed by transient edema is characteristic of patients who surreptitiously abuse diuretics.

Clinical observations on edema associated with potassium deficiency resulting from laxative abuse or diarrhea have led to the proposal that this phenomenon can be explained on the basis of glomerular filtration rate or increased Na,H exchange between the renal tubule and renal tubular cell. Perhaps the most enlightening study was performed by Lennon and Lemann. Using human volunteers, these investigators induced potassium deficiency by administering ammonium chloride. When ammonium chloride was stopped, the investigators separated their subjects into two groups, one receiving a diet containing normal amounts of potassium chloride and another the same diet deficient in potassium. Those receiving the potassium supplement rapidly returned to their base-line weight. Those continuing to ingest the potassium-free diet gained up to 3 kg above their base-line weight and accumulated 750 mEq of sodium and 625 of chloride. They showed pitting edema by the sixth or seventh day of the potassium-deficient diet, at which point their potassium loss averaged about 305 mEq. Creatinine clearance was clearly elevated in both groups of subjects. In addition, urinary aldosterone excretion was less in the group ingesting the potassium-free diet, suggesting that neither reduced glomerular filtration rate nor excessive aldosterone production was responsible for the salt and water retention. Simultaneous measurements of acid balance indicated that enhanced Na,H exchange across the tubule could not explain their observations. Experimental studies on potassium-deficient dogs show decreased glomerular filtration rate and increased rates of sodium chloride reabsorption. All of the experimental observations show that the occurrence of edema in potassium-deficient subjects is markedly attentuated by administration of sufficient potassium salts to correct the deficit.

Unfortunately, the precise cause of edema in potassium deficiency remains poorly defined. Since potassium deficiency possibly affects secretion and metabolism of a number of peptides and hormones capable of affecting sodium and chloride excretion, the phenomenon would appear to be a useful area for continuing investigation.

HYPERKALEMIA

Symptomatic manifestations of hyperkalemia are mostly cardiovascular and neuromuscular. The symptoms of hyperkalemia are not specific and are often those related to the underlying disease that caused hyperkalemia. Hyperkalemia almost never occurs in the absence of renal insufficiency. The rare exceptions to this rule are those in which large doses of potassium chloride or other potassium salts have been mistakenly infused intravenously or potassium salts of drugs, such as penicillin, have been infused rapidly in large quantities. It is of interest that hyperkalemia induced by infusing potassium salts into experimental animals reduces bicarbonate reabsorption by the proximal nephron and, as a result, causes acute hyperkalemic metabolic acidosis. Chronic hyperkalemic states may be associated with reductions of ammonia production by the kidney so that excretion of hydrogen ions by this important mechanism is eliminated. This particular set of circumstances has been observed in patients with type IV renal tubular acidosis, in whom elimination of hyperkalemia by administration of disodium polystyrene sulfonate (Kayexalate) leads to increased ammonia production and reduction of metabolic acidosis.

Cardiovascular Effects of Hyperkalemia

The most important effects of hyperkalemia are cardiovascular. Classic electrocardiographic findings occur in the following order:

1. Increased T Wave amplitude in the presence of a normal or a decreased Q-T segment.
2. Increased duration of the P-R segment.
3. Disappearance of the P wave.
4. Prolongation of the QRS complex.
5. Development of a sine wave that may precede ventricular flutter, fibrillation, or standstill.

Cardiotoxic hyperkalemia, complete heart block, and Stokes-Adams attacks have been observed in patients with primary hypoaldosteronism. Some patients with parkinsonism are unable to produce aldosterone normally and may manifest similar findings. It is important to realize that hyperkalemic cardiotoxicity may result in electrocardiographic changes that resemble an acute myocardial infarction. Thus, elevation of the J point with coving of the S-T segment may replicate changes seen on acute myocardial injury. These changes disappear quickly on correction of hyperkalemia or infusion of calcium salts so as to oppose the electrical effects of hyperkalemia.

It is critically important to realize that for any given level of hyperkalemia, the electrical abnormalities will be worse in the presence of either a low sodium concentration or a low calcium concentration (Fig. 11). In contrast, a person with frank hyperkalemia who is also hypercalcemic, such as may exist in patients with Addison's disease, may show relatively few electrocardiographic changes of hyperkalemia. Perhaps the most profound electrocardiographic abnormalities of hyperkalemia occur in patients with acute renal failure because of the frequent association of severe hypocalcemia. It must be emphasized that improvement of electrocardiographic changes of hyperkalemia treated by insulin or alkalinization with bicarbonate infusion occurs as a result of reducing serum potassium concentration. By contrast, correction of

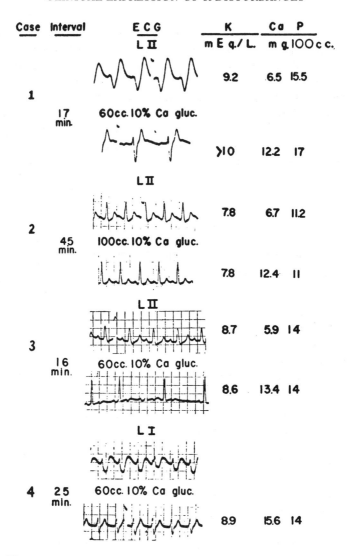

FIG. 11. Effects on the electrocardiograms of four uremic patients with advanced potassium intoxication of intravenous infusion of calcium.

hyperkalemic electrocardiographic toxicity with calcium does not produce reductions of serum potassium concentration.

Skeletal Muscle in Hyperkalemia

In the presence of a rising serum potassium concentration, patients may complain of paresthesias and demonstrate muscular fasciculations. Tremulousness and fasciculations probably represent the electrical effects of reducing the resting membrane potential to a level that approaches the activation potential of the skeletal muscle cells. Under such conditions, spike potentials are of sufficient magnitude to depolarize the muscle cell and result in local contractions. As hyperkalemia becomes more advanced, the patient may demonstrate ascending or Landry type paralysis and eventually flaccid quadriplegia. In a classic instance, there will be preservation of cerebral and cranial nerve function and a notable absence of respiratory paralysis. Nevertheless, diaphragm and intercostal muscle paralysis may occur and be responsible for death.

REFERENCES

1. Akaike, N. (1981): Sodium pump in skeletal muscle central nervous system-induced suppression by α-adrenoreceptors. *Science*, 213:1252–1254.
2. Beeson, P. B., and Rowley, D. (1959): The anticomplementary effect of kidney tissue: Its association with ammonia production. *J. Exp. Med.*, 110:695–698.
3. Berl, T. (1980): Water metabolism in potassium depletion. *Miner. Electrolyte Metab.*, 4:209–215.
4. Better, O. S., Goldschmid, Z., Chaimowitz, C., and Alroy, G. G. (1972): Defect of urinary acidification in cirrhosis. *Arch. Intern. Med.*, 130:77–83.
5. Biglieri, E. G., and McIlroy, B. B. (1966): Abnormalities of renal function and circulatory reflexes in primary aldosteronism. *Circulation*, 303:78–86.
6. Bilbrey, G. L., Herbin, L., Carter, N. W., and Knochel, S. P. (1973): Skeletal muscle resting membrane potential in potassium deficiency. *J. Clin. Invest.*, 52:3011–3018.
7. Clausen, T., Kjeldsen, K., and Norgaard, A. (1985): Acute and long-term regulation of the Na,K pump in skeletal muscle. In: *The Sodium Pump*, edited by I. M. Glynn and J. C. Ellory, pp. 707–711. Company of Biologists, Ltd., Cambridge.
8. Cunningham, J. N. Jr., Carter, N. W., Rector, F. C. Jr., and Seldin, D. W. (1971): Resting transmembrane potential difference of skeletal muscle in normal subjects and severely ill patients. *J. Clin. Invest.*, 50:49.
9. Fourman, P. (1954): Experimental observations on the tetany of potassium deficiency. *Lancet*, 2:525–528.
10. Fourman, P., and Hervey, G. R. (1955): An experimental study of edema in potassium deficiency. *Clin. Sci.*, 14:75–97.
11. Galvez, O. G., Roberts, B. W., Bay, W. H., et al. (1976): Studies of the mechanism of polyuria with hypokalemia. *Kidney Int.*, 10:583.
12. Gardner, L. I., Talbot, N. B., Cook, C. D., Berman, H., and Uribe, C. (1950): The effect of potassium deficiency on carbohydrate metabolism. *J. Lab. Clin. Med.*, 35:592–602.
13. Gaynor, M. L., Ferguson, E. R., and Knochel, J. P. (1982): The effect of prostaglandin synthesis inhibitors on glucose tolerance in potassium deficiency. *Clin. Res.*, 30:571.
14. Helderman, J. H., Elahi, D., Andersen, D. K., et al. (1983): Prevention of the glucose intolerance of thiazide diuretics by maintenance of body potassium. *Diabetes*, 32:106–111.
15. Knochel, J. P. (1986): Clinical effects of potassium deficiency on skeletal muscle. In: *Potassium in Cardiovascular and Renal Medicine*, edited by P. K. Whelton, A. Whelton, and W. G. Walker, pp. 97–109. Marcel Dekker, New York.
16. Knochel, J. P. (1987): Metabolism and potassium. In: *Current Topics in Membranes and Transport. Potassium Transport: Physiology and Pathophysiology*, edited by G. Giebisch, pp. 383–400. Academic Press, Orlando, FL.
17. Knochel, J. P., and Carter, N. W. (1976): The role of muscle cell injury in the pathogenesis of acute renal failure after exercise. *Kidney Int.*, 10:S-58–S-64.
18. Knochel, J. P., and Schlein, E. M. (1972): On the mechanism of rhabdomyolysis in potassium depletion. *J. Clin. Invest.*, 51:1750–1758.

19. Layzer, R. B. (1985): Mineral and electrolyte disorders. In: *Neuromuscular Manifestations of Systemic Disease*, pp. 47–54. Davis, Philadelphia.
20. Lennon, E. J., and Lemann, J. Jr. (1968): The effect of a potassium-deficient diet on the pattern of recovery from experimental metabolic acidosis. *Clin. Sci.*, 34:365–378.
21. Muchrcke, R. C. (1960): Prolonged potassium deficiency in chronic pyelonephritis in man and animals. In: *Biology of Pyelonephritis*, pp. 581–603. Little, Brown, Boston.
22. Richardson, R. M. A., and Kunau, R. T. Jr. (1985): Potassium deficiency and intoxication. In: *The Kidney: Physiology and Pathophysiology*, edited by D. W. Seldin and G. Giebisch, pp. 1251–1267. Raven Press, New York.
23. Robertson, P. (1983): Hypothesis: PGE, carbohydrate homeostasis, and insulin secretion. *Diabetes*, 32:231–234.
24. Ruder, M. A., Flaker, G. C., Alpert, M. A., and Bertuso, J. (1985): Hypokalemia as a cause of cardiac arrest: Results of electrophysiologic testing and long-term follow-up. *Am. Heart J.*, 110:490–491.
25. Sastrasinh, S., and Tannen, R. L. (1981): Mechanism by which enhanced ammonia production reduces urinary potassium excretion. *Kidney Int.*, 20:326–331.
26. Shapiro, W. (1978): Correlative studies of serum digitalis levels and the arrhythmias of digitalis intoxication. *Am. J. Cardiol.*, 41:852–859.
27. Shear, L., and Gabuzda, G. J. (1979): Potassium deficiency and endogenous ammonium overload from kidney. *Am. J. Clin. Nutr.*, 23:614–618.
28. Streicher, H. Z., Gabow, P. A., Moss, A. H., Kono, D., and Kaehny, W. D (1981): Syndromes of toluene sniffing in adults. *Ann. Intern. Med.*, 94:758–762.
29. Surawicz, B. (1967): Relationship between electrocardiogram and electrolytes. *Am. Heart J.*, 73:814.
30. Sweadner, K. J., and Goldin, S. M. (1980): Active transport of sodium and potassium ions. *N. Engl. J. Med.*, 302:777–783.
31. Tolins, J. P., Hostetter, M. K., and Hostetter, T. H. (1987): Hypokalemic nephropathy in the rat: Role of ammonia in chronic tubular injury. *J. Clin. Invest.*, 79:1447–1458.
32. Walker, W. G., Sapir, D. G., Turin, M., and Cheng, J. T. (1973): Potassium homeostasis and diuretic therapy. In: *Modern Diuretic Therapy*, edited by A. F. Lant and G. M. Wilson, pp. 331–342. Excerpta Medica, Amsterdam.

General Review Articles

33. De Fronzo, R. A., and Bia, M. (1985): Extrarenal potassium homeostasis. In: *The Kidney: Physiology and Pathophysiology*, edited by D. W. Seldin and G. Giebisch, pp. 1179–1206. Raven Press, New York.
34. Epstein, F. H. (1980): Signs and symptoms of electrolyte disorders. In: *Clinical Disorders of Fluid and Electrolyte Metabolism*, edited by M. H. Maxwell and C. R. Kleeman, pp. 499–530. McGraw-Hill, New York.
35. Knochel, J. P. (1982): Neuromuscular manifestations of electrolyte disorders. *Am. J. Med.*, 72:521–535.
36. Roy, D. R., and Jamison, R. L. (1985): Countercurrent system and its regulation. In: *The Kidney: Physiology and Pathophysiology*, edited by D. W. Seldin and G. Giebisch, pp. 903–932. Raven Press, New York.
37. Sterns, R. H., Cox, M., Feig, P. U., and Singer, I. (1981): Internal potassium balance and the control of the plasma potassium concentration. *Medicine*, 60:339–354.

The Regulation of Potassium Balance, edited by Donald W. Seldin and Gerhard Giebisch, Raven Press, Ltd., New York © 1989.

10

Potassium Deficiency: Pathogenesis and Treatment

Victor L. Schuster

Department of Internal Medicine and Veterans Administration Medical Center, University of Iowa, Iowa City, Iowa 52242

Definitions: Hypokalemia Versus Potassium Depletion
Etiologies of Hypokalemia Without Potassium Depletion
  Alkalemia—Bicarbonate Administration • Insulin • Beta-Adrenergic Drugs • Periodic Paralysis • Miscellaneous Causes
Cellular Potassium Depletion with Hypokalemia: Cell K/N Low
  Measurement of Total Body Potassium and Exchangeable Potassium • Dietary Insufficiency • Enhanced Gastrointestinal Loss • Enhanced Renal Loss
Potassium Depletion without Hypokalemia: Cell K/N Normal
Potassium Depletion without Hypokalemia: Cell K/N Low
Treatment of Established Potassium Depletion
  Prevention of Hypokalemia and K Depletion
References

Hypokalemia and potassium depletion are serious clinical manifestations of a substantial number of disease states. The prevalence of severe potassium depletion in a population of hospital inpatients has been estimated from a survey of serum potassium concentrations in over 58,000 inpatients. Assuming that a serum K less than 2.5 mEq/liter reflects substantial intracellular K depletion, fully 1% of the patients surveyed had such a degree of K depletion. Obviously, milder degrees of depletion are even more common. Thus, all clinicians must understand the etiology, pathogenesis, and treatment of hypokalemia and K depletion.

DEFINITIONS: HYPOKALEMIA VERSUS POTASSIUM DEPLETION (15–19)

Table 1 provides several definitions critical to understanding clinical disorders of K metabolism. The term "hypokalemia" refers only to a reduction in the serum K concentration. Although hypokalemia may reflect decreased intracellular K concentration, it need not; tissue K concentrations may be perfectly normal.

The term "potassium depletion" means that the amount of K inside cells is reduced, i.e., there is depletion of total body K stores. This can occur in one of two ways; either (1) K is lost but tissue (particularly muscle) mass is not or (2) K is lost in proportion to loss of tissue mass. The latter has sometimes been referred to as "pseudodepletion" because it has somewhat different pathophysiologic implications from true depletion. In either case, the serum K concentration is most often low but may be normal or high.

One way to conceptualize the difference between true K depletion and pseudodepletion is to consider the intracellular potassium/nitrogen (K/N) ratio. Potassium lost from cells in excess of intracellular proteins would lower the intracellular K/N ratio, whereas commensurate loss of K and tissue proteins would leave the intracellular K/N ratio constant. It must be emphasized that we use the K/N ratio here as a convenient shorthand way to differentiate the pathophysiology in these two conditions. Although the intracellular K/N ratio in normal tissue has certainly been measured (it is about 3), the ratio is not clinically available. It does represent, however, a useful framework within which to consider the pathophysiology of K depletion and, as such, is used in this chapter.

"Redistribution" refers to the transfer of K from the serum into cells. Because the ratio of intracellular/extracellular K content is about 50:1, even if one could transfer all extracellular K into the intracellular compartment (a lethal thought-experiment, incidentally), this maneuver would raise the intra-

TABLE 1. *Hypokalemia and potassium depletion: Definitions*

Term	Definition
Hypokalemia	Low concentration of serum K; normal or low intracellular K concentration.
Potassium depletion	Loss of intracellular K; cell potassium/nitrogen ratio may be low (↓ K/N) or normal (nl K/N); serum K may be low, normal, or high
Redistribution	Transfer of K from serum into cells; cell K/N is normal

cellular K concentration by a trivial amount. Thus, as shown in Table 1, redistribution results in a normal cell K/N ratio.

ETIOLOGIES OF HYPOKALEMIA WITHOUT POTASSIUM DEPLETION

Table 2 shows general categories by etiologies for hypokalemia and K depletion. We start our discussion by considering the pathophysiology of hypokalemia without cellular K depletion, i.e., redistribution of K from the extracellular to the intracellular space. This process is discussed in Chapter 1, and here we concern ourselves with the more clinically relevant causes of K redistribution.

Alkalemia—Bicarbonate Administration

Alkalemia, i.e., an elevation in arterial pH, is associated with a mild degree of shift of K into cells. Although many older textbooks give the impression

TABLE 2. *Etiologies of hypokalemia and potassium depletion*

Hypokalemia without K depletion: Cell K/N normal
Alkalemia/bicarbonate administration
Insulin
Beta-adrenergic drugs
Periodic paralysis
Miscellaneous
K depletion with hypokalemia: Cell K/N low
Dietary insufficiency
Enhanced gastrointestinal loss
Enhanced renal loss
Mineralocorticoid excess
Glucocorticoid excess
Diuretics
Bartter's syndrome
Distal nephron delivery of poorly absorbed anion, including alkalosis
Miscellaneous
K depletion without hypokalemia: Cell K/N normal
Dietary insufficiency
Glucocorticoid excess
K depletion without hypokalemia: Cell K/N low renal failure
Congestive heart failure
Cirrhosis
Diabetic ketoacidosis

that alterations in serum H^+ concentration produce large changes in serum K concentration due to K-H exchange across cell membranes, in fact, in most cases the degree of hypokalemia produced by alkalemia is small. In general, respiratory alkalosis with alkalemia lowers serum K by about 0.1 to 0.4 mEq/liter per 0.1 rise in pH units. Metabolic alkalosis and alkalemia, produced acutely by infusing various buffers, lower serum K by only 0.1 to 0.3 mEq/liter per 0.1 pH unit rise. The bicarbonate ion seems to have a special ability, however, to lower the serum K concentration via redistribution of K into cells. In experimental animals, one can raise serum pH to comparable degrees by lowering PCO_2 (acute respiratory alkalosis) or by infusing bicarbonate. The drop in serum K concentration with bicarbonate administration is much larger than with PCO_2 reduction, indicating that the bicarbonate ion *per se* has a special ability to translocate K into cells. The mechanism of this special effect is not clear at present.

Insulin

Insulin promotes translocation of K ions into skeletal muscle and hepatic cells. Likewise, glucose administration, by stimulating release of endogenous insulin, also causes hypokalemia via redistribution, although this effect is usually transient. Insulin-induced hypokalemia becomes clinically important in two circumstances. First, insulin is used in the acute treatment of hyperkalemia precisely because of its ability to redistribute K into cells. Overzealous use of insulin in this circumstance can lead to frank hypokalemia. Second, insulin administered as part of the treatment of diabetic ketoacidosis has the serious potential to cause hypokalemia. Intracellular K depletion can coexist with a normal serum K concentration in ketoacidosis. In fact, the hyperglycemia that accompanies ketoacidosis may produce frank hyperkalemia concurrent with intracellular K depletion (Tables 2 and 3). In this setting, insulin administration as part of the treatment of ketoacidosis shifts K into K-depleted cells and may result in severe acute hypokalemia. Thus, serum K must be monitored closely, and replacement should be effected appropriately during the treatment of ketoacidosis.

Beta-Adrenergic Drugs

As discussed in Chapter 1, beta$_2$-adrenergic agonists promote uptake of K by cells, probably by stimulating activity of Na,K-ATPase. Intravenous infusion of epinephrine in doses sufficient to achieve blood levels comparable to those seen, e.g., in acute myocardial infarction produces a drop in serum K concentration of about 0.7 mEq/liter. The beta$_2$ agonist albuterol (Proventil or Ventolin) used in the treatment of bronchospasm in patients with reversible airways disease, can lead to hypokalemia if used to excess.

TABLE 3. *Examples of relationship between serum and cell potassium*

Condition	Cellular K		Serum K
	K	K/N	
Periodic paralysis	N[a]	N	↓
Glucocorticoid excess	↓	N	N
Mineralocorticoid excess, diuretics, gastrointestinal loss	↓	↓	↓
Diabetic ketoacidosis	↓	↓	↓ , N, or ↑
Heart failure, cirrhosis	↓	↓	N

[a]N, normal.

Periodic Paralysis

Table 2 lists the disease periodic paralysis as an etiology of hypokalemia via shift of K into cells. There are three forms of this interesting disease, one associated with normokalemia, one with hyperkalemia, and one with hypokalemia. These forms and their pathophysiology are discussed in Chapter 12. Here we concern ourselves with the hypokalemia variety. Hypokalemic periodic paralysis is inherited with an autosomal dominant pattern. Symptoms begin in childhood, and the peak incidence occurs in the second decade of life, i.e., in the teens. Attacks of profound muscle weakness are precipitated by large meals (particularly those high in carbohydrates), rest after strenuous exercise, trauma, infections, or alcohol intake. Not surprisingly, administration of insulin or epinephrine also induces an attack. Although muscle weakness may involve only a single muscle group, more commonly it is generalized, except for muscles of respiration and speech. Seldom fatal, the attacks range in duration from 6 to 48 hr. Abundant evidence indicates that hypokalemic periodic paralysis is a disease in which K redistributes from the serum into cells in response to the various stimuli described. It was discovered fortuitously that acetazolamide in doses of 500 to 1000 mg per day eliminates severe attacks in the familial form of the disease. The mechanism by which acetazolamide works appears to be related to the accompanying mild metabolic acidosis, since ammonium chloride administration is effective in ameliorating the muscle cell membrane abnormalities in this disease. In some patients, acetazolamide is either ineffective or worsens the attacks; in such patients, the K-sparing diuretic triamterene has been found to be effective.

Miscellaneous Causes

Several miscellaneous causes of K redistribution into cells can be mentioned. Treatment of megaloblastic anemia with folate or vitamin B_{12} results in very rapid erythropoiesis and K uptake by newly forming cells, occasionally causing hypokalemia. Hypothermia is associated with excess K uptake by cells, as is poisoning with barium salts.

CELLULAR POTASSIUM DEPLETION WITH HYPOKALEMIA: CELL K/N LOW (1–7,9,11,13,14)

There is a whole range of disease states characterized by a decrease in total body K content. To understand the concept of cellular K depletion, we consider the techniques used to estimate cellular K concentration.

Measurement of Total Body Potassium and Exchangeable Potassium

The naturally occurring isotopes of K exist as 93.1% ^{39}K, 6.9% ^{41}K, and 0.118% ^{40}K. The last of these can be counted in a whole body counter. ^{40}K is a very stable isotope with a half-life of 1.3×10^9 years. Because the normal ratio of ^{39}K/^{40}K is known, one can count the emitted gamma radiation (^{40}K) for roughly 1,000 sec and determine a whole body K value (^{39}K plus ^{41}K plus ^{40}K) that is reproducible to 5%. Once this value (raw counts of gamma radiation from the total body) is obtained, it must be expressed in proper terms so that the number reflects cellular K concentration. From cadaver studies using chemical analysis, it is clear that factoring for body weight is not adequate and that factoring for fat-free body weight yields much more consistent data. Unfortunately, it is very difficult to determine fat-free body weight accurately in a living person. One way to improve on factoring total body K for body weight is to factor for total body water (measured using tritiated water), although this still gives results more variable than the cadaver measurements using fat-free body weight.

Another method that complements total body counting of ^{40}K is that of measuring exchangeable potassium, or K_e. The short-lived isotope ^{42}K is injected intravenously, and from its resulting dilution K_e can be determined. Values for K_e are usually about 90 to 95% of those obtained by total body counting. It must be kept in mind that both total body counting and K_e represent averages of intracellular plus extracellular K content. There are two problems: (1) the proportion of cellular/extracellular K content may change, and (2) the intracellular K concentration, which would be calculated from either measurement as an average concentration, in fact varies widely among tissues (5 mmoles/liter in adipose cells, 15 mmoles/liter in bone, 39 mmoles/liter in skin, and 94 mmoles/liter in muscle). Thus, total body K and K_e measurements only provide general estimates of cellular K concentration. Nonetheless, the resulting data are useful in considering mechanisms and etiologies of cellular K depletion.

In most disease states characterized by a decrease in total body K content, there is also a decrease in the average intracellular K concentration. Thus, one can consider that K is lost from cells disproportionate to other intracellular components, e.g., nitrogen, and that in these conditions the cellular K/N ratio is low (Table 3).

An example of renal K loss in excess of N loss, which would lead to a lowering of the K/N ratio in cells, is shown in the right-hand panel of Fig. 1. ACTH administration produces mixed hypercortisolism and hyperaldosteronism. The provision of adequate dietary Na allows enough distal nephron Na delivery so

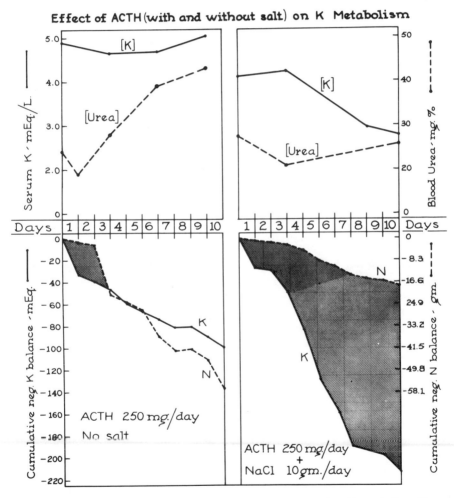

FIG. 1. Effect of ACTH (with and without supplemental dietary salt) on K metabolism. (Courtesy of Dr. D. W. Seldin.)

that the aldosterone effect predominates. Under these conditions the K/N ratio in the urine far exceeds the normal ratio of about 3 in tissues; i.e., K loss occurs in excess of N loss in mineralocorticoid excess.

A decline in cell K concentration usually is accompanied by a decline in serum K concentration. The states discussed subsequently generally produce a drop in serum K concentration of about 1 mEq/liter for a fall in total body K content of about 200 mEq. For example, the severely low serum K concentration of 1.5 mEq/liter is associated with a body K deficit of 400 to 800 mEq. It must be kept in mind, however, that other factors, such as those described previously, can shift the balance of intracellular/extracellular K and thus change the relationship between serum K and cell K content. The most common and clinically important causes of K depletion associated with hypokalemia are discussed in the following sections.

Dietary Insufficiency

K depletion resulting from inadequate dietary intake is an unusual, but real, cause of cellular K depletion because of the ubiquity of K in foods (Table 4). Although exact figures are not available, it appears that the average K intake is about 75 mEq/day. Once dietary K restriction is in place, its ability to produce cellular K depletion can be understood only in light of the physiology of renal K conservation. Maximal conservation of K by the normal kidney lowers the urinary K concentration to only about 10 mEq/liter. Thus, one would predict that a dietary K intake ≤ 10 mEq/day would result in K depletion. In fact, balance studies show this rough guide to be correct. In one of the most important clinical studies on the topic, healthy male volunteers on a 25 to 27 mEq/day K diet came into balance after 4 to 7 days on the diet. On an intake of 14 to 16 mEq/day, the subjects went into negative K balance, achieving a urinary K concentration of only 19 to 27 mEq/day. Subjects on 1 mEq/day of K lowered their urinary K concentrations to 4 to 5 mEq/day, at the expense of severe negative K balance. Thus, severe K depletion can be expected to develop on a K intake less than about 25 mEq/day.

Two conditions commonly predispose to diet-induced K depletion. The first is a weight-reduction method known as the "protein modified fast." This method consists of a roughly 500 Kcal/day meat diet. From Table 4 one can see that such a diet is likely to be poor in K. Because the K intake on such a diet can be as low as 25 mEq/day, it is not surprising that cardiac arrhythmias and sudden death have been reported in patients treated for obesity with liquid protein diets. The second dietary situation capable of producing K depletion is alcoholism. Although beer and wine do contain some K, the components consumed by a hard-liquor alcoholic, including club soda, ginger ale, tonic water, and distilled liquors, have virtually no K. One can deduce from this information and the data in Table 4 that an alcoholic consuming a

TABLE 4. *Potassium content and concentration in commonly used foods*[a]

Type of food	mEq/100 g		mEq/100 Kcal	
	Range	Mean	Range	Mean
Fresh vegetables	2.4–18.8	10.3	7.8–50	23.1
Fruit juices	2.6–6.0	4.5	4.2–26.9	17.2
Fresh fruits	2.8–15.4	6.5	3.0–40	11.1
Milk	3.9–5.9	4.1	6.4–12	9.3
Dry vegetable seeds	25.2–43.0	29.8	7.3–12.6	8.5
Dried fruits	16.4–24.1	17.4	6.0–9.6	6.2
Fowl	7.3–10.7	8.6	2.2–10.8	6.0
Shellfish	4.6–8.1	5.9	4.6–7.0	5.9
Meat	7.3–14.6	10.5	2.1–8.7	4.7
Whole grain flour	4.1–40.0	16.9	1.1–10.5	4.5
Nuts	10.5–30.7	14.9	1.5–6.7	3.4
Breakfast cereals	2.4–32.5	9.1	0.5–12.4	2.8
Candy	6.7–15.7	10.7	1.5–5.7	2.3
Breads with refined flour	1.9–7.4	4.3	0.67–3.5	1.8
Refined flour	2.3–4.3	3.7	0.6–1.0	0.8
Cheese	2.0–4.8	2.8	0.52–1.1	0.77
Salt substitutes Adolph's (6.1 mEq/5 g) Diamond's (6.6 mEq/5 g) Morton Lite Salt (3.3 mEq/5 g)				

From ref. 14a.

steady diet of wine, bread, and cheese would soon develop K depletion; i.e., to the extent that the total daily caloric intake is in the form of empty calories from alcohol and not other foodstuffs, the K depletion will be worsened. Dietary insufficiency resulting in malnutrition may result in a decrease in total body K stores simply as a result of a decrease in lean body mass, without a decline in the cellular K/N ratio; this condition is discussed later in this chapter.

Enhanced Gastrointestinal Loss

Table 5 lists approximate K concentrations of various gastrointestinal fluids. Fluids emanating from the upper gastrointestinal tract tend to have lower K concentrations than colonic secretions, undoubtedly because the colon normally is responsible for considerable K secretion. Under normal conditions, gastric, pancreatic, biliary, and small intestinal fluids, although secreted into

TABLE 5. *Approximate sodium and potassium concentrations in gastrointestinal fluids*[a]

Fluid	Na (mEq/liter)	K (mEq/liter)
Gastric fluid	20–80	10–15
Pancreatic fluid	140	5
Biliary fluid	148	5
Small bowel fluid	80–110	5
Colonic fluid	60	30
Diarrheal stools	120	25

[a]From ref. 9a.

the gut lumen at the rate of 3 to 6 liters/day are reabsorbed distally and, hence, do not exit the body. When vomiting or diarrhea occurs, however, extracorporeal K loss may be significant. Although gastric secretions contain the highest K concentration of the upper gastrointestinal secretions, it must be kept in mind that the usually severe K depletion associated with protracted vomiting results primarily from renal K loss. This renal K loss, in turn, results from excess renal HCO_3 excretion and the consequences of extracellular fluid volume depletion. The full pathophysiology of K depletion owing to vomiting is discussed further below.

Other than vomiting (Table 6), loss of K via the gastrointestinal tract occurs with acute and chronic diarrhea, externally draining gastrointestinal fistulas, the (now defunct) surgical procedure of ureterosigmoidostomy, and villous adenomas.

Acute diarrhea severe enough to cause K depletion is seen in cholera, in which daily stool losses may total 8 liters in volume and 130 mEq in K. Viral or other bacterial infections may also produce watery diarrhea sufficient to waste K. Chronic diarrhea associated with gastrointestinal K loss is seen in islet (non-beta) cell tumors of the pancreas that stimulate small intestinal secretion via vasoactive intestinal polypeptide, in which case daily stool losses may total 6 liters in volume and 300 mEq of K. K loss in chronic diarrhea is

TABLE 6. *Causes of gastrointestinal potassium loss*

Vomiting or nasogastric suction (with accompanying metabolic alkalosis)

Acute diarrhea (cholera; viral or other bacterial)

Chronic diarrhea (vasoactive intestinal polypeptide-producing tumor; laxative abuse)

Externally draining enteric fistula

Ureterosigmoidostomy

Villous adenoma

seen also with laxative abuse. Such patients often complain of chronic constipation or alternating diarrhea and constipation. The diagnosis of laxative abuse can be difficult, requiring a search of the patient's personal belongings and analysis of stool and urine for phenolphthalein.

In both acute and chronic diarrhea, the pathophysiology of K loss is similar. The colon is very similar to the cortical collecting tubule in terms of K transport; the colon actively secretes K, and this process is stimulated by aldosterone. In diarrheal states, there are several components to stool K loss. First, enhanced delivery of Na-containing fluid to the colon itself augments K secretion. Second, slough of K-rich small intestinal mucosal cells adds to K depletion. Third, concomitant volume depletion stimulates the renin-angiotensin-aldosterone axis, and aldosterone stimulates both colonic K secretion and renal (collecting duct) K secretion.

Ureterosigmoidostomies are not performed anymore as urinary diversion procedures, having been supplanted by ureteroileostomies, precisely because the former caused gastrointestinal K wasting. Patients with ureterosigmoidostomies developed K loss because Na delivered into the sigmoid colon via the ureter stimulated K secretion by that intestinal segment. The same problem can occur, although much less frequently, in patients with ureteroileostomies, i.e., ileal loops, if these loops are unusually long or undergo stomal obstruction.

Villous adenomas, unlike the much more common pedunculated type, are sessile. Rather than having K loss via watery diarrhea, patients with these tumors more often have normally formed stools but leak nearly continuously a characteristic, K-rich mucuslike material. Careful questioning may be necessary to elicit this feature in the history.

Enhanced Renal Loss

Enhanced renal loss of K probably represents a more common etiology of K depletion than either reduced dietary intake or enhanced gastrointestinal loss. Table 2 lists five major categories of enhanced renal K loss: mineralocorticoid excess, glucocorticoid excess, diuretics, Bartter's syndrome, and distal nephron delivery of a poorly absorbed anion. In addition, a miscellaneous category is given. The patient's blood pressure is a clue to differentiating among these possibilities. Patients with either mineralocorticoid or glucocorticoid excess usually have hypertension; patients with renal K loss due to the other etiologies have normal blood pressure.

Mineralocorticoid Excess: Etiologies and Pathophysiology

Mineralocorticoid excess is usually caused by increased levels of circulating aldosterone. Aldosterone binds to specific receptors in the cortical collecting tubule, where it increases Na reabsorption and K secretion. The degree to which aldosterone is able to exert this effect is in part a function of the rate of Na delivery to the collecting duct. Low dietary Na intake or enhanced proximal tubule Na reabsorption, by decreasing distal Na delivery, decrease the K-wasting effect of aldosterone. Conversely, diuretics administered to the patient with excess aldosterone produce severe K loss by markedly enhancing Na delivery to the K-secreting collecting duct.

High aldosterone levels can result from either primary or secondary aldosteronism. Primary aldosteronism means that the adrenal cortex is synthesizing aldosterone autonomously. Patients with primary aldosteronism have modest hypertension, no edema, variable degrees of hypokalemia (in some cases, serum K concentration is normal), and chloride-resistant metabolic alkalosis. Primary aldosteronism may be responsible for as much as 2% of cases of hypertension. Primary aldosteronism can result from an adrenal adenoma, from bilateral adrenal hyperplasia, or (rarely) from an adrenal carcinoma. In each of these cases, plasma renin levels are usually, but not always, suppressed, presumably in response to the subtle volume expansion accompanying aldosterone excess.

The pathophysiology of hyperaldosteronism resulting from bilateral adrenal hyperplasia is interesting. One form of the disease results from excessive sensitivity of the aldosterone-synthesizing area of the adrenal cortex, the zona glomerulosa, to ACTH. This produces so-called glucocorticoid-suppressible idiopathic hyperaldosteronism. This disease is familial, and it is rare. The diagnosis is made by administering 0.5 mg dexamethasone daily for 5 to 7 days. Patients with this disease show suppression of aldosterone levels and a reduction in blood pressure with this maneuver, whereas patients with the more common form of hyperplasia do not demonstrate these effects.

A much more common form of primary aldosteronism manifests itself pathologically as bilateral adrenal hyperplasia. This form accounts for 40% of cases of primary aldosteronism. The obvious question in this disease has been: What stimulates the hyperplasia and overproduction of aldosterone? The answer to this question is uncertain. It is clear that the well-known stimuli, ACTH, angiotensin II, and K, do not seem to be causative in this disease. Rather, there is evidence for the existence of other factors that can stimulate aldosterone synthesis or that might modify the threshold responses of the adrenal cortex to ACTH, angiotensin II, or K. One of these putative factors has been termed "aldosterone-stimulating factor," a glycoprotein of pituitary origin that is not suppressed by dexamethasone. This peptide circulates in patients with the disease and stimulates aldosterone synthesis *in vitro* at these circulating concentrations. Because pharmacologic manipulation of the dopaminergic system modulates aldosterone secretion (dopamine infusion reduces plasma aldosterone concentrations to normal in patients with idiopathic hyperaldosteronism), it has been speculated that dopaminergic mechanisms in the pituitary might regulate secretion of this aldosterone-stimulating factor. However, this scenario remains speculative.

In contrast to primary aldosteronism, secondary aldosteronism results from high circulating levels of renin, which, in turn, usually result from renovascular disease, including renal artery stenosis, malignant hypertension, vasculitis, or scleroderma. Secondary aldosteronism can also result from rare renin-secreting tumors arising from the juxtaglomerular apparatus.

Other mineralocorticoids can also stimulate renal K secretion. Figure 2 shows synthetic pathways for adrenocortical steroid synthesis. Deficiencies of the enzymes 11-beta-hydroxylase and 17-alpha-hydroxylase result in reduced synthesis of cortisol. The low circulating cortisol levels, in turn, stimulate ACTH release. This excess stimulation of the adrenal cortex by ACTH leads to overproduction of deoxycorticosterone and corticosterone in the case of 17-alpha-hydroxylase deficiency or of deoxycorticosterone alone in the case of 11-beta-hydroxylase deficiency. Both deoxycorticosterone and corticosterone possess mineralocorticoid activity and, thus, can stimulate the cortical collecting tubule to secrete excess K. As might be expected, the greater mineralocorticoid effect would be predicted for 17-alpha-hydroxylase deficiency; indeed, these patients have much more hypokalemia than those with 11-beta-hydroxylase deficiency.

Mineralocorticoids may also be ingested. Fludrocortisone is available as a prescription drug for the treatment of hypoaldosteronism and is a component of several nasal sprays. Glycyrrhizinic acid is a nonsteroidal plant compound possessing mineralocorticoid activity; it is present in licorice and in licorice-containing chewing tobacco and can cause a clinical syndrome indistinguishable from primary aldosteronism. In contrast, prescription glucocorticoids, such as prednisone or dexamethasone, have little propensity to cause renal K wasting, since they have less mineralocorticoid activity than aldosterone.

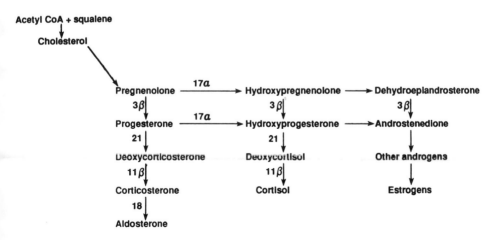

FIG. 2. Pathways for biosynthesis of glucocorticoids and mineralocorticoids. (From ref. 10a.)

Glucocorticoid Excess

Pure glucocorticoids increase the glomerular filtration rate, Na excretion rate, and urinary flow rate. Renal K wasting with glucocorticoids has a more rapid onset and shorter duration than that seen with minerolocorticoids. Changes in dietary Na intake have no effect on the renal K loss seen with glucocorticoids, whereas mineralocorticoid-induced renal K loss is proportional to distal nephron Na delivery and, hence, Na intake. The serum K concentration falls with mineralocorticoid excess but stays normal with glucocorticoid excess. The contrasting effects of mineralocorticoids versus glucocorticoids on renal K loss are highlighted in Table 7.

The concepts of loss of K and N in proportion to their intracellular ratios (glucocorticoid excess) or of K loss out of proportion to N (mineralocorticoid excess) are illustrated in Fig. 1. The data shown are from a balance study in a patient with rheumatoid arthritis who was given ACTH for two 10-day periods. ACTH stimulates overproduction of both glucocorticoids and mineralocorticoids. The relative effect of each could be brought out in this study by manipulating dietary Na intake and thus distal nephron Na delivery. The left panel in Fig. 1 shows the first 10-day period during which the patient was on a Na-free diet. This restriction of distal Na delivery allows glucocorticoid effects on K and N to predominant. Note that, except for the first 2 days (when K was excreted slightly in excess of N), the urinary excretion of K and N was more or less in the same ratio as inside the cell (2.41); i.e., glucocorticoid excess caused commensurate K and N loss. Given the duration of this study, it is likely that the K and N losses were due, at least in part, to catabolic effects of glucocorticoids. This is also evidenced by the rise in blood

TABLE 7. *Comparison of renal K wasting induced by mineralocorticoids and glucocorticoids*

Parameter	Mineralocorticoids	Glucocorticoids
Glomerular filtration rate	No change	Usually increased
Na excretion	Reduced	Usually increased
Urine flow	Acutely reduced	Usually increased
Time course	Delayed; sustained	Rapid; transient
Dietary		
Na depletion	Prevents K loss	No effect
K repletion	Prevents K loss	No effect
Plasma (K)	Usually falls	Often rises
Spironolactone	Blocks K loss	No effect

Adapted from ref. 1.

urea concentration. Characteristic of a pure glucocorticoid effect, there was no change in the serum K concentration in this case.

The right panel of Fig. 1 shows the effect of mineralocorticoid excess. The same patient was studied again after a short interval free of interventions. The ACTH administration was then repeated, but the patient's diet was supplemented with 10 g/day NaCl. This maneuver served to increase distal nephron Na delivery and allowed the mineralocorticoid effects produced by ACTH to predominate. In this case, urinary K loss far outstripped N loss, and the serum K concentration fell. The urinary K/N ratio was well above that measured in tissues. Thus, K was clearly leaving cells in excess of N, and this produced the fall in serum K concentration.

In general, hypokalemia is mild in Cushing's syndrome resulting from bilateral adrenocortical hyperplasia because pure glucocorticoids are produced. Cushing's syndrome can also result from excess ACTH secretion by the pituitary (so-called Cushing's disease) or by ectopic secretion of ACTH by such tumors as oat cell carcinoma. Because ACTH stimulates synthesis of deoxycorticosterone and corticosterone, both of which possess mineralocorticoid activity, K wasting and hypokalemia resulting from Cushing's disease or ectopic ACTH excretion are more pronounced than in hypercortisolism due to bilateral adrenal hyperplasia (Fig. 1). In fact, severe hypokalemia occurring in the clinical setting of Cushing's syndrome should raise the question of either ectopic ACTH secretion or adrenal carcinoma.

Clinical Approach to Hypokalemia with Hypertension

As stated previously, in contrast to other causes of renal K wasting, mineralocorticoid and glucocorticoid excess produce renal K wasting with elevated blood pressure. Clinically, once one has established the coexistence of K depletion and hypertension, one needs to be able to distinguish among the various mineralocorticoid and glucocorticoid excess states. Figure 3 shows an algorithm for the workup of hypokalemia with hypertension. First, a 24 hr urine collection for K is obtained to ensure that there is renal K wasting, not extrarenal loss. The next step serves to establish whether the renin-angiotensin system is likely to be stimulating aldosterone synthesis; this is accomplished by measuring plasma renin activity. Suppressed plasma renin concentrations suggest that mineralocorticoid excess is primary and is causing suppression of renal release via subtle volume expansion. Measurement of aldosterone levels under conditions that should suppress aldosterone release is an important next step. Volume expansion by intravenous saline infusion or a high Na diet represent adequate ways to suppress aldosterone release that is being driven physiologically by the renin-angiotensin system. A high Na diet before measuring the aldosterone concentration offers an advantage; the enhanced distal Na delivery promotes K wasting in true primary

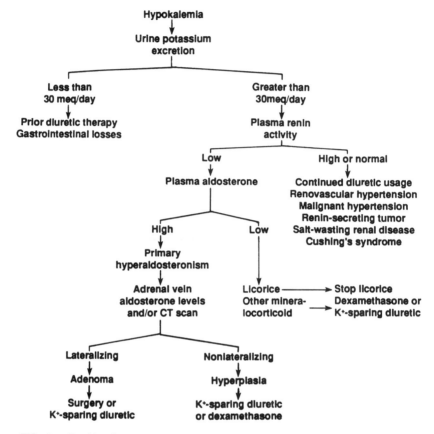

FIG. 3. Algorithm for workup of hypokalemia in hypertensive patients. (From ref. 10b.)

aldosteronism and produces or worsens hypokalemia. This simple clinical test thus provides a clue to the diagnosis before the aldosterone serum levels return from the laboratory.

Low aldosterone levels suggest the presence of exogenous mineralocorticoids. High aldosterone levels mean that one is dealing with primary hyperaldosteronism. In the latter case, the issue then becomes that of differentiating bilateral adrenal hyperplasia from benign adenoma or, rarely, carcinoma. The distinction is worth making, since adenoma is best treated by surgical resection, whereas bilateral hyperplasia is best managed with a K-sparing diuretic (amiloride, spironolactone, or triamterene) in combination with hydrochlorothiazide. The difficulty lies in making the distinction accurately. Adrenal venography, isotopic adrenal scintiscanning, computed tomography, and adrenal vein sampling all have been advocated. The last procedure, though offering the highest sensitivity and specificity, suffers the drawback that it is invasive and requires considerable experience and skill. Although several noninvasive tests have been proposed, none as yet is completely satisfactory, and adrenal vein sampling probably will be necessary in many cases.

Diuretics and Potassium Depletion

The topic of diuretics and K depletion is discussed in Chapter 13. There is little question that diuretics do cause K depletion, but the degree of depletion produced is highly variable, being largely a function of the reason for which the diuretics are given. If diuretics are given to treat edematous states, such as congestive heart failure, cirrhosis, or nephrotic syndrome, the potential exists for renal K wasting in large amounts. The reason for this is simple; these conditions are associated with a decreased effective plasma volume and stimulation of the renin-angiotensin-aldosterone system. Under these conditions, diuretics enhance Na delivery to the distal convoluted tubule and to a cortical collecting duct primed for K secretion by aldosterone. The resulting renal K wasting can be substantial. Thus, careful attention must be paid to K balance when patients with edema are treated with diuretics. The treatment methods necessary for K replacement under these conditions are discussed later in this chapter.

The situation is different when diuretics are administered chronically in the treatment of hypertension, but without edema. There is currently considerable controversy about the extent and importance of K depletion in this situation. A large number of total body K studies using ^{40}K or ^{42}K have examined the degree of K loss resulting from thiazide diuretics in essential hypertension. Of roughly 20 such studies, the mean deficit was about 150 mEq of K. Because total body K is about 3,000 mEq, this represents a roughly 5% fall in cellular K content. This degree of K depletion would appear to be inconsequential for the health of normal individuals. Although furosemide is a more potent diuretic than hydrochlorothiazide, furosemide used twice daily for the treatment of hypertension produces less renal K wasting than a regimen of thiazides. This may be related to the site of action in the nephron of the two diuretics; thiazides act just proximal to the main K-secretory segment, and thus enhanced Na delivery resulting from thiazides might be translated directly into enhanced K secretion. In contrast, furosemide acts more proximally, so that some intervening compensation of Na excretion may take place before delivery of urine to the collecting duct.

Despite this relatively small decrease in total body K produced by thiazide diuretics, these drugs do lower the serum K concentration significantly and do so in a dose-dependent manner. The average reductions in serum K concentration produced by hydrochlorothiazide as a function of dose in one large study were as follows: 0.45 mEq/liter (25 mg/day), 0.50 mEq/liter (50 mg/day), and 0.70 mEq/liter (75–150 mg/day). In another study, the percentage of patients with serum K concentrations less than 3.5 mEq/liter was 48% of those taking hydrochlorothiazide versus 5% of those taking furosemide. When the lower limit of a normal serum K was reduced to 3.0 mEq/liter, 7% of patients taking thiazides but only 0.2% of patients taking furosemide were below this value. Thus, it would appear that thiazide diuretics have the greater propensity to cause hypokalemia and that they do so in a dose-dependent fashion.

A great deal of attention has been paid to the issue of cardiac arrhythmias resulting from thiazide-induced hypokalemia. Several initial clinical trials involving ambulatory monitoring of heart rhythm have concluded that thiazides increase the number of ventricular extrasystoles. However, several subsequent studies with essentially equivalent experimental design have concluded the opposite. Careful inspection of these studies suggests that the results obtained depend on the patient group studied. Patients with clinical evidence of heart disease, such as an abnormal resting electrocardiogram or an enlarged heart, appear definitely to develop increased extrasystoles when placed on thiazides. In contrast, patients without clinical heart disease almost certainly do not. Moreover, it is not at all clear that an increase in ventricular extrasystoles is harmful. In this regard it is necessary to discuss the Multiple Risk Factor Intervention Trial (MRFIT) results. This large epidemiologic study of patients treated for hypertension found a slight increase in coronary heart disease deaths in thiazide-treated patients compared to controls (some of whom may also have received thiazides). This increase in mortality occurred in men with hypertension at entry whose base-line resting electrocardiograms showed signs of abnormalities, suggesting that perhaps thiazides had resulted in fatal ventricular arrhythmias. Two very important points should be made concerning this aspect of the trial. First, the increase in mortality was not statistically significant; the paper reads ". . . These findings are not conclusive. . . ." Second, a subsequent clinical hypertension trial (Hypertension Detection and Follow-Up Program, HDFP) specifically reexamined the MRFIT thiazide issue from the viewpoint of the HDFP data. There was no increase in mortality in the thiazide group. The paper concluded that: "These HDFP findings therefore offer no support for the hypothesis raised in MRFIT that intensive diuretic therapy may increase the mortality rate of hypertensive patients with resting ECG abnormalities" (ref. 6).

A recent study from the Glasgow Blood Pressure Clinic (10a) also examined this issue. In this study, 3,783 patients with nonmalignant hypertension were followed for an average of 6.5 years. Serum K fell in 414 patients given diuretics with or without other drugs except beta blockers. This fall in serum K was similar to the fall in those who died of ischemic heart disease (3.71 mEq/liter) and in those who survived (3.72 mEq/liter). Age-adjusted mortality in deaths per 1,000 patient-years in the lowest quartile of serum K (3.7 mEq/liter) was actually lower, although not statistically so, than mortality rates in those with higher K concentrations. Thus, this study does not support a role for K depletion in causing cardiac death.

One test of the harmfulness of increased ventricular ectopy would be an increase in mortality from arrhythmias during myocardial infarction in patients taking thiazides. In theory, this might seem particularly likely, since catecholamine levels rise steeply with infarction, driving K into cells via beta-adrenergic receptors. One large study of patients with acute myocardial infarctions in Scandinavia concluded that, in fact, there was an enhanced risk of ventricular fibrillation with infarction in patients on diuretics. However, the data warrant very careful scrutiny; although there was a correlation between diuretics and hypokalemia on admission and a correlation between hypokalemia and ventricular fibrillation, no correlation was present between diuretic use and ventricular fibrillation. Thus, this most direct statistical test of the hypothesis is negative.

Based on all of these data, it seems reasonable to conclude that the degree of hypokalemia and K depletion produced by diuretics is modest, being more pronounced with thiazides than with furosemide. The risk of death from thiazide-induced ventricular arrthymias depends on the underlying heart disease, but even in the presence of heart disease, this risk may not be great. There is no proof at this point that thiazides increase the risk of sudden death during myocardial infarction. The best policy appears to be one of reasonable prevention. Serum K concentration should be kept above 3.5 mEq/liter in patients taking digoxin or with overt heart disease, including ectopy on a resting electrocardiogram. Patients without heart disease should have their serum K concentration maintained above 3.0 mEq/liter. The most effective means by which to accomplish this are discussed at the end of this chapter.

Bartter's Syndrome

Bartter's syndrome is a rare disorder that presents with hypokalemia; alkalosis and hypomagnesemia sometimes are present. The blood pressure is normal despite hyperplasia of the juxtaglomerular apparatus histologically, hyperreninemia, and hyperaldosteronism. Most patients present in childhood with short stature, failure to thrive, polyuria, and weakness, all no doubt as a result of K depletion and hypokalemia. The pathophysiology of Bartter's syndrome is uncertain; it has been postulated to result from decreased NaCl absorption by the thick ascending limb. This hypothesis rests mostly on the similarity between the signs and symptoms of Bartter's syndrome and those of excessive furosemide use. In fact, it can be clinically difficult to distinguish Bartter's syndrome from surreptitious diuretic abuse. In a recent human clearance study, fractional distal Cl reabsorption was measured in eight patients with Bartter's syndrome, eight patients with comparable degrees of hypokalemia of different etiologies, and seven normal subjects. A low fractional distal Cl reabsorption was found only in patients with Bartter's syndrome. Thus, K depletion and hypokalemia *per se* do not appear to produce Cl wasting; rather, chloruresis is a specific feature of Bartter's syndrome.

Another similarity between diuretic abuse and Bartter's syndrome relates to the status of prostaglandins. Urinary excretion of PGE_2 is elevated both in Bartter's syndrome and with furosemide administration. Thus, for a while, there was great interest in using prostaglandin synthesis inhibitors to treat Bartter's syndrome. However, this maneuver, although reducing prostaglandin excretion rates and renin and aldosterone levels, does not ameliorate the renal K wasting.

Several recent papers suggest that the angiotensin-converting enzyme inhibitor enalapril is effective in treating Bartter's syndrome. In these studies, total body K values rose, there was (as expected) a further rise in renin and a decline in aldosterone, serum K rose (in one study from 2.4 ± 0.5 to 3.9 ± 0.6 mEq/liter), and symptoms of fatigue and tetany disappeared. This modality may prove to be the most effective to date in this disease.

Most cases that appear clinically to be due to Bartter's syndrome are, in fact, cases of clandestine laxative abuse, vomiting, or diuretic abuse. The first two of these can be distinguished from Bartter's syndrome by measuring the urinary concentration of Cl. Patients with Bartter's syndrome waste urinary Cl in addition to K, whereas those with laxative abuse or vomiting conserve renal Cl; urinary Cl concentrations in these patients are less than 10 to 15 mEq/liter. Surreptitious diuretic abuse can be more difficult to diagnose. If the patient has ingested the diuretic just before the urine Cl collection, the urinary Cl concentration may be high. In contrast, if the diuretics have been taken for several days and then stopped, e.g., a day before the urine test, the urine Cl concentration may be low. In either case, K will have been wasted, and the patient will appear clinically to have possible Bartter's syndrome.

Distal Nephron Delivery of a Poorly Reabsorbed Anion, Including Alkalosis

K secretion by the cortical collecting tubule responds to the voltage across the tubule wall. A more negative voltage in the lumen compared to the blood drives higher rates of secretion of the positively charged K ion. We can conceptualize the creation of a lumen-negative voltage as resulting from charge separation; to the extent that a positively charged Na ion is reabsorbed without an accompanying anion, the tubule lumen will be electronegative with respect to the blood. Na absorbed with a readily permeable anion (Cl) will generate less of a lumen-negative voltage than Na absorbed with a relatively impermeable anion (e.g., HCO_3). Thus, distal delivery of an impermeable or poorly reabsorbed anion in the setting of avid Na reabsorption would generate a large lumen-negative voltage and thus substantial K secretion.

This is precisely the situation in metabolic alkalosis. The classic example of renal K loss accompanying metabolic alkalosis is seen with vomiting. The generation of metabolic alkalosis with vomiting is illustrated in Fig. 4. Hydrochloric acid (HCl) is lost from the stomach (recall from Table 5 that gastric secretions contain relatively little K). This loss elevates the plasma HCO_3 concentration acutely and lowers the plasma Cl concentration reciprocally. The increase in filtered load of HCO_3 exceeds the ability of the proximal tubule to reabsorb it adequately, causing enhanced delivery of HCO_3 to the downstream nephron segments, especially the cortical collecting tubule. As mentioned previously, HCO_3 is poorly reabsorbed in the collecting duct compared to Cl. Thus, Na reabsorption takes place with a poorly permeable anion (HCO_3), the tubule lumen becomes substantially electronegative, and K secretion is stimulated. In essence, HCl is lost from the stomach and $KHCO_3$ is lost via the urine.

If this situation persists, several secondary events occur that serve to further perpetuate the state of alkalosis. Because the major extracellular anion is Cl, loss of Cl via gastric secretions causes a decrease in extracellular fluid volume and thus in effective vascular volume. This hypovolemia, in turn, activates the renin-angiotensin-aldosterone system. The resulting high aldosterone levels have two major effects on cortical collecting tubule K-secreting cells: (1) enhanced Na absorption, and (2) enhanced K secretion at any given transtubular voltage. Thus, the tendency for renal K wasting that began in the collecting duct as a result of excess HCO_3 delivery is now exacerbated by these aldosterone effects on Na reabsorption and K secretion. Total body K depletion ensues.

This decrease in total body K, in turn, is thought to produce changes in the transport of HCO_3 by the proximal and perhaps collecting tubules. K loss

VOMITING

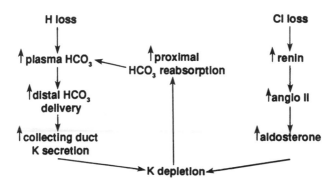

FIG. 4. Mechanisms of urinary K loss in the generation and maintenance of metabolic alkalosis.

from proximal tubule cells results in H^+ uptake by these cells via K-H exchange, and this stimulates HCO_3 reabsorption by the proximal tubule. Classic teaching holds that K-depleted collecting tubules reabsorb excess HCO_3, although recent studies using *in vitro* rabbit collecting tubules question this. Nonetheless, overall it appears that total body K depletion that originally resulted from metabolic alkalosis now plays a crucial role in maintaining alkalosis. Replacement of K to replenish body K stores is crucial for the correction of this form of metabolic alkalosis.

HCO_3 delivered to the distal nephron as a poorly absorbable anion also occurs with renal tubular acidosis (RTA) type 2 (proximal). Here, decreased proximal HCO_3 reabsorption from the glomerular filtrate leads to enhanced distal delivery. This is especially a problem when one treats type 2 RTA with oral alkali; high plasma HCO_3 concentrations cause higher filtered loads of HCO_3, which, in turn, exceed the proximal tubule's ability for reabsorption. Thus, worsening hypokalemia and renal K wasting on treating an RTA patient with alkali represent clues that the RTA is proximal.

Beta-hydroxybutyric acid and acetoacetic acid, delivered distally in excess in diabetic ketoacidosis also contribute to renal K wasting. Finally, penicillins, given as Na salts, are nonreabsorbable anions. Carbenicillin is given in large quantities (up to 36 g/day), and thus renal K wasting is most likely with this form of penicillin.

Miscellaneous Causes of Potassium Depletion with Hypokalemia

Gentamicin causes renal K wasting, an effect that may persist after the drug is stopped. Hypomagnesemia causes renal K loss, and repletion of K in this circumstance will be ineffective in raising serum K concentrations and body K stores until the Mg deficit is corrected. Primary polydipsia increases urinary flow rates such that, even at the lowest achievable urinary K concentrations of 5 to 10 mEq/liter, substantial K wasting may occur. Finally, several of the leukemias, particularly those associated with lysozymuria, may be associated with excess renal K excretion.

POTASSIUM DEPLETION WITHOUT HYPOKALEMIA: CELL K/N NORMAL

In this section, two conditions are discussed that can be associated with K depletion, a normal cell K/N ratio, and no hypokalemia: dietary insufficiency and glucocorticoid excess. Both conditions appear in Table 2 under the heading "K Depletion without hypokalemia: Cell K/N normal."

If dietary K insufficiency occurs as a part of generalized malnutrition, the resulting reduction in lean body mass is associated with a marked decrease in total body K. Although malnutrition certainly may be associated with a decrease in the cell K/N ratio, this is not necessarily the case. Likewise, glucocorticoids produce a catabolic state resulting in proportionate loss of K and N from cells. Early after the start of administering glucocorticoids, there is disproportionate K loss due to an increased glomerular filtration rate, but after this effect subsides, the catabolic effect produces a slow, steady, and proportional negative balance of K and N (Fig. 1).

POTASSIUM DEPLETION WITHOUT HYPOKALEMIA: CELL K/N LOW

As shown in Table 2, several chronic diseases, such as heart failure, cirrhosis, and renal failure can be associated with a 10 to 15% fall in body K stores but a normal serum K concentration. This effect occurs without diuretic therapy. The K deficit is resistant to attempts at repair by K replacement. There is some evidence that this poor response results from impaired function of the cell membrane Na,K-ATPase and thus that cellular uptake of K by the Na pump is impaired.

Diabetic ketoacidosis represents another disorder in which K depletion may be substantial but in which there is no associated hypokalemia. In this condition, K depletion arises by way of glucose-mediated osmotic diuresis. On clinical presentation to the physician, the osmotic diuresis usually has been prolonged, allowing substantial total body K wasting. However, several mechanisms may supervene that raise serum K to normal levels, including (1) K loss from cells that are ischemic from hypoperfusion, (2) loss of K from cells via solvent drag, which occurs as cell water leaves cells in osmotic response to hyperglycemia, (3) poor reuptake of K by cells because of insulinopenia, insulin resistance, poor beta-adrenergic tone (due to diabetic autonomic neuropathy), or hypoaldosteronism. Although previously it was believed that the acidosis *per se* of diabetic ketoacidosis played a major role in producing hyperkalemia, multiple recent studies have shown that this is not correct. Organic acids produce virtually no change in the distribution of K between cells and the extracellular fluid. Nonetheless, there are usually ample other mechanisms by which serum K may be maintained at least in the normal range while intracellular K stores are depleted. From a therapeutic standpoint, it is crucial to recognize that this situation can occur. Treatment with extracellular fluid volume expansion and insulin will translocate K from the plasma into K-depleted cells, producing acute hypokalemia and a risk of rhabdomyolysis.

TREATMENT OF ESTABLISHED POTASSIUM DEPLETION (8,10,12)

Treatment of K depletion is crucial if certain serious consequences, such as rhabdomyolysis or life-threatening ventricular ectopy, are to be avoided. In this section, we discuss strategies for acutely treating established K deficiency. The prevention of K depletion and hypokalemia during chronic diuretic therapy is addressed in the next section.

The first and sometimes most difficult step in treating K depletion is estimating the size of the deficit. Because bedside total body K determinations are not feasible for routine clinical use, one is left using the serum K concentration as a tool by which to estimate body K stores. Unfortunately, as was made clear in the preceeding sections, significant cellular and total body K depletion may exist with normokalemia or even hyperkalemia. Such an estimation of K stores can, therefore, represent a risky venture. Using data derived from uncomplicated diet-induced K depletion in normal subjects, one can use the following rough guideline. A decline of the serum K concentration from 4 to 3 mEq/liter means a loss of about 200 to 400 mEq intracellular K per 70 kg body weight. A further decline to 2.0 mEq/liter signifies a total body K deficit of roughly 600 to 700 mEq per 70 kg body weight. Further decreases in total body K tend to be unassociated with a drop in serum K concentration below 2.0 mEq. Despite these general guidelines, it must be emphasized that the serum K concentration provides only a rough estimate of intracellular K concentration. In any given clinical case, one must consider carefully the influences on K distribution across cell membranes that might be disturbed. Perhaps the most common error would be underestimating the degree of cellular K depletion based on a normal or near-normal serum K concentration.

In the case of K depletion, K can be repleted either orally or intravenously. If the patient can take medicines orally, oral KCl replacement is the preferred method for two reasons. First, it is frequently difficult to replace K intravenously at an adequately rapid rate, since the limit of 60 mEq/liter (higher concentrations cause vein sclerosis) necessitates large volumes of intravenous fluid administration. Second, the Cl salt of K is most effective at raising the serum K concentration. Other K salts with more palatable anions, such as HCO_3 or gluconate, seem not to be effective in raising plasma K concentrations. Moreover, the need for K replacement often arises in the setting of Cl depletion metabolic alkalosis. In this case, the Cl salt of K provides the anion necessary for correction of the alkalosis.

Oral KCl should be given at 100 to 150 mEq/day, recognizing that the total body K deficit may be several hundred mEq. Liquid KCl tastes bitter and is irritating to the gastric mucosa in high concentrations, so it must be diluted in water or fruit juice. KCl cannot be given in tablet form because this causes perforation, ulceration, and obstruction of the small bowel. Either wax-matrix or microencapsulated forms of KCl are free of these problems; however, these preparations are expensive on a per mEq basis compared to liquid KCl.

Intravenous K replacement is necessary either when the patient cannot take oral medicines (e.g., after gastrointestinal surgery) or when the K deficit is very severe and is acutely causing cardiac arrhythmias, quadriplegia, respiratory failure, or rhabdomyolysis. When the situation is simply that the patient cannot take oral KCl and when the K deficit is only moderate, K can be given intravenously at 10 to 20 mEq/h (60 mEq/liter maximum concentration). The vehicle solution should be chosen carefully. Addition of a small concentration of KCl, e.g., 20 mEq/liter, to a dextrose solution actually may lower the serum K concentration because insulin release is stimulated, causing K translocation into cells.

There are very rare occasions, mentioned previously, in which K replacement must be given intravenously at a more rapid rate. Paralysis of respiratory muscles and severe ventricular arrhythmias constitute grounds for such management. Cases have been reported in which solutions containing up to 180 mEq/liter of K were infused into a large peripheral vein at rates up to 100 mEq/h. Because K must traverse a small extracellular fluid pool in order to reach the much larger, albeit depleted, intracellular pool, such rapid infusion rates are extremely risky. Measurement of serum K concentration at very frequent intervals and continuous electrocardiographic monitoring are essential if such replacement is to be attempted. The degree of vigilance required to prevent iatrogenic hyperkalemia with such vigorous replacement cannot be stressed too much.

Prevention of Hypokalemia and Potassium Depletion

A separate issue from replacement of an established K deficit is the prevention of hypokalemia or K depletion when using chronic diuretic therapy, especially in hypertension. This applies only to thiazides. Furosemide, when used to produce diuresis in the presence of edema or ascites, certainly causes K loss. However, furosemide used in the absence of edema for the treatment of hypertension causes little, if any, renal K loss. As discussed earlier in this chapter, the actual magnitude of K depletion produced by thiazide diuretics is small, averaging 150 mEq, yet 48% of patients treated with thiazides develop serum K concentrations less than 3.5 mEq/liter. In certain patients (those on digoxin therapy, those with diabetes, or those with unequivocal clinical heart disease), it is desirable to maintain the serum K concentration above 3.5 mEq/liter. There are a number of treatment options, including salt substitutes, K-rich foods, liquid K preparations, K-containing capsules, and the K-sparing diuretics triamterene, amiloride, and spironolactone. Detailed studies comparing all of these agents to each other are not available. However, a comparison of available studies on K-raising effects of K supplements, amiloride, triamterene, and spironolactone showed that the rank order of efficacy was spironolactone > triamterene > amiloride > K supplements. A problem with spironolactone, however, is the number of side effects. These include impotence, decreased libido, and gynecomastia in males, and amenorrhea, irregular menses, hirsutism, postmenopausal bleeding, and deepened voice in females. Because of these problems, triamterene or amiloride is probably preferable to spironolactone for maintaining normal serum K concentration with thiazides.

Table 8 compares the relative costs of these various forms of K supplementation or sparing, normalized to the cost of generic liquid KCl. Typical doses of K-sparing diuretics are given. It is clear that grocery store K substitutes constitute the least expensive method, and there is some evidence that these sources of K are moderately effective as K replacement. Unfortunately, the least expensive K-sparing diuretic (spironolactone) has the most undesirable side effects. On the other hand, amiloride and triamterene cost no more, and often less, than KCl in various forms and are more effective in raising serum K concentration. Thus, either of these drugs would appear to be optimal.

There is one last caution concerning treatment or prevention of K depletion. The Boston Collaborative Drug Surveillance Program (8) showed that K replacement carries its own risks. Of 16,048 inpatients monitored, 4,921 received K therapy, 87% of these for "prophylaxis." Of these 4,921 patients, 3.6%, or 179, developed hyperkalemia. Of these, the hyperkalemia caused 7 deaths and 21 near-deaths. In a more recent study of severe, sustained hyperkalemia found in 172 patients, KCl or K-sparing diuretics were contributory in 72. The frequency of hyperkalemia complicating K therapy increases with age and renal failure. Because K must traverse a small extracellular pool

TABLE 8. Costs for K therapy
(normalized to 50 mEq/day generic KCl)[a]

Source	Cost
Salt substitutes	
Morton	0.4
Co-Salt	0.8
Foods	
Bananas (5/day)	4.3
Tomatoes (5/day)	4.3
Orange juice (4 cups/day)	4.3
Liquid K supplements	
Kaon (K gluconate)	7.3
Kaon-Cl (KCl)	4.5
K-lyte Orange (KHCO$_3$)	5.0
Klorvess (KCl)	2.6
Generic KCl	1.0
K tablets	
K-Tabs	3.6
Klotrix	3.3
Micro-K Extentabs	3.5
K-sparing diuretics	
Triamterene (100 mg/day)	3.3
Amiloride (10 mg/day)	3.8
Spironolactone (100 mg/day)	2.2

[a]Costs obtained at retail pharmacies.

to reach the intracellular pool, K therapy requires great attention to detail on the part of the physician.

REFERENCES

1. Field, M. J., and Giebisch, G. (1985): Hormonal Control of Renal Potassium Excretion. *Kidney* Int., 27:379–387.
1a. Freis, E. D. (1986): The cardiovascular risks of thiazide diuretics. *Clin. Pharmacol. Ther.*, 39:239–244.
2. Gennari, F. J., and Cohen, J. J. (1975): Role of the kidney in potassium homeostasis: Lessons from acid-base disturbances. *Kidney Int.*, 8:1–8.
3. Gill, J. R. (1980): Bartter's syndrome. *Annu. Rev. Med.*, 31:405–419.
4. Harrington, J. T., Isner, J. M., and Kassirer, J. P. (1982): Our national obsession with potassium. *Am. J. Med.*, 73:155–159.
5. Hene, R. J., Koomans, H. A., Dorhout Mees, E. J., van de Stolpe, A., Verhoef, G. E., and Boer, P. (1987): Correction of hypokalemia in Bartter's syndrome by enalapril. *Am. J. Kidney Dis.*, 9:200–205.
6. Hypertension Detection and Follow-Up Program Cooperative Research Group. (1984): The effect of antihypertensive drug treatment on mortality in the presence of resting electrocardiographic abnormalities at baseline: The HDFP experience. *Circulation*, 70:996–1003.
7. Kaplan, N M. (1984): Our appropriate concern about potassium. *Am. J. Med.*, 77:1–4.
8. Lawson, D. H. (1974): Adverse reactions to potassium chloride. *Q.J. Med.*, 53:433–440.
9. Morgan, D. B., and Davidson, C. (1980): Hypokalaemia and diuretics: An analysis of publications. *Br. Med. J.*, 1:905–908.
9a. Ornt, D. B., and Scandling, J. D. (1986): Disorders of Potassium Balance. In: *Pathophysiology of Electrolyte and Renal Disorders*, edited by H. D. Humes, Churchill Livingstone, New York.
10. Papademetriou, V., Burris, J., Kukich, S., and Freis, E. D. (1985): Effectiveness of potassium chloride or triamterene in thiazide hypokalemia. *Arch. Intern. Med.*, 145:1986–1990.
10a. Robinson, J. W., Isles, C. G., Brown, I., et. al. (1986): Mild hypokalaemia is not a risk factor in treated hypertensives. *J. Hypertens.* 4:603–608.
10b. Rose, B. D. (1984): *Clinical Physiology of Acid-Base and Electrolyte Disorders*, McGraw-Hill, New York.
11. Sebastian, A., McSherry, E., and Morris, R. C. Jr. (1971): Renal potassium wasting in renal tubular acidosis (RTA): Its occurrence in types 1 and 2 RTA despite sustained correction of systemic acidosis. *J. Clin. Invest.*, 50:667.
12. Sopko, J. A., and Freeman, R. M. (1977): Salt substitutes as a source of potassium. *JAMA*, 237:608–610.
13. Tierney, W. M., McDonald, C. J., and McCabe, G. (1985): Serum potassium testing in diuretic-treated outpatients. A multivariate approach. *Med. Decision Making*, 5:89–104.
14. van de Stolpe, A., Verhoef, G. E., Hene, R. J., Koomans, H. A., and vander Vijver, J. C. (1987): Total body potassium in Bartter's syndrome before and during treatment with enalapril. *Nephron*, 45:122–125.
14a. Whang, R. (1983): *Potassium: Its Biological Significance*. CRC Press, Boca Raton, FL.

General Review Articles

15. Biglieri, E. G. (1984): The pituitary and idiopathic hyperaldosteronism. *N. Engl. J. Med.*, 311:120–121.
16. Brown, R. S. (1984): Potassium homeostasis and clinical implications. *Am. J. Med.*, 77:3–9.
17. Nardone, D. A., McDonald, W. J., and Girard, D. E. (1978): Mechanisms in hypokalemia: Clinical correlation. *Medicine*, 57:435–446.
18. Sterns, R H., Cox, M., Feig, P. N., and Singer, I. (1981): Internal potassium balance and the control of the plasma potassium concentration. *Medicine*, 60:339–354.
19. Weinberger, M. H. (1984): Primary aldosteronism: Diagnosis and differentiation of subtypes. *Ann. Intern. Med.*, 100:300–302.

The Regulation of Potassium Balance, edited
by Donald W. Seldin and Gerhard Giebisch,
Raven Press, Ltd., New York © 1989.

11

Potassium Intoxication: Pathogenesis and Treatment

John B. Stokes

*Department of Internal Medicine, College of Medicine, University of Iowa,
Iowa City, Iowa 52242*

The maintenance of serum K concentration within the narrow range of 3.5
to 4.8 mEq/liter represents the interaction of a host of control mechanisms
whose ultimate aim is protection against a potentially lethal increase in plasma
K concentration. The systems responsible for maintaining normal extracellular
K concentration must defend against two constant threats. The first is the
threat of extravasation of K from within the intracellular space where 98% of
the body stores of K reside, and the second threat is the organism's daily

intake of dietary K. In this chapter, the problems of hyperkalemia are discussed. To establish the framework for the evaluation and management of clinical problems, certain aspects of normal K balance are considered, and those processes thought to be relevant for understanding the pathophysiology of hyperkalemia are emphasized.

DISPOSITION OF POTASSIUM INTAKE: ACHIEVEMENT OF THE STEADY STATE (6,11,19,28,29,31–35)

The intake of K is matched precisely by the elimination of K from the body. Such a situation defines the steady state, the study of which has led to a clearer understanding of K transport by each segment of the nephron, a more detailed understanding of the molecular mechanisms of K transport across cell membranes, and a more integrated, albeit elementary, understanding of how an organism adjusts to increases and decreases in K intake.

Adjustment to alterations in intake is in some ways more easily understood for Na than for K. The inescapable conclusion from a large number of studies is that long-term regulation of K excretion normally is determined by some function of total body K. Of course, this principle obtains under conditions where other homeostatic regulatory mechanisms are not impaired. Profound alterations in this relationship can be detected, e.g., in subjects given diuretics or other agents that interfere with one of the mechanisms regulating K excretion. In normal subjects, the ability to increase K excretion after step increments of K intake occurs after a period of positive K balance. Similarly, reduction in K excretion following a reduction of K intake (leading to the new steady state) occurs after a period of negative K balance.

The concept that alterations in total body K provide a signal regulating renal K excretion is deduced readily from data on experimental animals and humans. The major question is, "What is the nature of this signal?"

One of the most obvious factors for determining the magnitude of K excretion is the plasma K concentration. It is likely that plasma K is usually correlated with intracellular K and thereby provides a major link in the regulation of K excretion. It should be appreciated that amplification of the plasma K increment is so enormous that a high K intake, producing a barely perceptible increase in steady state plasma K, may eventuate in a urine K concentration of 300 mEq/liter. In the following discussion on the normal steady state, the idea is used that the plasma K reflects total body K and that total body K is a primary determinant of the factors that govern the magnitude of K secretion.

By viewing the plasma K concentration as a variable that both reflects total body K and regulates other factors responsible for the secretion of K by the distal nephron, we can begin to assess the importance of these other factors in steady state K balance. The two best studied factors are aldosterone production and Na intake.

Aldosterone and Na intake are considered by clinicians to be important regulators of renal K secretion. It is solidly established that one of the causes of hypokalemia (total body K depletion) is an aldosterone-producing tumor; removing the tumor corrects the hypokalemia. It also is clearly established that the hypokalemia so produced can be corrected by severely restricting dietary Na. Such dramatic clinical situations provide powerful insights into the cellular nature of the K secretory process. K secretion by the distal nephron is Na dependent.

But how does the body adjust to the more common and more physiologic situation of changing the K when there is an unchanged Na intake? One critical factor is the effect of increased plasma K in stimulating aldosterone production, thereby increasing secretion. In general, increasing K intake when there is a fixed Na supply results in four important adaptive changes: (1) There is a small but statistically significant increase in plasma K concentration. The magnitude of this increase is dependent on the increment of K intake but is usually 0.5 mEq/liter or less. (2) There is a significant increase in plasma aldosterone production and plasma aldosterone concentration without significant changes in plasma cortisol concentration. (3) Although the plasma aldosterone concentration is increased, the plasma renin activity (PRA) is not consistently elevated, although it is not depressed. This discrepancy between the increase in PRA and plasma aldosterone has been interpreted as being the result of the direct effect of increasing plasma [K] to stimulate aldosterone secretion. However, there is better evidence to support the idea that, in the high K intake situation, aldosterone secretion is more sensitive to any given level of PRA. (4) A consistent observation following K loading is a transient natriuresis. Carefully conducted studies demonstrate that after the steady state has been achieved, there is a significant reduction in the extracellular fluid (ECF) volume.

The important point of these observations is that a high K intake produces only small changes in plasma K and an increase in K excretion. The steady state is attended by an increase in aldosterone production, but contrary to what would be expected from the well-established effects of aldosterone on Na balance, there is a Na diuresis. These results demonstrate that the natriuretic effect of high K intake is antagonistic to the Na-retaining effect of higher circulating aldosterone. The effects of high K intake on aldosterone clearly are separate from its natriuretic effect.

These interactions between the effects of K intake on aldosterone production and ECF volume are depicted in Fig. 1. The generally accepted response to increased K intake via aldosterone is shown in the center, and the feedback loop maintaining the ECF volume at lower than otherwise normal levels is shown on the left. The interactions between ECF volume and aldosterone production are identified by solid lines, and the broken line indicates the tendency of aldosterone to increase ECF volume. The important point is that for any given state of aldosterone production set by a given Na intake, the

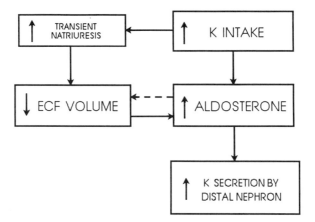

FIG. 1. Sequence of events following an increase in K intake without changing Na intake. A primary increase in K intake leads to an increase in aldosterone production and an increase in circulating plasma aldosterone as well as a transient natriuresis. On reaching the steady state, the extracellular fluid (ECF) volume is somewhat low, further causing an increase in aldosterone production. The increase in aldosterone production will tend to increase ECF volume, as shown by the broken line. The increase in K secretion by the distal nephron is primarily owing to the increase in aldosterone and may also be owing to intrarenal shifts of Na absorption from more proximal segments to the distal nephron.

effect of increasing K intake will produce a steady state increase in aldosterone and a reduction in ECF volume.

The nature of this effect of increasing K intake on Na balance is not completely understood. It is possible that K loading produces subtle effects that reduce the glomerular filtration rate. Alternatively, there may be alterations in the tubular reabsorption of Na. In this regard, the process of K recycling in the renal medulla may play a central role. We examine this process when we discuss disposition of an acute K load.

Given the fact that steady state K excretion rates are determined by some function of total body K, which in turn is related to intake, we can begin to dissect the factors that are important in changing the total body K and how plasma aldosterone concentration and Na intake influence K excretion.

Effect of Aldosterone and Sodium Intake on Steady State Potassium Excretion

The relationship between total body K and K excretion in normal subjects is of fundamental importance in understanding the effect of aldosterone and Na intake on these parameters. Normally, in the steady state, a high K intake produces only a modest (0.1–0.3 mEq/liter) increase in plasma K; i.e., the ratio of the increment in K excretion to increase in plasma K is large. What happens to this relationship when we maintain Na intake constant and fix plasma aldosterone concentration at one of three values: high, normal, and low? As demonstrated in Fig. 2, the higher plasma aldosterone concentrations shift the relationship up and to the left. For any K intake on a fixed Na intake, raising the plasma aldosterone causes a fall in plasma K, reflecting a reduction in total body K. This relationship demonstrates the central importance of aldosterone to the body K content.

In addition to the clearly documented effects of aldosterone on steady state K excretion, there is good evidence that Na intake, and thus Na excretion, can be an important determinant. When plasma aldosterone and K intake are held constant, an increase in Na intake will increase K excretion for any given value of plasma K. Figure 3 demonstrates this effect in adrenalectomized dogs replaced with constant amounts of aldosterone. When Na intake is low, steady state excretion of a given amount of K occurs at a higher plasma K concentration than when Na intake is high.

These experiments point out the dual nature of the effect of Na intake on K excretion in the intact animal. The first effect of decreasing Na intake is to increase the production of aldosterone. Thus, through the effect of increasing plasma aldosterone concentration, a low Na diet will maintain K balance even when distal Na delivery is reduced. The second effect of dietary Na on K excretion (in the absence of changes in plasma aldosterone) is the opposite. The higher the Na intake, the higher the K excretion.

The explanation for the positive correlation between Na intake and K excre-

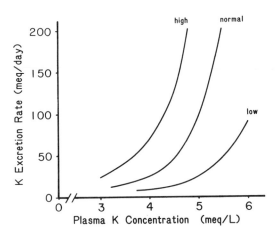

FIG. 2. Effect of high, normal, and low plasma aldosterone concentrations on K excretion rates at various plasma K concentrations. In this experiment, dogs given a constant infusion of normal plasma aldosterone concentrations displayed a rather steep increase in the magnitude of K excretion once plasma K concentration exceeded 4.5 mEq/liter. Higher fixed plasma aldosterone concentration shifted the curve to the left. When dogs were given only low plasma aldosterone concentrations, K intake >100 mEq/day caused dangerous hyperkalemia. (From ref. 35.)

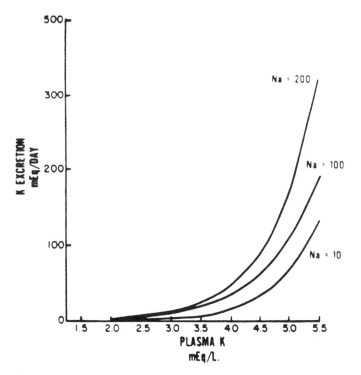

FIG. 3. The effect of varying Na intakes on plasma K concentration and K excretion. All dogs were given a constant infusion of aldosterone to maintain normal plasma concentrations. At very low Na intake (10 mEq/day), K balance was maintained only at the expense of very high plasma K concentrations. At high Na intake (200 mEq/day), K intakes of 300 mEq/day could be accommodated easily within the normal range of plasma K. These experiments demonstrate the importance of the Na intake on the steady state plasma K levels at any given intake of K. (From ref. 33.)

tion is probably not hormonal. Rather, it is likely the consequence of augmented distal tubule flow rate and Na delivery that results from the high Na intake. The two major physical factors that govern distal nephron K secretion are axial volume flow (in the distal convoluted tubule) and the luminal Na concentration (in the cortical collecting tubule). These two factors, the product of which constitutes Na delivery, are those that produce the aldosterone-independent effect of Na intake on K excretion.

The interrelationship between these two variables, aldosterone and Na excretion (intake), on K excretion exemplifies the complexities of some of the control systems for K excretion. The opposite effects of Na intake and aldosterone secretion on K excretion are teleologically reasonable. In conditions of high Na intake, K secretion can proceed without the need for major hormonal stimulation. With a low Na intake, substantial hormonal stimulation is necessary to compensate for the reduced distal Na delivery. Thus, the influence of Na intake on K excretion in the intact organism is a balance between the magnitude of aldosterone production and the physical factors (flow and lumen [Na]) present in the distal nephron.

Potassium Adaptation: How Is a Large Potassium Intake Excreted?

An increase in K intake from normal amounts of 60 mEq/day to amounts of 150 to 200 mEq/day produces a transient positive K balance, leading to an expansion of total body K followed by reestablishment of the steady state. This steady state is characterized by a slightly higher aldosterone concentration and plasma K concentration and a slight reduction in ECF volume.

The organ primarily responsible for this adaptation is the kidney. The colon also plays a role in K adaptation, using cellular mechanisms that are similar to those used by the kidney. Under normal circumstances, the colon is responsible for excreting 5 to 20% of the ingested K load. In patients with kidney disease, the fraction of colonic K excretion can be larger, and the magnitude can reach 30 mEq/day. For purposes of this discussion, we focus on the ways the kidney responds to high K intake.

Animals that have been fed high K diets for several days or weeks are adapted, and their kidneys exhibit some striking changes. Historically, one of the first things investigators noticed was that the amount of K excreted in K-adapted animals exceeded the filtered load. This situation can be explained only by invoking tubular secretion of K. This observation provided a firm foundation for the subsequent demonstration that the major site of K secretion was the distal nephron, specifically, the distal convoluted tubule and the cortical collecting tubule.

K-adapted animals can be distinguished easily from control animals by the fact that they drink more water and excrete more urine. The flow of urine through the distal tubule and collecting duct is, therefore, increased. In addition to the increase in tubular flow, the distal nephron displays (1) an increase in magnitude of the voltage across the epithelium, (2) an increased capacity to absorb Na, (3) an increased capacity to secrete K, (4) an enhanced ability to maintain high K concentrations in the tubular fluid, (5) hypertrophy of the cells responsible for K secretion, (6) enhancement of the area of the basolateral cell membrane (the side of the epithelial cell facing the blood), and (7) an enhancement of the activity of the Na,K pump.

An understanding of the significance of these changes is best approached by considering the cellular pathways for K secretion. These pathways are considered in detail in Chapter 6 and are simplified for our consideration. Figure 4 A represents a typical K-secreting cell. The process involves three steps. First, Na is absorbed from the lumen across the luminal (apical) cell membrane. Second, after entering the cell, it is pumped out across the blood side of the cell (basolateral cell membrane) by the Na,K pump (Na,K-ATPase).

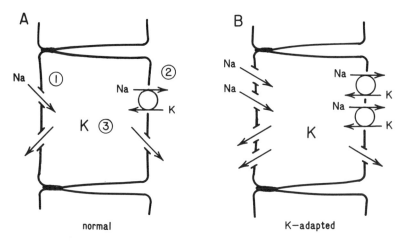

FIG. 4. K secretion by the distal nephron. **A:** K secretion under normal conditions. Three steps are important: (1) Na entry across the luminal membrane into the cell, (2) Na extrusion into the blood by the Na,K pump, and (3) the exit of K that has accumulated in the cell as a result of pump activity either across the luminal membrane or back into the blood. **B:** Hypertrophy of the K secretory system after K adaptation. There are more Na and K channels on the luminal membrane, more pump units on the basolateral (blood) membrane, but probably fewer K channels on the basolateral membrane.

The extrusion of three Na ions is accompanied by a transfer of two K ions into the cell. This charge translocation creates a flow of current (positive charge) from the lumen to the blood and accounts for the lumen-negative voltage across distal nephron segments. The third step in the K-secretory process involves the flow of K out of the cell either into the lumen (secretion) or back into the blood.

Several features are important to note. First, all of the energy for the ion translocation comes from Na,K-ATPase. The other translocations occur down an electrical or chemical gradient and, therefore, require no direct input of energy. Second, the process of K secretion is critically dependent on the presence of Na in the lumen. Agents that block the entry of Na (e.g., amiloride or triamterene) prevent K secretion. Likewise, physiologic states of intense Na retention can cause such avid Na proximal absorption that Na concentrations in the cortical collecting tubule can fall to values well below those optimal for K secretion. Thus, for maximal K secretion, an adequate supply of Na to the distal nephron is necessary.

Finally, Fig. 4 A demonstrates that the magnitude of K secretion is in large part dependent on the fraction of the K exiting the cell across the apical membrane versus the basolateral membrane. These relative rates of K transport are, in turn, determined by the electrical and chemical gradients across the two membranes, together with their relative permeabilities.

K adaptation affects all three steps. It increases the entry of Na across the

TABLE 1. *Cellular expressions of potassium adaptation on the distal nephron*

Primary increase	Manifestation
Apical Na channels	Greater voltage across the cell Greater Na absorption
Na, K pump activity (may be partly secondary to 1)	Greater Na, K-ATPase activity Enlargement of basolateral membrane area
Apical K channels	Greater K secretion Higher lumen [K]

apical membrane by increasing the number of Na channels, it increases the number of Na,K-ATPase units on the basolateral membrane, and it increases the apical membrane K permeability also by increasing the number of channels. These primary effects of K conditioning are depicted in Fig. 4 B, and their linkage with the observed physiologic parameters are shown in Table 1. These effects are applicable generally to the distal convoluted tubule, the connecting tubule, and the cortical collecting tubule, although the cellular details of the transport process may vary slightly. Similar principles obtain for the colon, although the specific membrane transport processes are not completely understood.

Stimuli for Distal Nephron Potassium Adaptation

The major alteration causing functional changes in the distal nephron in states of high K intake is the increased secretion of aldosterone. Numerous studies have shown that plasma aldosterone concentration increases as a result of increasing K intake. Furthermore, administration of aldosterone produces virtually all of the changes documented in K conditioning except for the change in plasma K. Whereas the K-adapted animal has slightly elevated plasma K values, animals treated with aldosterone (with normal Na intake) are hypokalemic. However, mineralocorticoid treatment produces qualitatively the same changes in the distal nephron as does K adaptation.

Aldosterone is not the only factor involved in K adaptation. There is now good evidence indicating that adrenalectomized animals placed on a constant infusion of aldosterone and fed a high K diet display qualitatively similar functional changes in the distal nephron as do animals with intact adrenal glands. Although the magnitude of the changes is blunted in the absence of adrenal glands, the clear conclusion is that a high K diet can enhance distal nephron K secretion independent of increases in aldosterone production. Clearly, aldosterone is not producing the entire effect.

Among the several possible candidates, two are worth considering seriously: high plasma K concentration and high urine flow rates. As mentioned previously, animals fed a high K diet have a small but significant elevation in plasma K. The long-term effect(s) of this elevation is not clear, but it is possible that it may be substantial over the period where adaptation takes place (days). For example, it is possible that the small membrane depolarization produced by elevated plasma K would contribute to these effects. It is also possible that a secondary effect of high K concentration (such as increased insulin secretion) may cause a trophic effect on the distal nephron disproportional to its effect on more proximal segments. It seems likely that there is either a primary or a secondary (hormonal) effect of high K intake that causes an increase in K secretion.

The second possible effect of K loading that may be related importantly to aldosterone-independent K adaptation is flow rate and distal Na delivery. Distal Na delivery is a term used to indicate the product of volume flow and Na concentration. In the intact kidney, it is often difficult to separate these variables because maneuvers that tend to increase flow to the distal nephron also tend to increase Na concentration at various points along the distal nephron. These variables can be separated experimentally, however. It is now clear that under physiologically relevant conditions, K secretion by the distal convoluted tubule is flow dependent and less dependent on lumen Na concentration. In contrast, K secretion by the cortical collecting tubule is critically dependent on the presence of adequate Na in the lumen (more than 30 mEq/liter).

The explanation for these differences involves the fundamental properties of the respective epithelia. The distal convoluted tubule can secrete K extremely quickly but can do so only up to a certain concentration of K in the lumen. In normal rats, lumen K concentration increases from 2 mEq/liter to 20 mEq/liters in less than 2 sec. However, concentrations greater than 20 mEq/liter are seen only under special conditions (e.g., high K diet). In contrast, the cortical collecting tubule can increase lumen K concentration to over 100 mEq/liter, but it requires minutes to do so. The distal convoluted tubule thus exemplifies a high capacity–low gradient K secretory system, whereas the cortical collecting tubule exemplifies a high gradient–low capacity system. This axial arrangement of high capacity systems operating in more proximal portions of the nephron than the lower capacity but high gradient systems is a recurring theme in renal solute transport. It appears to obtain for Na, Cl, and glucose absorption as well as H^+ and K secretion. The practical consequence of this functional array is that it permits the kidney to maintain steep chemical gradients with maximal efficiency.

The role of flow rate and lumen Na concentration may help explain the enhanced distal nephron K secretion in animals fed high K diets and maintained on a fixed infusion of mineralocorticoid hormone. There is recent evidence that, in this experimental setting, K loading increases distal nephron Na,K-

ATPase, the basolateral membrane area, and the magnitude of K secretion. The factor(s) responsible for this adaptation may include some function of the more elevated K concentration. Other factors, such as chronically increased Na delivery, also may play a role. There is recent evidence that diuretics increase the basolateral membrane area in the distal nephron of adrenalectomized rats on a fixed aldosterone infusion. If high K diets increase distal Na delivery and thereby produce the chronic changes described, there must be an intermediate step, not currently appreciated, that poises the distal nephron to secrete more K. It is likely that this step is closely associated with the increase in plasma K concentration (reflecting the increase in total body K).

DISPOSITION OF AN ACUTE POTASSIUM LOAD (7–9,13,17,25,26,40)

Extrarenal Potassium Disposition

The body's defense against hyperkalemia must include not only the ability to excrete the daily intake of K but also the ability to dispose of the absorbed K resulting from a normal meal. If we assume that a normal meal contains 30 mEq of K, a normal 70 kg man having approximately 14 liters of extracellular space would experience an increase in plasma K to 6.3 mEq/liter if the absorbed K remained only in the extracellular compartment. An increase in plasma K of 60% after a meal is not seen normally. Obviously, the absorbed K does not remain in the extracellular space. The increase in plasma K is disposed of by two mechanisms; it goes into cells, and it is excreted by the kidney.

The extrarenal disposition of K has been studied in considerable detail. Four important hormones regulate intracellular–extracellular balance: insulin, glucagon, adrenergic agents, and aldosterone. In addition, acid-base balance and plasma tonicity influence the distribution of potassium. The mechanisms regulating transport into cells have been reviewed in Chapter 1.

Renal Potassium Disposition

One of the most reproducible observations in studies examining the acute disposition of K is that following ingestion, renal K excretion increases. The events leading to this phenomenon are not yet completely understood. However, there are enough clues to allow us to construct a framework in which to interpret past experiments and evaluate future ones.

Several general observations are relevant. Carefully timed measurements demonstrate that plasma K and urine K secretion is not tightly coupled. Infusion of K intravenously produces a brisk rise in plasma K concentration and a delayed rise in urinary K excretion. When K infusion is stopped, plasma K concentration falls more rapidly than does the rate of K excretion. This pattern suggests that at least two mechanisms promote K excretion, one of which may be closely related to plasma K concentration and the other a secondary response to the K load. Candidates for delayed kaliuresis are hormones (e.g., aldosterone) or mobilization of a temporarily sequestered K pool that accumulated during the initial phase of K loading. These possibilities are not mutually exclusive. A third widely observed change following a K load is an acute natriuresis and diuresis. The rate of increase and peak natriuresis usually slightly precede the kaliuresis, and the magnitude of the natriuresis is often greater than that of the kaliuresis.

These three generally observed features of acute K administration have not been integrated into a generally accepted model of acute K excretion. However, the explanation of these findings can be approached using recently formulated concepts of K recycling to the medulla.

Process of Potassium Recycling and Accumulation in Renal Medulla

K recycling can be best envisioned as a four-step process (Fig. 5). The first step is secretion by the distal convoluted tubule and cortical collecting tubule into the tubular lumen. Without this K secretion, K recycling is greatly impaired if not impossible. Because of this secretion, K concentration increases along the cortical collecting tubule. In the section passing through the outer medulla, active K secretion stops because the transport processes necessary for K secretion are not present. The lumen K concentration, which has been elevated as a result of K secretion and water absorption, becomes higher than the medullary interstitial K. In the second step of K recycling, a fraction diffuses out of the medullary collecting tubule, thereby raising interstitial K and setting up the third step. In this step, the high medullary K diffuses into the descending limb of Henle's loop, elevating the K concentration of the fluid entering the ascending limb. The fourth step of K recycling is absorption by the ascending limb. (The magnitude of this process may be species dependent or diet dependent.) The net effect of these transport steps is to increase K concentration in all of the structures of the renal medulla.

The importance of this accumulation to K excretion probably rests with its effect on NaCl absorption by the thick ascending limb of Henle's loop. It is this structure that, by virtue of its ability to absorb NaCl without absorbing water, provides the energy necessary to produce a hypertonic medulla. A hypertonic medulla is essential for excretion of a concentrated urine. The accumulation of K in the medulla inhibits NaCl absorption by the thick ascending limb, perhaps in accord with the following mechanism: K recycling, by increasing the interstitial concentration of K, results in a depolarization of the cells of the ascending limb. In consequence intracellular Cl concentration would increase at the same rate that the driving force for NaCl entry at the

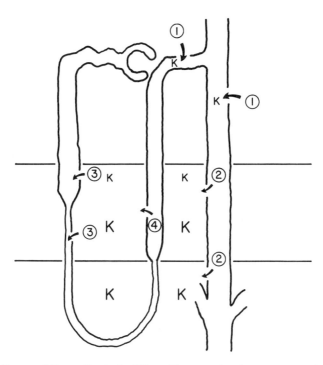

FIG. 5. Pathways of K recycling in the kidney. There are four important steps in K recycling: (1) K secretion by the distal nephron, (2) diffusion of K from the lumen of the collecting duct into the interstitium of the medulla, (3) diffusion of K from the medullary interstitium to the thin descending limb of Henle's loop, and (4) active extrusion of K by the medullary thick ascending limb. These steps serve to accumulate K in the medulla as a function of the magnitude of K secretion by the distal nephron. Such accumulation acts as a diuretic and prevents maximum absorption of NaCl by the thick ascending limb. (Adapted from ref. 40.)

apical membrane would diminish. The net effect would be inhibition of NaCl reabsorption.

Thus, K recycling can have the same effect as a diuretic; it can reduce NaCl absorption by the ascending limb, reduce the concentrating capacity of the kidney, and, secondary to these two effects, deliver more Na and H_2O to the nephron segments distal to the thick limb, two factors of importance for optimal K secretion. Viewed from the perspective of K secretion, K recycling is a function of the magnitude of K secretion by the distal nephron. It provides a mechanism to amplify K excretion by providing more optimal conditions for distal nephron K secretion.

One of the attractive features of this model is that it provides a reasonable explanation for the diuresis and natriuresis seen in acute K loading. It is possible that inhibition of Na reabsorption in the proximal tubule participates in the acute response to K loading and that it is synergistic with the effects of K recycling.

The diuretic response to K loading and K recycling may not be confined to the few hours after an acute K load. Similar patterns of natriuresis and diuresis are reported commonly for animals on high K diets. Medullary K accumulation, by inhibiting NaCl absorption by the thick ascending limb of Henle's loop, shifts the location of Na absorption to more distal sites, thereby allowing Na-dependent K secretion to occur under more optimal conditions.

CONSEQUENCES OF HYPERKALEMIA

The elaborate biologic systems that have evolved to dispose of the potentially wide-ranging variations in K intake have, as their central purpose, the maintenance of extracellular K concentration within narrow limits. As a consequence, the intracellular/extracellular K ratio also is maintained within fairly narrow limits.

When the K disposal mechanisms are defective and plasma K increases, the immediate and most important effects are on those cells possessing excitable membranes, i.e., nerves and muscle. Alterations in the membrane voltage change profoundly the ability of the nerve to conduct action potentials and of muscles to contract. The resting membrane voltage of most cells is fixed by the ratio of intracellular/extracellular K. Because hyperkalemia increases extracellular K concentration proportionally more than intracellular K, hyperkalemia depolarizes cells.

The most important clinical consequence of hyperkalemia is on the heart. The cause of death from hyperkalemia is cardiac arrest in diastole. The electrocardiographic changes of hyperkalemia should be known to every clinician because prompt recognition and initiation of therapy can be lifesaving.

Figure 6 A displays an electrocardiogram from a patient with a plasma K of 6.2 mEq/liter and demonstrates clearly the earliest abnormalities of hyperkalemia. The predominant feature is the tall, peaked T waves in the precordial leads. This characteristic shape results from the reduced duration of repolarization. Abnormalities of the QRS complex (depolarization) are not yet evident. With increasing plasma K concentrations, abnormalities in the P wave emerge. Atrial conduction slows, and the P wave amplitude is reduced; discernible P waves can be absent. The effects on the QRS complex occur at still higher K concentrations. Figure 6 B displays the ability of plasma K concentrations of over 8 mEq/liter to produce delayed depolarization, resulting in a prolonged QRS complex. The P waves have disappeared, and one has difficulty discerning whether the rhythm is sinus or nodal in origin. Sinus arrest, A-V dissociation, ventricular fibrillation, and finally cardiac arrest occur at somewhat higher K concentrations (*see* Chapter 3).

Although one can describe a reasonable predictable sequence of ECG events in response to increasing plasma K concentrations, the exact rate of progression depends on individual factors that may not be apparent at the time of discovery. Two such factors are the rate of rise of plasma K and the base-line K concentrations. In general, patients who are chronically hyperkalemic do not necessarily display ECG abnormalities at a given plasma K concentration typical for normal patients who have become hyperkalemic more quickly.

A second dramatic effect of hyperkalemia can be manifested on skeletal muscle. Familial hyperkalemic periodic paralysis is a rare disorder, the symptoms of which are produced by an unexplained, rapid elevation in plasma K. This disorder results from one or more abnormalities of the system(s) regulating the intracellular/extracellular K ratio. The familial disorders of K balance are discussed in Chapter 12.

A third and important metabolic effect of chronically elevated plasma K concentration is a depression in the renal synthesis of NH_3. Because NH_3 is the major urinary buffer, reduction in its production impairs the kidney's ability to excrete an acid load.

ETIOLOGIES OF HYPERKALEMIA (1–3,14–16,20,22,27)

Five major categories of hyperkalemia can be identified (Table 2):

1. Factitious: A laboratory artifact posing no threat to the patient and requiring no therapy.

2. Exogenous loads: A situation usually responding well to discontinuation of K therapy.

3. Endogenous loads: Resulting from cell lysis and release of cell contents, usually requiring concerted monitoring and therapy designed to put the patient into negative K balance.

4. K shifts from intracellular to extracellular: A problem requiring rapid diagnosis and, on occasion, rapid correction of the underlying disorder. Sometimes therapy must be in two or three stages: removal of extracellular K, correction of the underlying problem, and possible K replacement.

5. Impaired renal excretion: The most complex group of disorders, requiring careful assessment in order to avoid worsening of the condition. Impaired excretion often is found in combination with the other etiologies.

Factitious Hyperkalemia

The artifactually elevated concentration of K comes from lysis of blood cells. Lysis of red blood cells can occur in conditions where the red cell membranes are sensitive to injury (e.g., spherocytosis). More commonly, red cell lysis is caused by careless venipuncture technique. One potential clue to traumatic red cell lysis is the pink color of plasma caused by hemoglobin.

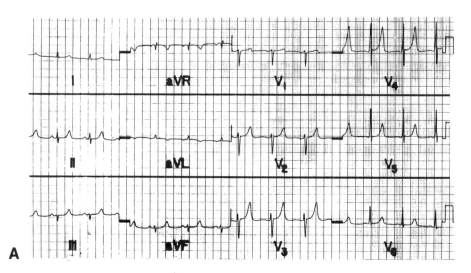

A

FIG. 6. Effects of hyperkalemia on the electrocardiogram. **A:** Early abnormalities of peaked T waves. **B:** More advanced and potentially lethal hyperkalemia (precordial leads only).

Although not all hemolyzed specimens will have abnormal elevations of K concentration, in the presence of hemolysis, all elevations of plasma or serum K must be suspected as being artifactual.

The elevated K values caused by lysis of platelets or white blood cells are almost always seen in the setting of thrombocytosis or leukocytosis. In the majority of cases, these cells are abnormal and, therefore, susceptible to cell membrane injury. Thus, nonhemolytic factitious hyperkalemia is usually accompanied by platelet counts of more than 800,000 and white blood cell counts of more than 50,000.

The correct procedure for collecting venous blood in cases of suspected factitious hyperkalemia is to (1) use a wide-bore needle (19 gauge or larger) attached to a heparinized syringe (to prevent coagulation artifacts), (2) loosen the tourniquet before applying suction to the syringe, and (3) aspirate the blood sample very gently to minimize shearing forces. The blood should be transferred immediately to a test tube (not under vacuum) and centrifuged gently.

Exogenous Loads

Normal animals have an enormous capacity to excrete K. Adults can excrete over 200 to 300 mEq/day with only a mild increase in plasma K concentration. However, there are some situations in which K intake can produce hyperkalemia in otherwise normal individuals. In general, there are two such circum-

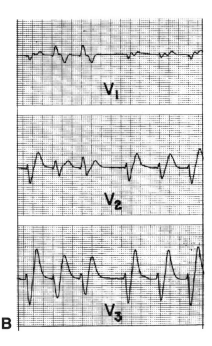

FIG. 6. (*Continued.*)

stances. The first is when Na intake is severely restricted, and the second is when K is ingested or infused rapidly.

Clinical experiments in normal humans have demonstrated that when dietary Na is reduced to less than 10 mEq/day, K intakes of up to 150 mEq/day are tolerated without clinically threatening hyperkalemia. However, intakes of K over 200 mEq/day often are associated with dangerous hyperkalemia. It is most unlikely that a person could, even intentionally, ingest that much potassium other than with K supplementation.

A more common setting for hyperkalemia as a result of increased intake is the patient who, perhaps because of mild hypokalemia, is placed on K supplementation. The ability to dispose of an acute K load depends on the previous history of K intake. K-adapted animals display less of a rise in plasma K concentration after a K load than do normal animals. Hypokalemia may predispose to K retention and may thus render the patient more susceptible to hyperkalemia following attempts at rapid correction.

A reasonable guideline regarding K replacement therapy is to give no more than 20 mEq/hr. It is far better to delay the recovery from hypokalemia than to have to treat arrhythmias resulting from hyperkalemia.

Endogenous Loads

Because more than 98% of the body K is located within cells, the organism is continuously threatened by the risk of hyperkalemia from within. If only

TABLE 2. *Etiologies of hyperkalemia*

Factitious
  Hemolysis
  Thrombocytosis
  Leukocytosis

Exogenous K loads
  Rapid K administration
  High K intake on severe Na restriction
  Bleeding into internal cavity, with subsequent
    absorption

Endogenous k loads (cell injury)
  Trauma and burns
  Rhabdomyolysis
  Tumor lysis
  Hemolysis

Intracellular to extracellular shift
  Hyperkalemic periodic paralysis
  Exercise
  HCl acidosis
  Hypertonicity
  Diabetes
  Drugs (digitalis, succinylcholine)

Impaired renal excretion
  Renal insufficiency (acute or chronic)
  Inadequate distal Na delivery
    Prostaglandin inhibitors
    Very low Na diet
    Gordon's syndrome?
    NaCl retaining states
  Impaired distal nephron function
    Interstitial nephritis
    Sickle cell disease
    Obstructive nephropathy
    Systemic lupus erythematosus
    Transplant nephropathy
    K-sparing drugs (amiloride, triamterene,
      spironolactone)
  Mineralocorticoid deficiency
    Addison's disease
    Enzyme defect (21-hydroxylase, corticosterone
      methyl oxidase)
    Idiopathic hypoaldosteronism
    Heparin (chronic therapy)
  Defective renin secretion
    Defective prostaglandin production
    Autonomic insufficiency
    Diabetes mellitus

2% of the intracellular K were suddenly to leak into the extracellular space, the result would be catastrophic. It is no surprise that extensive cell injury can be accompanied by severe hyperkalemia requiring intensive efforts to prevent cardiac arrhythmias.

The most dramatic setting for this form of hyperkalemia is the crush injury. When large portions of extremities are damaged, hyperkalemia must be monitored carefully. As is true for rhabdomyolysis, the hyperkalemia resulting from dying cells is accompanied by the appearance in the plasma of other intracellular substances. Thus, the elevation of plasma phosphorus and enzymes associated with muscle cells (aldolase, creatine kinase, lactate dehydrogenase, and transaminases) provides major clues about the origin of the elevated K.

Besides the death or injury of muscle cells, the death of tumor cells also can release large quantities of K with sufficient rapidity to produce serious hyperkalemia. Again, there is associated release of other intracellular products. Of special concern is the killing of rapidly growing cells, resulting in the release of precursors of uric acid. Therefore, allopurinol should be given prophylactically to patients in whom substantial tumor cell lysis may be expected.

The therapeutic objective for this group of disorders is to remove K from the ECF. To promote effective and fast renal excretion, saline should be given so that adequate distal Na delivery and copious urine flow (e.g., 100 ml/hr or more) can be ensured. Other, more aggressive measures (outlined under Therapy) may be necessary.

One of the ever threatening complications in these clinical settings is acute renal failure. After muscle injury, release of myoglobin can cause acute tubular necrosis. After tumor cell lysis, the release of purines predisposes to enhanced production of uric acid, which can produce urate nephropathy. The superimposition of acute renal failure in a setting of endogenous K release can produce extremely dangerous situations mandating hemodialysis. Early recognition of these problems should lead to institution of preventive measures. Infusion of bicarbonate solution to alkalinize the urine will assist in preventing both myoglobin-induced renal failure and urate nephropathy. These two therapeutic goals, alkalinization of the urine and Na diuresis, can be best accomplished by infusing 1 liter of half-normal saline and 1 ampule (44 mEq) of $NaHCO_3$ solution every 6 to 8 hr.

Intracellular to Extracellular Shift

The release of cell K by lysis or severe injury is not the only way intracellular K can cause hyperkalemia. There are several physiologic and pathophysiologic situations where K leaks out of the cell faster than it can be taken up or faster than it can be excreted. The importance of these situations lies primarily in the recognition that complete correction must have as its major goal the restoration of normal amounts of intracellular K.

The purest example of hyperkalemia resulting from such a shift is the rare syndrome of familial hyperkalemic periodic paralysis. The pathophysiology of these syndromes is covered in Chapter 14.

Some insight into the problem of K balance can be gained from the studies on exercising humans. When it is sufficiently heavy, exercise produces a significant increase in plasma K owing to muscle K loss. The local effect of this hyperkalemia is to dilate the blood vessels supplying the bed, and thus this physiologic K leak serves an important function for the exercising muscle. Shortly after reduction in the intensity of exercise, plasma K values return to near normal. This process of release and reuptake of muscle K appears to be heavily influenced by the adrenergic nervous system, since beta-blocking agents exaggerate the hyperkalemia. This reuptake seems to be mediated by $beta_2$ receptors; therefore, selective $beta_1$ agonists (atenolol, metoprolol) should, in proper doses, have minimal effect on plasma K.

One of the most pervasive misconceptions among practitioners of medicine about the etiology of hyperkalemia is the idea that acidosis produces hyperkalemia. It was originally thought that for any given plasma pH reduction, the plasma K would increase by a constant value. Over the past 10 to 15 years, numerous investigators have shown that this relationship is not correct. The correct interpretation of the data is as follows: When HCl is infused (or the equivalent mineral acid is allowed to accumulate), as the plasma pH falls, plasma K increases. However, if acidemia is induced by another acid form, such as lactic or beta-OH-butyric acid (or any organic acid), there is no change in plasma K. Similarly, acute or chronic respiratory acidosis produces little or no change in plasma K.

The most dramatic example of this relationship in humans was published by Orringer et al. They measured plasma pH, lactate, and electrolytes in patients during and after grand mal seizures. Although there was significant lactic acidosis, the plasma K was constant. Similar results obtain for infusions of other organic acids. The reason that the K shift occurs only with mineral acids probably has to do with the permeability of the relevant anion. Whereas organic acids are freely diffusible across cell membranes (by the process of nonionic diffusion of the undissociated form), Cl permeation must take specific transport pathways that are highly regulated. Since in HCl acidosis, the entry of H^+ into the cell is incompletely accompanied by Cl^-, electroneutrality must be maintained by movement of another ion. A portion of this counter-ion flow is the exit of K^+.

There is a second commonly encountered metabolic disturbance that can produce hyperkalemia, i.e., hypertonicity. Hypertonic states induced by administration of hypertonic saline, mannitol, or glucose will sometimes produce hyperkalemia. On the other hand, infusion of urea generally will not raise plasma K. The difference between these agents is that urea is freely permeable across cell membranes and thus exerts no effective osmotic pressure. Since NaCl, glucose, and mannitol are confined to the extracellular space, they cause cells to shrink. Numerous reasons have been proposed to explain this phenomenon. The most commonly advanced mechanism is that of solvent drag; as H_2O leaves the cell by osmosis, it drags K with it. Such an explanation seems unlikely given the nature of cell membrane H_2O and ion permeation. Another explanation invokes an increase in cell K concentration and the increase in chemical driving force for K exit. This latter explanation may be more to the point. However, cell shrinkage invariably is followed by a secondary increase in their volume by processes that increase cell K content. Thus, based on our knowledge of the cellular response to shrinkage, we would expect hypertonicity to be associated with hypokalemia and not hyperkalemia. Clearly, more investigation is needed on this topic.

Diabetes

The derangements of K concentration in diabetic ketoacidosis present the clinician with a complex array of possible causes. Diabetic patients commonly are hypokalemic owing to starvation, diuretic administration, and vomiting. The patient is K deficient and requires K administration. However, the diabetic in ketoacidosis who is hyperkalemic also may be K deficient. Several factors converge in this setting to produce a shift in K from the intracellular space to the ECF. The first is hormone deficiency. In the absence of insulin, cell K uptake mechanisms function suboptimally and hyperkalemia ensues. The two other hormones responsible for cell K uptake, beta-adrenergic agents and aldosterone, also may be deficient in diabetics. Diabetics with autonomic insufficiency may have suboptimal beta-adrenergic stimulation, and many diabetics have hypoaldosteronism. Thus, diabetics may be deficient in three hormones important for extrarenal K disposition.

The second problem complicating the assessment of K balance is the presence of hypertonicity. We have just reviewed the observations demonstrating the increase in extracellular K occurring as a result of hypertonicity. The diabetic may be particularly susceptible to this effect owing to marked hyperglycemia.

The third problem in ketoacidosis involving K balance is the acidosis. Although organic acids (i.e., beta-OH-butyrate) do not alter plasma K concentration, patients with ketoacidosis often do not have pure ketoacidosis (as estimated by the anion gap). Furthermore, most patients with ketoacidosis, when corrected, go through a phase of hyperchloremic acidosis before fully correcting the acid-base disorder. This phase of acidosis is thought to be owing to several factors: (1) There is a loss of bicarbonate equivalents (ketoacids) in the urine. Replacement therapy consisting of Cl solution replaces the lost acid anion with Cl. Regeneration of HCO_3 by the kidney takes a few days to complete. (2) Acidosis increases cell Cl via the Cl-HCO$_3$ exchangers. As HCO$_3$ concentration increases, Cl moves out of the cell and contributes to the hyperchloremic acidosis. (3) Most patients with ketoacidosis are volume contracted. Administration of NaCl solutions produces an expansion acidosis. Thus, for one or more of these reasons, treatment of diabetic ketoacidosis produces a transient hyperchloremic acidosis.

The importance of this phase of treatment of diabetic ketoacidosis is that it is functionally not different from HCl acidosis. Thus, correction can be expected to shift K into the cells. The key therapeutic point is that the clinician should expect to see a further reduction in plasma K as the patient receives insulin and assumes a more normal acid-base status.

Drugs

There are two drugs known to predispose to shifts of K from cells into the extracellular space. Succinylcholine, a muscle relaxant used in surgery, produces a prolonged depolarization of muscle membranes. In traumatized cells or in muscles affected by certain neuromuscular diseases, this depolarization can effect a massive release of K. In normal patients, the rise in plasma K generally is small and of no significance. In susceptible patients, the increase in plasma K can produce cardiac arrest. In patients susceptible to this effect, a better muscle relaxant is pancuronium.

The second drug capable of causing a shift in K into the extracellular space is digoxin. An inhibitor of the Na,K pump, its major mechanism of action is to enhance myocardial contractility via the increase in cell Ca^{2+} that occurs secondary to the (partial) pump inhibition. Used in appropriate therapeutic doses, there is no significant effect on plasma K. However, when digitalis toxicity is superimposed on conditions that predispose to hyperkalemia or when massive amounts of digitalis are taken, dangerous hyperkalemia can follow.

Impaired Renal Excretion

The inability of the kidney to excrete K normally is the most common group of disorders resulting in hyperkalemia. The knowledge that K is secreted by the distal nephron by a process dependent on the absorption of Na leads directly to the conclusion that K secretion depends on an adequate glomerular filtration rate (GFR). Therefore, any disease that impairs GFR has the potential to reduce K secretion and produce hyperkalemia. Given this circumstance, it is perhaps surprising that hyperkalemia is not a major problem in patients with chronic renal disease until the GFR falls below 20 ml/min. Even at rates of 10 ml/min, the adaptive capacity of the distal nephron is adequate to maintain K homeostasis at the cost of only modest increases in plasma K (to 5–6 mEq/liter). The adaptive changes in response to reduction in nephron mass appear to be similar to those operating in normal kidneys. The hypertrophy of the secretory system probably is dependent on intact aldosterone secretion and adequate Na delivery owing to diminished proximal reabsorption. With reduced nephron mass, osmotic diuresis through residual nephrosis, increased filtration per nephron of nonreabsorbable anions, and effective volume expansion may account for the suppression of more proximal Na reabsorption.

As discussed earlier, optimal K secretion depends on an adequate delivery of Na to the distal nephron as well as an adequate urine flow rate. In the presence of very high intakes, it is possible to reduce Na intake so that K secretion is inadequate to maintain a normal serum K. Although this is unusual because of the extreme difficulty in eliminating Na from the diet, there is a more common situation with hyperkalemia that develops as a result of impaired distal Na delivery. The setting for the problem most commonly occurs in the great salt-retaining states: cirrhosis, nephrotic syndrome, and heart failure.

In these pathologic conditions, the maintenance of the GFR has been shown repeatedly to be dependent on renal prostaglandin production, presumably PGI_2 production by the glomerulus. Prostaglandin production is also increased in the renal medulla. The major effect of medullary PGE_2 production is to inhibit NaCl absorption by the thick ascending limb of Henle's loop. Thus, under conditions calling for NaCl retention, renal prostaglandin production acts to preserve GFR and stabilize Na delivery to the distal nephron. From this perspective, it requires only a small integrative step to explain the reduction in GFR and increased plasma K concentration in these clinical settings after an inhibitor of prostaglandin production is given. Indomethacin and all of the nonsteroidal anti-inflammatory drugs, by virtue of inhibiting cyclooxygenase, produce reductions in GFR and distal Na delivery in all conditions characterized by a tendency to retain NaCl.

Another setting where decreased distal Na delivery appears to limit normal K secretion is the rare syndrome reported by Gordon et al. The patient had hypertension, hyperkalemia, low plasma renin activity, and low plasma aldosterone concentrations. All abnormalities were corrected by either NaCl restriction or diuretics. The exact pathophysiology of this syndrome is not completely clear, but it seems likely that it is in some way connected to overly avid NaCl absorption in a section of the nephron proximal to the K secretory segment. The resulting Na delivery to the distal nephron in the face of low plasma aldosterone concentrations was insufficient to maintain adequate K secretion.

Defective Tubular Secretion

Several disorders have been associated with an inability to excrete K disproportionate to the degree of renal insufficiency. Such disorders as interstitial nephritis can display exaggerated defects in distal nephron function, including severe acidosis and hyperkalemia. Similar problems have been reported in the setting of urinary tract obstruction. Presumably, the increased pressure within the collecting system damages the collecting duct cells, rendering them resistant to the action of aldosterone. Sickle cell disease, systemic lupus erythematosus, and transplanted kidneys all have been reported to display defects in K excretion. The incidence of these defects is not known; presumably in many patients they may be mild.

An important subgroup of agents causing defective K secretion is the K-sparing diuretics. Amiloride and triamterene prevent K secretion by blocking Na channels in the luminal membrane of K-secreting cells. As shown in Fig. 4, without Na absorption K secretion falls to unmeasurably low values. Spironolactone acts by another mechanism. It interacts with the aldosterone receptor to prevent stimulation of the transport system. Presumably, the basal level of Na absorption and K secretion is not altered. Thus, spironolactone has minimal effects in adrenalectomized animals, whereas amiloride and triamterene can be effective in the absence of aldosterone. Clinically important hyperkalemia is found more commonly in patients taking the Na channel blocking drugs. When they are used in conjunction with other diuretics in patients with normal renal function, hyperkalemia is seldom a problem. However, the use of potassium-sparing diuretics in conjunction with K supplementation in patients with renal insufficiency or in patients predisposed to K retention must be carefully monitored. Two drugs predisposing to hyperkalemia, particularly when given with these diuretics, are beta blockers and angiotensin-converting enzyme inhibitors; both act by diminishing angiotensin production, thereby reducing aldosterone secretion.

Mineralocorticoid Hormone Deficiency

Few patients display a pure defect in aldosterone secretion, but when it occurs, it must be carefully documented and appropriately treated. In its complete manifestation, the syndrome can be documented readily by the signs of volume contraction, abundant Na in the urine, hyperkalemia, and acidosis. It is a major part of Addison's disease. Other causes of aldosterone deficiency include enzyme defects (21-hydroxylase and corticosterone methyl oxidase), idiopathic hypoaldosteronism, and a poorly understood defect in adrenal glomerulosa cells. An acquired form of aldosterone deficiency has been reported in patients receiving chronic heparin therapy.

In its pure state, mineralocorticoid hormone deficiency is associated with elevated PRA that does not suppress with salt loading. However, it is more commonly encountered in conjunction with defects in the renin secretory system. Whether these defects result from atrophy of the mineralocorticoid hormone system from lack of renin-angiotensin II stimulation or whether there are disorders that produce selective paralysis of both systems has not been determined.

Defective Renin Secretion

As one of the dominant influences on the production of aldosterone, renin via angiotensin II can play a major role in K excretion. It is now clear that an intact adrenergic system and an intact prostaglandin system are important for full adequate expression of renin secretion. Therefore, disorders characterized by deficiencies in prostaglandin production or autonomic dysfunction may be associated with blunted renin response. Drugs most commonly associated with this situation are beta-adrenergic blockers and nonsteroidal anti-inflammatory agents.

In addition to drugs, diabetes mellitus often is associated with reduced renin production. The syndrome, hyporeninemic hypoaldosteronism, may arise from a primary defect in the ability of the juxtaglomerular cells to produce renin. It has been postulated that the vascular disease seen in diabetics, which can disproportionately affect the efferent arteriole of the glomerulus, may be related to the problem of renin secretion. An alternative explanation, that in diabetics there is expanded ECF volume and, therefore, a reduced stimulus to renin secretion, has received considerable attention. The disturbances in diabetics are subtle and complex and as yet are incompletely understood.

HYPERKALEMIA IN TYPE IV RENAL TUBULAR ACIDOSIS
(4,5,10,12,16,18,21,23,24,30)

The myriad factors involved in K balance and the consequences of the organism's failure to maintain normal K homeostasis are best exemplified in the syndrome of type IV renal tubular acidosis (RTA). The classic forms of RTA (i.e., proximal and distal) are actually rare (although they serve as examples of the consequences of defective proximal and distal acidification). Type IV RTA, however, is common and exemplifies the interaction of several possible defects.

The syndrome was first described in the 1950s, when it was recognized in a series of patients with renal disease. Its features are hyperkalemia, hyperchloremic acidosis (non-anion gap), and urine pH less than 5.2. These features form a distinct entity Neither proximal nor classic distal RTA is characterized by hyperkalemia, uremic acidosis occurs with an anion gap (owing to the accumulation of unmeasured and unexcreted anions), and the distal acidification mechanism appeared to be intact because the urine pH was acid. Subsequent studies in patients with this syndrome have demonstrated reduced PRA and plasma aldosterone concentration, reduced urinary ammonia excretion, depressed ability of the proximal tubule to absorb HCO_3, and reduced urinary excretion of prostaglandin. This constellation may not be present in every patient. From the variety of theories in the literature, it is clear that no single defect can explain completely the findings in every patient.

The syndrome is present in a variety of clinical settings. Although it can occur in patients in whom it is completely unexpected, there are two situations where it may be anticipated: progressive renal insufficiency and diabetes mellitus. When the two states coexist, the incidence of type IV RTA is common.

The fundamental problem in this syndrome is the inability to secrete K. There is a secondary defect in distal H^+ secretion (owing to a lack of buffer), but such defect alone will not produce the syndrome. The interactions of the systems regulating K secretion and its relationship to acid-base balance are outlined in Fig. 7. Emphasized in this schematic are the abnormalities tending to prevent normal K secretion and the effect of hyperkalemia in predisposing to acidosis.

The defective K secretion can be caused by any of a number of problems along the previously described chain of events regulating normal K secretion. There can be a tubular defect, defective aldosterone secretion, defective renin secretion, or a combination of all three. The complexity of the syndrome is exemplified in patients exhibiting a primary defect in renin secretion and thus having blunted aldosterone production but in whom aldosterone replacement fails to correct the disorder.

One of the most useful ways to separate patients with this syndrome is to determine whether or not they are volume contracted. Absence of hypotension and orthostatic reductions in blood pressure and tachycardia is evidence for a noncontracted extracellular volume. The presence of volume contraction implies a primary deficiency in aldosterone. (Rarely, children can have the syndrome secondary to distal nephron unresponsiveness to aldosterone.) In this setting, the long-term therapy must include as its major therapeutic objective mineralocorticoid hormone replacement. Careful documentation of the exact problem is, therefore, quite important.

Most patients with type IV RTA are not volume contracted; in fact, over half are hypertensive or have edema. These patients cannot have a primary deficiency in aldosterone production as a cause of the derangement. Many such patients will display a blunted aldosterone response to appropriate stimuli, but we can conclude with certainty that deficiency in aldosterone production is not the primary problem.

Integrated Pathophysiology of Type IV RTA

The typical patient with type IV RTA is an insulin-dependent diabetic of long duration, often with hypertension, diabetic retinopathy, peripheral neuropathy, and perhaps a small amount of ankle edema. The creatinine is moderately elevated, and hyperkalemic, hyperchloremic acidosis is present.

The patient clearly is not volume contracted. The presence of edema and mild hypertension reflect an expanded ECF volume. Measurements disclose both a low plasma renin and aldosterone activity. From the therapeutic point of view, there is no primary need for mineralocorticoid hormone replacement therapy. The problem facing the physician is to determine the reasons why the increased serum K has not stimulated the compensatory mechanisms normally invoked to correct the hyperkalemia.

According to Fig. 7, there are three reasons why such a patient might have this syndrome. The most important problem is the expansion of the ECF volume. The expanded volume will reduce renin secretion, which will reduce aldosterone secretion and will, through the reduction in distal nephron K secretion, raise plasma K concentration. Such a scenario can help explain the hyperkalemia but does not explain how the patient became volume expanded. It is probable that the reduction in GFR was primarily responsible. The importance of volume expansion in this syndrome is underscored by the clinical observation that most patients progressing to renal insufficiency pass through a phase where they manifest the syndrome of type IV RTA. The nature of the renal disease does not seem to play a major role in the incidence, although the underlying disease may be important in the severity of expression.

Two other problems may amplify the severity of the syndrome. The autonomic neuropathy may decrease the basal neural tone that sensitizes the juxtaglomerular cells to renin-releasing stimuli, and the kidney may be defective in its ability to produce prostaglandins. The impairment in prostaglandin production may further impair renin release and may, by increasing NaCl absorption in the thick ascending limb of Henle's loop, reduce distal Na delivery to the K-secreting site. Both of these effects will result in impaired K secretion.

The expansion of the ECF volume produces several further effects that may be additive in the production of type IV RTA. In addition to inhibiting renin release, it stimulates atrial natriuretic peptide (ANP), which in turn can suppress aldosterone production. One reason why ANP may be ineffective as a natriuretic agent is that the GFR is too low and Na delivery to the nephron site of action is insufficient for ANP to produce a significant natriuresis. The effect of volume expansion to reduce renal nerve traffic may dampen renin release, although if neuropathy is prominent, the contribution of this factor may be slight.

The fourth effect of volume expansion in the production of type IV RTA is on the production of acidosis. It has long been appreciated that volume expansion can reduce the maximal ability of the proximal tubule to absorb HCO_3 (T_m HCO_3). The cellular mechanisms underlying this effect are not clear, but its occurrence has produced speculation that a portion of the acidosis seen in this syndrome is owing to this effect. In support of this theory are

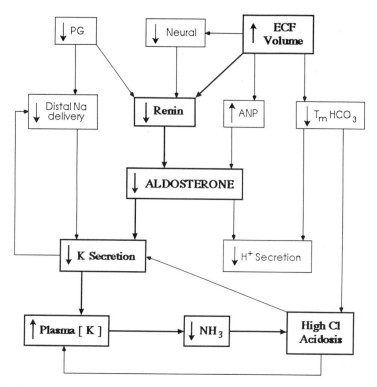

FIG. 7. Pathophysiology of type IV renal tubular acidosis. (PG) prostaglandin; (ECF) extracellular fluid; (ANP) atrial natriuretic peptide; (T_m) tubular maximum of HCO_3 reabsorption.

reports of patients with corrected T_m HCO_3 values following volume contraction.

From Fig. 7 we can see that the primary derangements, volume expansion, decreased renal nerve traffic, and decreased prostaglandin production produce secondary effects that, in general, suppress aldosterone production. In a sense, aldosterone is the cornerstone in the expression of the syndrome; without aldosterone (mineralocorticoid hormone), K secretion will be sluggish and hyperkalemia almost inevitable. Also from Fig. 7, we can see that type IV RTA syndrome could be produced by a pure deficiency in aldosterone. The major difference in the clinical expression is the presence or absence of an expanded ECF volume.

Aldosterone Deficiency and Type IV RTA

The lower portion of Fig. 7 emphasizes the consequences of aldosterone deficiency. The most important effect is on the distal nephron, where K secretion is suboptimal. The reduced K secretion may, in some situations, impair optimal Na delivery. By impairing K recycling, urine flow and Na concentration to the distal nephron may be inappropriately low, further impairing optimal K secretion.

However, the major effect of K retention on the syndrome is the reduction in NH_3 production. As discussed earlier, K depletion is a major stimulus to renal ammoniagenesis, and hyperkalemia does the opposite. In the absence of sufficient ammonia to provide a urinary buffer, acidification of the distal nephron tubular fluid is achieved rapidly, and the low pH limits further H^+ secretion. In this way, hyperkalemia limits the regeneration of HCO_3 by the distal nephron, and hyperchloremic acidosis ensues. The dominance of hyperkalemia in the production of acidosis is best exemplified by studies demonstrating complete correction of the acidosis after K removal by polystyrene resins.

Although hyperkalemia dominates the generation and maintenance of acidosis, two other factors contribute. As previously discussed, expansion of the ECF volume, commonly present in chronic renal insufficiency, suppresses the ability of the proximal tubule to absorb HCO_3 maximally. In addition to this proximal effect, aldosterone stimulates H^+ secretion, and in its absence distal tubular acidification would be suboptimal.

The acidosis could also worsen the hyperkalemia, although these effects are probably minor. The absence of urinary buffer (NH_3), by allowing the tubular pH to fall more rapidly, would reduce maximal K secretion. This mechanism involves direct reduction of apical membrane K permeability by acid solutions. A second contribution of the acidosis to the hyperkalemia may be a shift of K out of the cell. This shift in K would be analogous to that seen with mineral acid infusion.

Treatment of Type IV RTA

The approach to the patient with type IV RTA evolves naturally from consideration of the pathophysiology. As depicted in Fig. 8, the first decision is if the patient is volume contracted. Volume contraction leads one to consider strongly the diagnosis of aldosterone deficiency, aldosterone resistance, or Addison's disease. The exact diagnosis is important so that appropriate replacement therapy (mineralocorticoid or glucocorticoid hormone) can be selected.

If the patient is volume expanded, the primary problem is not mineralocorticoid hormone deficiency. There may be decreased aldosterone production even with hyperkalemia, but the first therapeutic approach is not administration of mineralocorticoid hormones. The first attempt at correction of the syndrome should be administration of diuretics. The diuretic of choice is a long acting agent that would be successful in inducing a mild natriuresis.

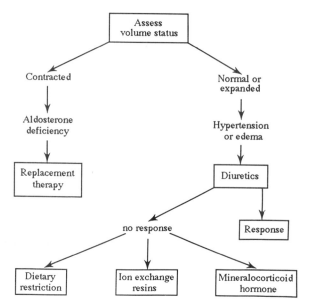

FIG. 8.   Approach to treatment of the patient with type IV renal tubular acidosis.

Chlorthalidone, hydrochlorothiazide, or any of the family of thiazidelike diuretics is appropriate in patients who have GFRs above 50 ml/min. For patients with GFRs lower than 25 ml/min, furosemide or one of the class of loop diuretics is often necessary. Since these agents often are relatively short acting, an extended natriuresis often requires twice daily dosage.

The logic for using diuretic therapy can be defended in several ways. For patients with hypertension or edema, the logic is self-evident. For correcting the hyperkalemia, diuretics will increase Na delivery to the sites of K secretion by blocking absorption in more proximal nephron segments. Loop diuretics may be more effective than thiazide diuretics because they tend to wash out the medulla and will, therefore, increase Na delivery to the distal nephron. A second effect will be to reduce ECF volume, thereby stimulating the renin-angiotensin-aldosterone system. Even with documented hyporeninemic hypoaldosteronism, long-term diuretic therapy may restore an element of responsiveness to the system.

The major goal of correcting the syndrome is to reduce plasma K to normal values. Correction of plasma K and contraction of ECF volume will tend to correct the acidosis. Reduction in plasma K will permit increased NH_3 production and improve the buffering capacity of the urine. Contraction of the extracellular fluid volume will enhance the proximal tubule T_m for HCO_3. Reduction in plasma K also will produce this effect.

If diuretics are not completely effective, several options remain. Unless there are intolerable side effects, such as hypotension, diuretic therapy should be continued. Reduction in K intake may help, and, if that option appears unlikely to work, polystyrene sulfonate resin (Kayexalate) can be given orally (*see* Therapy of Acute Hyperkalemia). The rationale for concentrating on reducing plasma K is well founded. It has been shown that normalization of plasma K corrects the acidosis.

If diuretics and efforts to reduce plasma K are unsuccessful, one can try mineralocorticoid hormone therapy. Ordinarily this modality should not be used in the presence of edema or hypertension. However, it can be useful (and even necessary) in patients with a tendency to hypotension.

THERAPY OF ACUTE HYPERKALEMIA

There are four modalities used to lower K acutely; they are aimed at alleviating the complications in three different ways. The first is to minimize the depolarizing effect on the myocardium, the second to shift K into the cells, and the third to create a net loss of K from the body.

Since K depolarizes the myocardium, it renders it more susceptible to arrhythmias (*see* Chapter 3). Therefore, administration of Ca^{2+} (as the chloride or gluconate) will reduce the threshold potential (make it less negative) and thereby render the myocardium less susceptible to arrhythmias. Intravenous administration of 1 g of Ca^{2+} will buy important time to allow other therapeutic modalities to function.

The second therapeutic objective is to shift K into cells. Two agents are available for this therapy, HCO_3 and insulin with glucose. HCO_3 therapy will immediately cause K to enter cells. Its mechanism of action is not clear, but its efficacy is well established. Insulin will also cause K to enter cells. To achieve a maximum effect, pharmacologic doses are required, and to prevent hypoglycemia, glucose must be administered simultaneously. A general guideline to be used in this setting is to infuse 10% glucose plus 1 ampule (44 mEq) $NaHCO_3$ at 500 ml/hr and 20 units of insulin/hr. It may be important not to infuse $NaHCO_3$ or glucose as hypertonic solutions. In many patients, hypertonicity exacerbates hyperkalemia.

The third therapeutic objective is to eliminate K from the body. The most effective way to accomplish this goal is to administer polystyrene sulfonate resin (Kayexalate). This resin has the capacity to exchange 3.4 mEq Na for 3.4 mEq K for each gram of resin. In practice, the quantity of K absorbed by the resin is variable and averages about 1 mEq/g. Because Na is exchanged for K, hypernatremia or edema may eventuate. One can see readily the need for careful monitoring of plasma electrolyte values and body weight in patients being so treated.

The route of administration of the resin can be either oral or rectal, although it is less effective when given as a retention enema than when given orally. By either route, sorbitol should be given concomitantly to prevent constipation. A cocktail of 25 g resin, 25 g sorbitol, and 100 ml H_2O can be given as often as every 30 min.

CONCLUSION

The approach to the patient with hyperkalemia must involve a careful assessment of the duration of the derangement as well as an assessment of the state of cardiac toxicity. Potent and effective measures are available to lower plasma K acutely.

REFERENCES

1. Adrogué, H. J., Chap, Z., Ishida, T., and Field, J. B. (1985): Role of the endocrine pancreas in the kalemic response to acute metabolic acidosis in conscious dogs. *J. Clin. Invest.*, 75:798–808.
2. Adrogué, H. J., and Madias, N. E. (1981): Changes in plasma potassium concentration during acute acid-base disturbances. *Am. J. Med.*, 71:456–467.
3. Adrogué, H. J., Wilson, H., Boyd, A. E., Suki, W. N., and Eknoyan, G. (1982): Plasma acid-base patterns in diabetic ketoacidosis. *N. Engl. J. Med.*, 307:1603–1610.
4. Batlle, D. C., Arruda, J. A. L., and Kurtzman, N. A. (1981): Hyperkalemic distal renal tubular acidosis associated with obstructive uropathy. *N. Engl. J. Med.*, 304:373–380.
5. Batlle, D. C., Mozes, M. F., Manaligod, J., Arruda, J. A. L., and Kurtzman, N. A. (1981): The pathogenesis of hyperchloremic metabolic acidosis associated with kidney transplantation. *Am. J. Med.*, 70:786–796.
6. Bauer, J. H., and Gauntner, W. C. (1979): Effect of potassium chloride on plasma renin activity and plasma aldosterone during sodium restriction in normal man. *Kidney Int.*, 15:286–293.
7. Bia, M. J., and DeFronzo, R. A. (1981): Extrarenal potassium homeostasis. *Am. J. Physiol.*, 240:F257–F268.
8. Bia, M. J., Tyler, K. A., and DeFronzo, R. A. (1982): Regulation of extrarenal potassium homeostasis by adrenal hormones in rats. *Am. J. Physiol.*, 242:F641–F644.
9. Brown, M. J., Brown, D. C., and Murphy, M. B. (1983): Hypokalemia from beta$_2$ receptor stimulation by circulating epinephrine. *N. Engl. J. Med.*, 309:1414–1419.
10. DeFronzo, R. A. (1980): Hyperkalemia and hyporeninemic hypoaldosteronism. *Kidney Int.*, 17:118–134.
11. Doucet, A., and Katz, A. I. (1980): Renal potassium adaptation: Na-K-ATPase activity along the nephron after chronic potassium loading. *Am. J. Physiol.*, 238:F380–F386.
12. Espinel, C. H. (1975): The influence of salt intake on the metabolic acidosis of chronic renal failure. *J. Clin. Invest.*, 56:286–291.
13. Fraley, D. S., and Adler, S. (1976): Isohydric regulation of plasma potassium by bicarbonate in the rat. *Kidney Int.*, 9:333–343.
14. Goldfarb, S., Cox, M., Singer, I., and Goldberg, M. (1976): Acute hyperkalemia induced by hyperglycemia: Hormonal mechanisms. *Ann. Intern. Med.*, 84:426–432.
15. Goldfarb, S., Strunk, B., Singer, I., and Goldberg, M. (1975): Paradoxical glucose-induced hyperkalemia. Combined aldosterone-insulin deficiency. *Am. J. Med.*, 59:744–750.
16. Gordon, R. D., Gedder, R. A., Pawsey, C. G., and O'Halloran, M. W. (1970): Hypertension and severe hyperkalemia associated with suppression of renin and aldosterone and completely reversed by dietary Na restriction. *Aust. Ann. Med.*, 4:287–294.
17. Higashihara, E., and Kokko, J. P. (1985): Effects of aldosterone on potassium recycling in the kidney of adrenalectomized rats. *Am. J. Physiol.*, 248:F219–F227.
18. Lathem, W. (1958): Hyperchloremic acidosis in chronic pyelonephritis. *N. Engl. J. Med.*, 258:1031–1036.

19. Liddle, G. W., Bennett, L. L., and Forsham, P. H. (1953): The prevention of ACTH-induced sodium retention by the use of potassium salts: A quantitative study. *J. Clin. Invest.*, 32: 1197–1201.
20. Makoff, D. L., Da Silva, J. A., Rosenbaum, B. J., Levy, S. E., and Maxwell, M. H. (1970): Hypertonic expansion: Acid-base and electrolyte changes. *Am. J. Physiol.*, 218:1201–1207.
21. Norby, L. H., Weidig, J., Ramwell, P., Slotkoff, L., and Flamenbaum, W. (1978): Possible role for impaired renal prostaglandin production in pathogenesis of hyporeninemic hypoaldosteronism. *Lancet*, 2:1118–1122.
22. Orringer, C. E., Eustace, J. C., Wunsch, C. D., and Gardner, L. B. (1977): Natural history of lactic acidosis after grand-mal seizures. A model for the study of an anion-gap acidosis not associated with hyperkalemia. *N. Engl. J. Med.*, 297:796–799.
23. Perez, G. O., Lespier, L. E., Oster, J. R., and Vaamonde, C. A. (1977): Effect of alterations of sodium intake in patients with hyporeninemic hypoaldosteronism. *Nephron*, 18:259–265.
24. Phelps, K. R., Lieberman, R. L., Oh, M. S., and Carroll, H. J. (1980): Progress in endocrinology and metabolism. Pathophysiology of the syndrome of hyporeninemic hypoaldosteronism. *Metabolism*, 29:186–199.
25. Rabinowitz, L., Sarason, R. L., and Yamauchi, H. (1985): Effects of KCl infusion on potassium excretion in sheep. *Am. J. Physiol.*, 249:F263–F271.
26. Rabinowitz, L., Sarason, R. L., Yamauchi, H., Yamanaka, K. K., and Tzendzalian, P. A. (1984): Time course of adaptation to altered K intake in rats and sheep. *Am. J. Physiol.*, 247:F607–F617.
27. Schambelan, M., Sebastian, A., and Biglieri, E. G. (1980): Prevalence, pathogenesis, and functional significance of aldosterone deficiency in hyperkalemic patients with chronic renal insufficiency. *Kidney Int.*, 17:89–101.
28. Silva, P., Ross, B. D., Charney, A. N., Besarab, A., and Epstein, F. H. (1975): Potassium transport by the isolated perfused kidney. *J. Clin. Invest.*, 56:862–869.
29. Stanton, B., Pan, L., Deetjen, H., Guckian, V., and Giebisch, G. (1987): Independent effects of aldosterone and potassium on induction of potassium adaptation in rat kidney. *J. Clin. Invest.*, 79:198–206.
30. Szylman, P., Better, O. S., Chaimowitz, C., and Rosler, A. (1976): Role of hyperkalemia in the metabolic acidosis of isolated hypoaldosteronism. *N. Engl. J. Med.*, 294:361–365.
31. Walser, M. (1985): Phenomenological analysis of renal regulation of sodium and potassium balance. *Kidney Int.*, 27:837–841.
32. Young, D. B. (1982): Relationship between plasma potassium concentration and renal potassium excretion. *Am. J. Physiol.*, 242:F599–F603.
33. Young, D. B., Jackson, T. E., Tipayamontri, U., and Scott, R. C. (1984): Effects of sodium intake on steady-state potassium excretion. *Am. J. Physiol.*, 246:F772–F778.
34. Young, D. B., McCaa, R. E., Pan, Y-J., and Guyton, A. C. (1976): The natriuretic and hypotensive effects of potassium. *Circ. Res.* [Suppl II]38:1184–1189.
35. Young, D. B., and Paulsen, A. W. (1983): Interrelated effects of aldosterone and plasma potassium concentration on potassium excretion. *Am. J. Physiol.*, 244:F28–F34.

General Review Articles

36. Good, D. W., and Wright, F. S. (1979): Luminal influences on potassium secretion: Sodium concentration and fluid flow rate. *Am. J. Physiol.*, 236:F192–F205.
37. Jamison, R. W. (1987): Potassium recycling. *Kidney Int.*, 31:695–603.
38. Sterns, R. H., Cox, M., Feig, P. U., and Singer, I. (1981): Internal potassium balance and the control of the plasma potassium concentration. *Medicine*, 60:339–351.
39. Stokes, J. B. (1981): Potassium secretion by cortical collecting tubule: Relation to sodium absorption, luminal sodium concentration and transepithelial voltage. *Am. J. Physiol.*, 241: F395–F402.
40. Stokes, J. B. (1982): Consequences of potassium recycling in the renal medulla. Effects on ion transport by the medullary thick ascending limb of Henle's loop. *J. Clin. Invest.*, 70: 219–229.

The Regulation of Potassium Balance, edited
by Donald W. Seldin and Gerhard Giebisch,
Raven Press, Ltd., New York © 1989.

12

Periodic Paralysis

Robert L. Ruff

*Department of Neurology, Cleveland Veterans Administration Medical Center,
and Case Western Reserve University, School of Medicine,
Cleveland, Ohio 44106*

Periodic paralysis refers to a group of muscle diseases in which patients are
afflicted by episodic attacks of weakness. They are frequently classified as
primary (familial) or secondary. In addition, they usually are classified according to the changes in serum potassium as hypokalemic, hyperkalemic, or
normokalemic periodic paralysis. In the primary types of periodic paralysis
and in periodic paralysis associated with thyrotoxicosis, episodes of weakness
can occur with relatively small changes in serum potassium. In contrast, in
the secondary or acquired forms of periodic paralysis associated with potassium loss or retention, the serum potassium level is always markedly abnormal during a paralytic attack. The pattern of electrolyte changes

TABLE 1. *Clinical features of periodic paralysis*

The paralytic attacks last hours to days.

The weakness can be focal but usually is generalized. Respiratory and cranial nerve innervated muscles tend to be spared.

The myotatic reflexes diminish or disappear, and the involved muscles become inexcitable to either direct electrical stimulation or motor nerve stimulation.

Rest immediately after vigorous exercise tends to provoke paresis of the exercised muscles. Continued mild exercise may abort weakness.

Exposure to cold may provoke weakness in primary periodic paralysis.

Strength is normal between attacks at the onset of the disease. Permanent weakness and irreversible pathologic changes in muscle may develop after repeated paralytic attacks in primary periodic paralysis.

---

usually is similar from attack to attack in a given patient; however, the same patient rarely will have paralysis associated with an elevated, depressed, or unchanged serum potassium level. The different forms of periodic paralysis share several clinical features that are described in Table 1.

Paralytic attacks in hypokalemic periodic paralysis are triggered by an excessive influx of potassium into muscle, whereas hyperkalemic paralysis is associated with an exaggerated efflux of potassium from muscle. The relationships of the paralysis to the changes in muscle and serum potassium have not been resolved completely, although it is clear that the paralysis results from a defect that is restricted to muscle fibers, since muscle will not contract during an attack in response to either stimulation of the nerve or direct stimulation of the muscle. Nerve conduction studies indicate that action potential propagation along axons is not impaired during paralytic attacks. Consequently, the paralysis must result from a defect in one or more of the steps of excitation-contraction coupling. As discussed subsequently, the defect appears to be in the muscle membrane. The following sections describe the different types of periodic paralysis, the pathophysiology of the serum and muscle potassium changes, and the rationale for various types of treatment.

CLINICAL FEATURES (2,4,8,10–12,16,17,21,24,30,32,33,36,39,40)

Familial Hypokalemic Periodic Paralysis

This form is transmitted as an autosomal dominant disorder with reduced penetrance in women. The male/female ratio is approximately 4:1. There are sporadic cases of this disease. The paralytic attack usually begins in the first or second decade of life. The episodes of paralysis occur infrequently during adolescence and may become more frequent during early adult life. In some patients, the episodes of paralysis cease when the patient reaches middle age. During an attack the serum potassium falls but not always below the normal range. The patients may become oliguric, with renal retention of sodium and potassium. The serum potassium returns to normal, with gradual recovery of muscle strength. Sinus bradycardia and other electrocardiographic signs of hypokalemia may develop when the serum potassium falls below the normal range. The serum concentration of creatine kinase and its MB isoenzyme may rise during a paralytic attack. The weakness usually is associated with hypotonia, but in rare instances, myotonia may be present as the weakness develops. Common precipitating factors include a meal rich in carbohydrates, rest immediately after exercise, cold exposure, and emotional excitement. Most patients usually have normal strength between attacks; however, a permanent proximal myopathy has been noted in patients with periodic paralysis, usually after the disease has been manifest for many years. A few patients have developed a cardiomyopathy in association with permanent extremity weakness.

The diagnosis is suggested by a normal serum potassium level between attacks, hypokalemia during a paralytic attack, and a positive family history for hypokalemic periodic paralysis. It is necessary to distinguish primary hypokalemic periodic paralysis from secondary hypokalemic periodic paralysis. In the latter disorder, the hypokalemia is due to renal or gastrointestinal potassium loss, and patients usually are hypokalemic between attacks. In addition, thyrotoxic periodic paralysis can resemble primary hypokalemic periodic paralysis. The diagnosis of hypokalemic periodic paralysis can be confirmed by inducing hypokalemic paralysis in a clinically controlled situation and then restoring strength with potassium replacement. There are several different protocols for provocative tests, most of which require that the patient be given glucose either orally or intravenously along with insulin. The combination of glucose administration and insulin will usually induce hypokalemia and paralysis within 2 to 3 hr. A method for inducing localized weakness is to inject a small amount of epinephrine into the brachial artery while evaluating the amplitude of the evoked compound muscle action potential in a hand muscle. A positive test is a greater than 30% reduction in the muscle action potential. Both of these tests must be carried out with extreme caution by experienced examiners. The administration of insulin can provoke hypoglycemia or extreme hypokalemia. Excessive intra-arterial epinephrine can produce severe vasospasm, resulting in ischemia.

Thyrotoxic Periodic Paralysis

The clinical presentation of thyrotoxic periodic paralysis may closely resemble that of familial hypokalemic periodic paralysis. Patients have recurrent episodes of weakness that can be precipitated by a carbohydrate meal, muscle cooling, or rest immediately after exercise. The serum potassium is usually, but not always, decreased during a paralytic attack. In addition to the presence of thyrotoxicosis, there are several other features that distinguish thyrotoxic periodic paralysis from familial hypokalemic periodic paralysis. The initial attack occurs when a patient is older than 20 years in over 90% of the cases of thyrotoxic periodic paralysis, whereas 60% of patients with familial hypokalemic periodic paralysis have their initial attack before 16 years of age. The male/female ratio is approximately 6:1 in thyrotoxic periodic paralysis compared with 4:1 in familial hypokalemic periodic paralysis. Most of the reported cases of thyrotoxic periodic paralysis have occurred in Orientals, whereas familial hypokalemic periodic paralysis is uncommon in Orientals. Although most of the cases of thyrotoxic periodic paralysis are sporadic, the observation that most patients are Oriental suggests a predisposing genetic factor. Interestingly, Oriental patients with thyrotoxic periodic paralysis have a higher frequency of certain HLA haplotypes, specifically A2BW22 and A19B17, than Oriental thyrotoxic patients without periodic paralysis or unaffected Oriental controls. The greater susceptibility of males to either primary hypokalemic periodic paralysis or thyrotoxic periodic paralysis is not yet understood.

Thyrotoxic periodic paralysis usually resolves with correction of thyroid function. Okihiro and Nordyke reported that a Japanese man with thyrotoxic periodic paralysis that resolved with thyroidectomy developed recurrent paralytic attacks when treated with thyroid hormone. Episodic paralysis also has been induced in Oriental and Caucasian euthyroid patients after administration of thyroid hormone. The Oriental patient developed paralysis with a dose of thyroid hormone that did not produce clinical signs of thyrotoxicosis. Excessive amounts of thyroid hormone did not appear to trigger paralytic attacks in patients with familial hypokalemic periodic paralysis. Engel reported that a patient with familial hypokalemic periodic paralysis given thyroid hormone did not develop weakness while receiving hormone therapy. However, when the thyroid treatment was withdrawn, the patient had repeated paralytic attacks.

Secondary Hypokalemic Periodic Paralysis

Severe potassium depletion usually produces generalized weakness, but occasionally, patients will develop episodic paralysis associated with hypokalemia. Rarely, attacks of paralysis will be triggered by insulin in hypokalemic patients. Secondary or acquired hypokalemic periodic paralysis can be separated from primary hypokalemic periodic paralysis by the presence of hypokalemia between attacks and the absence of a family history of episodic weakness. Some causes of secondary hypokalemic periodic paralysis are shown in Table 2.

TABLE 2. *Causes of secondary hypokalemic periodic paralysis*

Renal Potassium Wastage
    Associated with alkaline urine and metabolic alkalosis
    Primary hyperaldosteronism
    Excessive diuretic therapy or mineralocorticoid therapy
    Intoxication with natural licorice
    Bartter's syndrome
    Associated with alkaline urine and metabolic acidosis
    Fanconi's syndrome
    Primary and secondary renal tubular acidosis
    Associated with alkaline urine and renal failure
    Amphotericin B therapy
    Associated with acid urine and metabolic acidosis
    Recovery phase of acute renal tubular necrosis
    Bilateral ureterocolostomies
    Diabetic ketoacidosis
    Chronic ammonium chloride ingestion

Gastrointestinal Potassium Wastage
    Nontropical sprue
    Laxative abuse
    Pancreatic noninsulin-secreting tumor or villous adenoma of the colon
    Gastrointestinal fistula
    Severe or chronic diarrhea, vomiting, or gastrointestinal intubation
Barium Intoxication
    Associated with potassium influx into the intracellular compartment

Barium-Induced Periodic Paralysis

Barium-induced periodic paralysis is caused by a combination of hypokalemia and the direct effect of barium on the muscle membrane. The accidental ingestion of a barium salt induces a hemorrhagic gastroenteritis associated with vomiting, diarrhea, cardiac arrhythmia, muscle twitching, convulsions, hypokalemia, and muscle paralysis. The hypokalemia is caused in part by transfer of potassium into the intracellular compartment rather than solely by gastrointestinal wastage. Barium blocks potassium channels in the skeletal muscle membrane. A decreased efflux of potassium from muscle partly accounts for the hypokalemia. In addition, the reduction in potassium conductance results in a depolarization of the muscle membrane, which will result in membrane inexcitability due to inactivation of sodium channels.

Endemic periodic paralysis in western China, Pa-Ping, has been traced to barium in the local salt. Outbreaks of periodic paralysis have resulted from contamination of food products by barium salts.

Primary Hyperkalemic Periodic Paralysis

This form of periodic paralysis, also called adynamia episodica hereditaria, is a rare muscle disease with autosomal dominant inheritance. A few sporadic cases have been reported. Clinically, this disorder is similar to hypokalemic periodic paralysis; however, during episodes of muscle weakness, the serum potassium rises rather than falls. Three variants of primary hyperkalemic periodic paralysis have been described: (1) in combination with clinical or electromyographic myotonia, (2) without any signs of myotonia, and (3) in combination with paramyotonia. The last disease also has been called "paralysis periodica paramyotonica." The affected members of a given family always show the same variant of the disease. Attacks usually commence in childhood or adolescence. At the onset of an attack, the patient may develop myalgia, elevated serum creatine kinase, and electrocardiographic changes consistent with hyperkalemia. Hypocalcemia during paralysis was found in a few patients. Diuresis with elevated potassium excretion frequently accompanies the paralysis. Paralysis may be precipitate by rest after exercise, oral ingestion of potassium, cold exposure, pregnancy, or administration of glucocorticoids. Strength usually is normal between attacks, but a prominant proximal myopathy may develop after repeated episodes of paralysis.

The paramyotonic form of hyperkalemic periodic paralysis and paramyotonia congenita have many features in common: autosomal dominant inheritance, myotonia and weakness provoked by exposure to cold, and weakness produced by rest after exercise. The similarities between these disorders suggested that they might be a similar disease. However, there are slight differences that distinguish paramyotonia congenita and hyperkalemic periodic paralysis: (1) potassium loading does not provoke weakness in patients with paramyotonia, (2) repeated muscle contraction aggravates myotonia in paramyotonia congenita and lessens myotonia associated with hyperkalemic periodic paralysis, and (3) the attacks of weakness in paramyotonia may be associated with hypokalemia.

Secondary Hyperkalemic Periodic Paralysis

This usually results from renal potassium retention due to adrenal insufficiency or inhibition of mineralocorticoid action. The attacks are usually induced by rest after exercise, with an elevation of the serum potassium above 7 mEq/liter.

Normokalemic Periodic Paralysis

Normokalemic periodic paralysis is an autosomal dominant disorder characterized by paralytic attacks starting in childhood and provoked by rest after exercise or cold exposure. There usually is no consistent pattern of electrolyte change associated with paralysis. However, Chesson et al. reported a patient who initially had episodes characteristic of familial normokalemic periodic paralysis and then developed spontaneously occurring and provokable episodes of both hypokalemic and hyperkalemic periodic paralysis superimposed on a persistent proximal myopathy.

There are reports of other forms of periodic paralysis that are not associated with fluctuations in serum potassium levels. These disorders differ from the previously discussed forms of periodic paralysis in that they are associated with other skeletal cardiac or developmental anomalies. In one family reported by Iannoccone et al., the paralysis appeared to result from a structural defect in the sarcoplasmic reticulum that may have resulted in an inhibition in calcium release or storage.

MORPHOLOGIC CHANGES (25)

The characteristic histopathologic finding in periodic paralysis is a vacuolar myopathy. This has been described in primary hypokalemic, secondary hypokalemic, thyrotoxic, primary hyperkalemic, and normokalemic periodic paralysis. The vacuolation appears to be more prominent after repeated paralytic attacks and has been associated with permanent proximal myopathy. However, myopathy has developed in patients who have not been found to have vacuolar changes on muscle biopsy. The vacuoles are located in the center of the fiber, are usually lined with membrane, and may contain a periodic acid-Schiff-reactive material, which is probably glycogen. The vacuoles frequently are associated with swellings at the t-tubule and mitochondria and dilatation of the terminal cisternae of the sarcoplasmic reticulum. The origin of the vacuoles has been debated; an origin from the coalescence of dilated sarcoplasmic reticulum components or from proliferating t-tubule system membranes has been suggested. An alternative suggestion is that the vacuoles are the end results of focal fiber destruction. Pathologic changes in the myofibril and mitochondria and focal increase in muscle glycogen also have been noted, suggesting that there are changes in several parts of the muscle that may account for the permanent myopathy that develops after repeated paralytic attacks. Of note, many of the morphologic changes seen in the periodic paralyses may in part reflect intracellular potassium depletion, as clinical and experimental potassium depletion produces vacuolar changes that closely resemble those seen in the periodic paralyses.

ELECTROLYTE CHANGES (3,5,6,14,19,34,35,38,39,40)

Intracellular Electrolyte Changes

A common feature of skeletal muscle from patients with periodic paralysis is that the intracellular potassium is lower and the sodium and chloride contents

TABLE 3. *Muscle electrolytes in patients with primary periodic paralysis* [a,b]

Disease	Condition	Potassium (mEq/kg) [c]	Sodium (mEq/kg) [c]	Chloride	Water (ml/kg) [c]
Hypokalemic PP	Paralyzed	78	43	29	777
	Not paralyzed	79	44	26	767
Thyrotoxic PP	Paralyzed	84	40	—	786
	Not paralyzed	86	43	25	787
Hyperkalemic PP	Not paralyzed	84	42	22	775
Controls		95	35	21	782

[a] Adapted from ref. 40.
[b] Averages of values found in the literature.
[c] Tissue wet weight.

are higher than normal. This has been noted in patients with hypokalemic periodic paralysis, thyrotoxic periodic paralysis, and hyperkalemic periodic paralysis (Table 3). Placing a rat on a potassium-deficient diet will gradually result in total body potassium depletion. Interestingly, the potassium and sodium contents of neurons and cardiac muscle cells tend to be preserved at near normal levels, whereas in skeletal muscle, the potassium content is markedly depleted, and the sodium content is increased. Skeletal muscle from potassium-depleted rats shows vacuolar changes that are similar to those seen in muscle from patients with periodic paralysis. The potassium-depleted rats become weak in response to a carbohydrate and insulin challenge, and muscle from these rodents depolarizes and becomes electrically inexcitable when placed in a bathing solution with insulin and a low concentration of potassium. The potassium-depleted rat has served as an experimental model of hypokalemic periodic paralysis. Increased intracellular sodium may contribute to the changes in membrane electrical properties seen in muscle from patients with periodic paralysis and potassium-depleted rats.

Changes in Distribution of Electrolytes During Paralytic Attacks

Familial Hypokalemic Periodic Paralysis

The etiology of hypokalemia during paralytic attacks remains an intriguing question. One proposal was that intermittent hyperaldosteronism produced the hypokalemia due to renal potassium loss. This proposal was supported by the observations that hyperaldosteronism, mineralocorticoid treatment, and licorice ingestion could produce hypokalemic weakness. However, aldosterone levels usually are not elevated during paralytic attacks, and frequently there is urinary retention of sodium, potassium, and water. The occasional finding of elevated aldosterone production may be due to a decrease in the extracellular volume that sometimes accompanies a paralytic attack.

Based on arterial and venous plasma red cell measurement, Zierler and Andres found that influx of potassium into muscle produced the hypokalemia and spontaneous or induced paralytic attacks. The intracellular potassium store is much larger than the quantity of extracellular potassium, so that a shift of sufficient potassium into muscle to lower the serum potassium content less than 1.5 mEq/liter may produce little change in the potassium content of skeletal muscle (Table 3). Interestingly, red cell potassium transport is normal, and red cells do not accumulate potassium during paralytic attacks. With recovery from the paralysis, potassium moves from muscle into the extracellular space until the serum potassium is nearly normal. Potassium is released from muscle even when recovery is produced by potassium administration. The recovery frequently is followed by a potassium diuresis. The etiology of the episodic excessive influx of potassium into muscle is not known. It has been suggested that a block in muscle carbohydrate metabolism might result in an excess of nondiffusable phosphorylated anions during glycogen breakdown or synthesis, which could result in a net influx of cation and water into muscle cells. However, direct investigation of carbohydrate metabolism and mitochondrial respiration of muscle from patients with hypokalemic periodic paralysis has revealed no evidence of a defect. Intracellular potassium accumulation could result from excessive pumping of potassium into muscle cells. The basal Na,K-ATPase activity in skeletal muscle from patients with familial hypokalemic periodic paralysis appears to be normal. It is possible that the Na,K pump in skeletal muscle may be unusually sensitive to hormonal stimulation, but this has yet to be proven.

Thyrotoxic Periodic Paralysis

The electrolyte changes in this disorder are similar to those found in primary hypokalemic periodic paralysis. Hypokalemia is produced by muscle uptake of potassium. Thyroid hormone directly stimulates sodium-potassium transport in mouse skeletal muscle and enhances muscle sensitivity to beta-adrenergic stimulation. In human red blood cells isolated from patients with thyrotoxicosis, both passive sodium-potassium fluxes and active sodium-potassium transport were increased; however, passive fluxes exceeded the Na,K pump rate, resulting in a decreased intracellular potassium and elevated intracellular sodium content. This finding might partially explain why muscle from patients with thyrotoxicosis has excess intracellular sodium and is potassium depleted (Table 3). Enhanced beta-adrenergic sensitivity of the Na,K pump could explain why epinephrine induced hypokalemia. It is not known if there is also increased sensitivity to insulin-stimulated potassium uptake by muscle. However, for unknown reasons, insulin concentration is elevated during spontaneous attacks in thyrotoxic periodic paralysis.

Secondary Hypokalemic Periodic Paralysis

This disorder usually is associated with a depletion of total body potassium. Patients usually become paralyzed when the potassium falls below 2 to 3 mEq/liter. In most of the patients with secondary hypokalemia and episodic weakness, further fall in potassium is triggered by aggravation of the underlying potassium-losing disorder. In a man with mineralocorticoid-induced hypokalemia, insulin administration repeatedly produced hypokalemic paralysis. In addition, in potassium-depleted rats, insulin administration also produces hypokalemia in muscle paralysis.

In potassium-depleted mammals, intracellular potassium content of skeletal muscle is decreased, and the potassium content of heart, brain, and red cells is maintained at nearly normal levels. The density of ouabain binding sites and the sodium-potassium transport capacity are reduced in muscle and increased in red blood cells. The selective suppression of muscle sodium-potassium transport may be mediated in part by alpha-adrenergic stimulation as well as by muscle activity. Despite the decreased sensitivity of the Na,K pump, potassium-depleted muscle is able to increase sodium-potassium transport markedly when appropriately stimulated. Thus, it is possible that insulin stimulation of sodium-potassium transport could further lower serum potassium in potassium-depleted patients and experimental animals.

Primary Hyperkalemic Periodic Paralysis

Measurement of arterial and venous plasma potassium concentrations shows that the hyperkalemia during paralytic attacks results from a net efflux of potassium from muscle. In addition, there appears to be a marked disturbance of the regulation of plasma potassium. Patients frequently have several episodes of hyperkalemia daily, many of which may be asymptomatic. There appears to be a generalized impairment of potassium transport, since red blood cells also have diminished potassium influx and net potassium loss during paralytic attacks. The efflux of potassium from muscle is not caused by diminished secretion of insulin, catecholamines, or glucagon or elevated serum mineralocorticoid or glucocorticoid activity. The basal Na,K-ATPase activity in muscle is normal. However, it is possible that the sodium-potassium transport may be abnormally sensitive to hormonal stimulation.

Secondary Hyperkalemic Periodic Paralysis

Patients with adrenal insufficiency are prone to develop hyperkalemia for two reasons. First, these patients cannot increase mineralocorticoid output to compensate for a potassium loss. Second, diminished glucocorticoid activity reduces the sensitivity of muscle to adrenergic stimulation. Consequently, the ability of muscle to take up potassium is impaired due to reduced beta-adrenergic stimulation of the Na,K pump. A consequence of the decreased potassium uptake is that skeletal muscle may become potassium depleted in patients with secondary hyperkalemic periodic paralysis.

In summary, the electrolyte shifts associated with paralysis in the various forms of the periodic paralyses are due to excessive influxes or effluxes of potassium from skeletal muscle. The mechanisms for these abnormal potassium fluxes are currently unknown.

RELATIONSHIP OF ELECTROLYTE CHANGES TO MEMBRANE INEXCITABILITY (1,9,13,22,29,31)

The weakness in the various forms of periodic paralysis is caused by loss of muscle contractility. Nerve conduction and neuromuscular transmission are normal during hypokalemic paralytic attacks. Consequently, the loss of contractility could result from (1) surface membrane excitability, (2) impairment of the propagation of the electrical signal down the t-tubules, (3) decreased release of calcium from the sarcoplasmic reticulum, (4) defective myofibrillar calcium-stimulated contraction, or (5) depletion of ATP or other high energy phosphates. The currently available data suggest that mechanisms 3 through 5 are not the cause of paralysis. Skinned muscle fibers (surface membrane mechanically or chemically removed) from patients with periodic paralysis have a normal contractile response to calcium. In addition, the maximum force generated by these muscle fibers was normal. The ATP content in paralyzed muscle was also normal. Calcium uptake by the sarcoplasmic reticulum was impaired during paralytic attacks and normal between attacks in patients with thyrotoxic periodic paralysis. Diminished calcium uptake by the sarcoplasmic reticulum would impair muscle relaxation but not necessarily affect the initiation of contraction. Unfortunately, calcium released from the sarcoplasmic reticulum has not been studied. T-tubule excitability and coupling to calcium release also remain to be studied. The t-tubules are dilatated in the various forms of periodic paralysis, but the triadic connections to the terminal cisternae appear to be preserved.

The available data suggest that the primary defect in periodic paralysis is sarcolemmal inexcitability. During paralytic attacks in primary hypokalemic or hyperkalemic periodic paralysis, EMG recording shows a progressive decline in the number of fibers that can be activated electrically. Extracellular record ing from single muscle fibers demonstrates a failure of the surface membrane to propagate an action potential. The amount of tension that a muscle can generate is directly proportional to the number of muscle fibers that remain electrically excitable. A difference between primary hyperkalemic and hypokalemic periodic paralysis is that there may be a brief period of increased muscle excitability with spontaneous action potential generation at the onset of a paralytic attack in the myotonic form of primary hyperkalemic periodic paralysis. Intracellular membrane potential recordings during paralysis usually demonstrated that the muscle fibers were depolarized (Table 4) and electrically inexcitable.

The loss of membrane excitability with depolarization in periodic paralysis is probably due to voltage-dependent inactivation of sodium channels. In mammalian muscle fibers, there are at least two voltage-dependent sodium channel inactivation processes that have different kinetics and voltage dependence. The fast inactivation process is able to close sodium channels on a millisecond time scale. The slow inactivation process acts on a time scale of minutes. The slow inactivation process is active at the resting potential, so that in rat fast twitch muscle fibers more than half of the available sodium channels are inactivated at the resting potential because of slow inactivation. The membrane must be depolarized by more than 30 mV to produce a similar reduction in sodium channel excitability due to the fast inactivation process. With the slow inactivation process, a 5 mV depolarization will result in about a 40% reduction in the number of sodium channels that can be excited, and a 10 mV depolarization will result in about a 70% reduction in the number of excitable sodium channels. Consequently, the reduced excitability of fibers from patients with hypokalemic or hyperkalemic periodic paralysis may result from the slight depolarization in the membrane increasing the amount of inactivation due to the slow inactivation process. In addition, there may be a shift in the voltage dependence of the inactivation process. Rudel et al. noted that muscle fibers from patients with hypokalemic periodic paralysis studied in a bathing medium with normal potassium concentration had decreased excitability and markedly reduced action potential amplitudes despite having resting potentials between -70 and -80 mV.

The excitability and action potential amplitude could be increased by hyperpolarizing the fibers. The muscle fibers from a patient with hyperkalemic periodic paralysis were inexcitable at membrane potentials that normally

TABLE 4. *Muscle membrane potentials in primary periodic paralysis*

Type	Not paralyzed (mV)	Paralyzed (mV)	Reference
Hypokalemic	-86	-77	8
	-75	-71	36
	-75	-54	29
Hyperkalemic	-69	-52	8
	-72	-45	2
	-83	-64	22
Control	-88		9

would not be sufficiently positive to inactivate sodium channels. These findings suggested that there was excessive sodium channel inactivation at or near the resting potential possibly due to a shift in the voltage dependence of the inactivation processes. Interestingly, the myotonia seen in some patients with hyperkalemic periodic paralysis appears to be associated with a class of sodium channels that is resistant to voltage-dependent inactivation.

ORIGIN OF MUSCLE MEMBRANE DEPOLARIZATION (9,20,22,29,33)

The membrane potential is determined by the intracellular and extracellular concentrations of sodium, potassium, and chloride ions, the permeability of these ions, and additional contributions from electrogenic pumping, the most significant from the Na,K pump. The intracellular and extracellular concentration of the important ions are such that the equilibrium potential for sodium is approximately 65 mV, and the equilibrium potentials for potassium and chloride are approximately -95 mV. The resting membrane permeability for potassium and chloride ions is much larger than for sodium ions. Consequently, the resting membrane potential is close to the equilibrium potential for potassium and chloride ions. During an action potential, the sodium permeability increases and the membrane potential approaches the sodium equilibrium potential.

The skeletal muscle membrane depolarization seen during paralytic attacks of hypokalemic or hyperkalemic or thyrotoxic periodic paralysis is in excess of what would be expected based on the extent of change in the serum potassium concentration and potassium equilibrium potential. Cunningham et al. demonstrated that in normal rats and humans, the muscle membrane potential closely follows the potassium equilibrium potential. The membrane depolarization seen in the periodic paralyses could result from a reduction in the potassium and chloride permeabilities, an increase in the sodium permeability, or a reduction in the electrogenic potential produced by the Na,K pump.

Layzer proposed that in hypokalemic periodic paralysis, the potassium permeability was reduced and the membrane potential was maintained at near normal values between attacks by an increase in the membrane depolarization produced by the Na,K pump. During an attack, the extracellular potassium could fall to sufficiently low intervals to reduce Na,K pump activity and the membrane depolarized. This is an interesting proposal; however, it does not appear likely because the extracellular potassium concentration never gets sufficiently low enough to inactivate the Na,K pump.

The ability of either elevated or reduced extracellular potassium to depolarize the muscle membrane can be explained partially by the passive membrane properties of skeletal muscle. The resting potassium conductance is carried by inward rectifier channels that allow potassium to flow into cells much more easily than it passes out. The conductance of the inward rectifier potassium channels depends on the membrane potential and the extracellular potassium concentration. As the extracellular potassium concentration is lower, the potassium conductance at a given membrane potential decreases. Given the behavior of the skeletal muscle potassium channels, why do normal muscle fibers hyperpolarize in solutions with low extracellular potassium concentrations? The answer probably is that in normal muscle fibers the potassium conductance is so much larger than the sodium conductance that even though extracellular potassium is lowered and consequently the potassium conductance is lowered, the potassium conductance still exceeds the sodium conductance and the membrane potential approaches the potassium equilibrium potential and hence hyperpolarizes.

Figure 1 shows that as the ratio of sodium/potassium permeability is increased (proceeding from curve A to curve B), the inward rectifier characteristics become more prominent, and the membrane will depolarize as the extracellular potassium is reduced. Thus, the inward rectifying characteristics of the potassium channel can explain partially the depolarization in low potassium solutions if one also assumes that the ratio of the sodium/potassium permeability at the resting potential is greater than normal. The consequences of increased sodium/potassium permeability ratio are that the resting membrane potential would be less negative and that either high or low extracellular potassium concentrations could produce depolarizations. The resting mem-

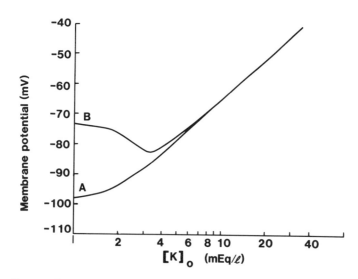

FIG. 1. Computed membrane potential plotted as a function of the serum potassium, assuming that the sodium permeability is 2.5×10^{-8} cm/sec, the chloride permeability is 10^{-6} cm/sec, and the potassium conductance in the linear portion of the permeability vs. membrane potential relationship is 2×10^{-5}/ohm-cm^2 (curve A) or 10^{-5}/ohm-cm^2 (curve B). Similar curves can be generated by increasing the sodium permeability.

brane potentials of patients with periodic paralysis may be depolarized compared to normal values (Table 4).

The depolarizing capacity of either elevated or reduced serum potassium was seen in a patient suffering from an attack of hypokalemic periodic paralysis, described by Sestoft, who was given an intravenous injection of potassium. After an initial improvement, his condition became much worse than at onset; he was now hyperkalemic and his muscle fibers were depolarized. Therefore, the potassium treatment turned a hypokalemic paralysis into a hyperkalemic paralysis presumably due to membrane depolarization and resultant inexcitability due to sodium channel inactivation.

The possibility that increased sodium permeability caused the membrane depolarization in both hypokalemic and hyperkalemic periodic paralysis was suggested by the finding of a lower than normal input resistance in depolarized fibers. In addition, procaine, a local anesthetic that blocks sodium channels, can partially repolarize the membrane potential of paralyzed muscle fibers.

Rudel et al. presented direct evidence that the paradoxical membrane depolarization seen in muscle fibers from patients with hypokalemic periodic paralysis was associated with an increased steady state sodium conductance. The muscle fibers from patients depolarized when bathed in a potassium solution apparently due to the opening of an atypical sodium channel. The chloride and potassium permeabilities were not significantly altered, but the inward rectifying property of the potassium channels allowed the persistent inward sodium current to be more effective in depolarizing the muscle fibers from patients with hypokalemic periodic paralysis. The abnormal sodium current was not blocked by agents that block normal sodium channels. Consequently, the muscle membrane depolarization in patients with hypokalemic periodic paralysis may be mediated by a separate class of altered sodium channels.

Hyperkalemic periodic paralysis also seems to be associated with a sodium channel abnormality. Lehmann-Horn et al. studied muscle fibers from two patients with hyperkalemic periodic paralysis. The mechanism of paralysis appeared to be slightly different for the fibers from each patient. Muscle fibers from both patients developed an excessive depolarization compared to control in response to elevating the extracellular potassium. Fibers from the first patient were more sensitive, with depolarization occurring as the extracellular potassium was increased from 3.5 to 7 mM. The muscle fibers from the first patient were spontaneously active at membrane potentials between -60 mV and -70 mV. When the extracellular potassium was increased to 7 mM, the fibers depolarized to -50 mV and were electrically inexcitable. The depolarization was associated with an increased sodium conductance. Fibers from the second patient depolarized without activity in elevated extracellular potassium concentrations. The fibers from the second patient became electrically inexcitable and paralyzed at resting potentials that were not sufficiently positive to inactivate normal muscle fibers. In both patients, membrane depolarization was produced by an increased sodium conductance. The muscle fibers from the first patient, who had myotonia associated with hyperkalemic periodic paralysis, appeared to contain a class of sodium channels that activated at more negative potentials than normal, so that these fibers were spontaneously active at the resting potential. In contrast, the fibers from the second patient may have been excessively sensitive to voltage-dependent inactivation.

An additional factor that may increase the sodium/potassium conductance ratio in periodic paralysis is the increased intracellular sodium concentration. Intracellular sodium ions can enter potassium channels and compete with potassium ions so that the potassium channels will be partially blocked, thereby reducing the potassium conductance when the cell is depolarized and potassium and sodium ions tend to leave the cell.

Possible Action of Insulin in Hypokalemic Periodic Paralysis

Studies of an animal model of hypokalemic periodic paralysis, the potassium-depleted rat, indicate that insulin may contribute to the depolarization of the muscle fibers by reducing the conductance of the inward rectifier potassium channel (Fig. 2). Insulin reduced the potassium conductance at depolarized membrane potentials so that the resting potassium conductance was normal, but when the membrane depolarized, the potassium conductance decreased. Consequently, insulin would exaggerate the effect of the abnormal sodium currents associated with hypokalemic periodic paralysis.

The muscle membrane inexcitability in hypokalemic and hyperkalemic periodic paralysis appears to result from surface membrane depolarization producing sodium channel inactivation. The voltage-dependent gating of sodium channels may be altered so that in patients with myotonia, channels may be resistant to inactivation, whereas in other patients, the channels may be excessively sensitive to inactivation. Insulin may contribute to the depolarization of the muscle fibers in primary and secondary hypokalemic periodic paralysis by reducing potassium conductance. Figure 3 illustrates the possible mechanisms of paralysis in hypokalemic periodic paralysis.

RATIONALE FOR THERAPY (7,15,18,20,23,26–28,37,39,40)

Primary Hypokalemic Periodic Paralysis

Acute attacks can be treated with oral potassium supplementation. Exercise or electrical stimulation of motor nerves may also improve the strength of contracting muscles. The beneficial effect of exercise is possibly due to accu-

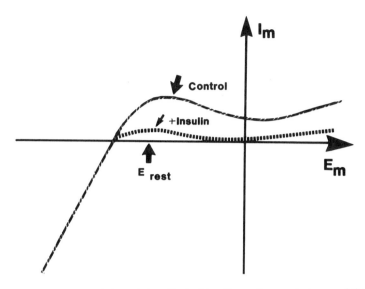

FIG. 2. A qualitative description of the effect of insulin on the conductance of the inward rectifying potassium channels of skeletal muscle from potassium-depleted rats. The inward rectifying property of the skeletal muscle potassium channels that are open at the resting potential is demonstrated by the difference in the conductance of these channels depending on the direction that potassium is flowing. At membrane potentials that are more negative than the resting potential (E_{rest}) and the potassium equilibrium potential, potassium current flows into the cell, and the slope of the current-voltage relationship (I_m vs. E_m) is steep, indicating large conductance. At potentials more positive than E_{rest}, the conductance of the channel decreases. Consequently, this channel will allow potassium to enter the cell more easily than it allows potassium to leave. When insulin is applied, the conductance of the channel at potentials positive to E_{rest} is much lower. Therefore, insulin exaggerated the inward rectifying properties of this class of potassium channels.

mulation of potassium in the extracellular space surrounding muscle fibers, which can increase the conductance of inward rectifying potassium channels.

Prophylactic treatment includes maintenance of a negative sodium balance with a low sodium diet, diuretics, or a mineralocorticoid inhibitor, such as spironolactone. Sodium depletion may reduce the intracellular sodium content to more normal values, which may diminish the possible block of potassium channels by intracellular sodium ions. A low carbohydrate diet is sometimes beneficial and may act by minimizing postprandial insulin release. In a similar fashion, diazoxide may prove useful by reducing insulin secretion. Acetazolamide, a carbonic anhydrase inhibitor, can be useful by reducing insulin-induced hypokalemia. The metabolic acidosis produced by acetazolamide is important for its action. In normal individuals, metabolic acidosis results in an increase in extracellular potassium and may inhibit sodium channel inactivation. Some patients do not respond to acetazolamide, possibly because they become hypokalemic in response to the drug.

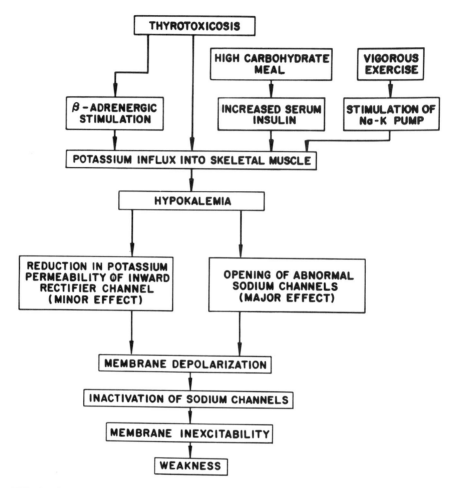

FIG. 3. Hypothesized scheme for the mechanisms of paralysis in primary hypokalemic periodic paralysis.

Thyrotoxic Periodic Paralysis

Treatment of thyrotoxic periodic paralysis is directed primarily at normalizing thyroid function. Until the patient becomes euthyroid, treatment of acute attacks and prophylactic measures are the same as for primary hypokalemic periodic paralysis. Acetazolamide usually is not effective in this disorder, since it fails to prevent hypokalemia. Propranolol, a beta-adrenergic blocker, can prevent attacks possibly by countering the effect of thyroid hormone to increase the beta-adrenergic sensitivity of the Na,K pump.

Primary Hyperkalemic Periodic Paralysis

Acute treatment of primary hyperkalemic periodic paralysis is directed at lowering serum potassium by facilitating cellular uptake of potassium using glucose and insulin. Epinephrine also can stop an attack. Intravenous calcium can abort attacks presumably due to a shift in the voltage sensitivity of sodium channels. Acetazolamide can prevent attacks by stimulating muscle and red blood cell potassium uptake and by stimulating insulin release. In addition, the metabolic acidosis produced by acetazolamide may shift the voltage dependence of sodium channel inactivation. The beta$_2$ agonist, salbutamol, which stimulates sodium-potassium active transport in muscle, is a very effective prophylactic agent. Other preventive measures are frequent meals of high carbohydrate content and low-dose diuretic therapy. The local anesthetic derivative tocanide may be useful in preventing myotonia and cold-induced weakness in patients with the myotonic or paramyotonic form of primary hyperkalemic periodic paralysis.

The treatment of secondary hypokalemic or hyperkalemic periodic paralysis is directed toward correcting the underlying electrolyte imbalance.

ACKNOWLEDGMENT

This work was supported by Merit Review Funding from the Veterans Administration.

REFERENCES

1. Bezanilla, F., and Armstrong, C. M. (1972): Negative conductance caused by entry of sodium and cesium ions into the potassium channels of squid axon. *J. Gen. Physiol.*, 60:588–608.
2. Brooks, J. E. (1969): Hyperkalemic periodic paralysis. *Arch. Neurol.*, 20:13–18.
3. Buruma, O. J., Dubbelman, T. M. A. R., deBruyne, A. W., and van Steveninck, J. (1978): Erythrocyte membrane studies in familial hypokalemic periodic paralysis. *Arch. Neurol.*, 35:615–616.
4. Chesson, A. L., Schocet, S. S., and Peter, B. H. (1979): Biphasic periodic paralysis. *Arch. Neurol.*, 36:700–704.
5. Clausen, T., Kjeldsen, K., and Norgaard, A. (1983): Effects of denervation on sodium, potassium and [^{3}H] ouabain binding in muscles of normal and potassium-depleted rats. *J. Physiol.*, 345:123–134.
6. Clausen, T., Wang, P., Orskov, H., and Kristensen, O. (1980): Hyperkalemic periodic paralysis: Relationships between changes in plasma water, electrolytes, insulin and catecholamine during attacks. *Scand. J. Clin. Lab. Invest.*, 40:211–220.
7. Conway, M. J., Seibel, J. A., and Eaton, R. P. (1974): Thyrotoxicosis and periodic paralysis improvement with beta blockade. *Ann. Intern. Med.*, 81:332–336.
8. Creutzfeldt, O. D., Abbott, B. C., Fowler, W. M., and Pearson, C. M. (1963): Muscle membrane potentials in episodic adynamia. *Electroencephalogr. Clin. Neurophysiol.*, 15:508–519.
9. Cunningham, J. N., Carter, N. W., Rector, F. C., and Seldin, D. W. (1971): Resting trans-

membrane potential difference of skeletal muscle in normal subjects and severely ill patients. *J. Clin. Invest.*, 50:49–59.

10. Engel, A. G. (1961): Thyroid function and periodic paralysis. *Am. J. Med.*, 30:327–333.

11. Engel, A. G. (1966): Electron microscopic observations in primary hypokalemic and thyrotoxic periodic paralysis. *Mayo Clin. Proc.*, 41:797–808.

12. Engel, A. G., Lambert, E. H., Rosevear, J. W., and Tauxe, T. N. (1965): Clinical and EMG studies in a patient with primary hypokalemic periodic paralysis. *Am. J. Med.*, 38:626–640.

13. Gordon, A. M., Green, J. R., and Lagonoff, D. (1970): Studies on a patient with hypokalemic familial periodic paralysis. *Am. J. Med.*, 48:185–189.

14. Grob, D., Johns, R. J., and Liljestrand, A. (1957): Potassium movement in patients with familial periodic paralysis. *Am. J. Med.*, 23:356–375.

15. Hoskins, B. (1977): Studies on the mechanism of action of acetazolamide in the prophylaxis of hyperkalemic periodic paralysis. *Life Sci.*, 20:343–350.

16. Huang, K. W. (1943): Pa-Ping: Transient stimulating family periodic paralysis. *Chin. Med. J.*, 61:305–312.

17. Iannoccone, S. T., Bove, K., Nagy, B., and Samaha, F. J. (1982): Familial dystrophy associated with periodic paralysis and a unique deficit of the major protein of sarcoplasmic reticulum. *Ann. Neurol.*, 12:108–109.

18. Johnsen, T. (1977): Effect upon serum insulin, glucose and potassium concentrations of acetazolamide during attacks of familial periodic paralysis. *Acta Neurol. Scand.*, 56:533–541.

19. Klein, R., Egan, T., and Usher, P. (1960): Changes in sodium, potassium and water in hyperkalemic familial periodic paralysis. *Metabolism*, 9:1005–1024.

20. Layzer, R. B. (1982): Periodic paralysis and the sodium-potassium pump. *Ann. Neurol.*, 11:547–552.

21. Layzer, R. B., and Goldfield, E. (1974): Periodic paralysis caused by abuse of thyroid hormone. *Neurology*, 24:949–955.

22. Lehmann-Horn, R., Rudel, R., Ricker, K., Lorkovic, H., Dengler, R., and Hopf, H. C. (1983): Two cases of adynamia episodica hereditaria: *In vitro* investigation of muscle cell membrane and contraction parameters. *Muscle Nerve*, 6:113–121.

23. Martin, A. R., and Levsinson, S. R. (1985): Contribution of the Na^+,K^+ pump to membrane potential in familial periodic paralysis. *Muscle Nerve*, 8:359–362.

24. Okihiro, M. M., and Nordyke, R. A. (1966): Hypokalemic periodic paralysis experimental precipitation of sodium lithyronine. *JAMA*, 198:277–279.

25. Pearson, C. M. (1964): The periodic paralysis: Differential features and pathological observations in permanent myopathic weakness. *Brain*, 87:341–358.

26. Ricker, K., Bohlen, R., and Rohkamm, R. (1983): Different effectiveness of tocainide and hydrochloralthiazide in paramyotonia congenita with hyperkalemic episodic paralysis. *Neurology*, 33:1615–1618.

27. Riggs, J. E., Griggs, R. C., and Moxley, R. T. (1984): Dissociation of glucose and potassium arterial-venous differences across the forearm by acetazolamide. *Arch. Neurol.*, 41:35–38.

28. Riggs, J. E., Griggs, R. C., Moxley, R. T., and Lewis, E. D. (1981): Acute effects of acetazolamide in hyperkalemic periodic paralysis. *Neurology*, 31:725–729.

29. Rudel, R., Lehmann-Horn, F., Ricker, K., and Kuther, G. (1984): Hypokalemic periodic paralysis: *In vitro* investigation of muscle fiber membrane parameters. *Muscle Nerve*, 7:110–120.

30. Ruff, R. L. (1979): Insulin-induced weakness in hypokalemic myopathy. *Ann. Neurol.*, 6:139–140.

31. Ruff, R. L., Simoncini, L., and Stuhmer, W. (1987): Comparison between slow sodium channel inactivation in rat slow- and fast-twitch muscle. *J. Physiol.*, 383:339–348.

32. Satoyoshi, E., Murakami, K., Kowa, H., Kinoshita, M., and Mishiyama, Y. (1963): Periodic paralysis in hyperthyroidism. *Neurology*, 13:746–752.

33. Sestoft, L. (1967): Direct transition from hypo- to hyperkalemic paralysis during potassium treatment of familial periodic paralysis. *Dan. Med. Bull.*, 14:157–160.

34. Shishiba, Y., Shizume, K., Sakuma, M., Yamauchi, H., Nakao, K., and Okinaka, S. (1966): Studies on electrolyte metabolism in idiopathic and thyrotoxic periodic paralysis. III. Intra- and extracellular concentrations of potassium and sodium in muscle and their changes during induced attacks of paralysis. *Metabolism*, 15:163–162.

35. Shizume, K., Shishiba, Y., Sakuma, M., Yamauchi, H., Nakao, K., and Okinaka, S. (1966):

Studies on electrolyte metabolism in idiopathic and thyrotoxic periodic paralysis. I. Arterio-venous differences of electrolytes during induced paralysis. *Metabolism*, 15:144–183.

36. Shy, M., Wanko, T., Rowley, P. T., and Engel, A. G. (1961): Studies in familial periodic paralysis. *Exp. Neurol.*, 3:53–121.

37. Wang, P., and Clausen, T. (1975): Treatment of attacks in hyperkalemic familial periodic paralysis by inhalation of salbutamol. *Lancet*, 1:221–223.

38. Zierler, K. L., and Andres, R. (1957): Movement of potassium into skeletal muscle during spontaneous attack in family periodic paralysis. *J. Clin. Invest.*, 36:730–737.

General Review Articles

39. Engel, A. G. (1986): Periodic paralysis. In: *Myology*, edited by A. G. Engel and B. Q. Banker, pp. 1843–1870. McGraw-Hill, New York.

40. Ruff, R. L., and Gordon, A. M. (1986): Disorders of muscle: The periodic paralysis. In: *Physiology of Membrane Disorders*, edited by T. E. Andreoli, J. F. Hoffmann, D. D. Fanestil, and S. G. Schultz, pp. 825–839. Plenum Press, New York.

The Regulation of Potassium Balance, edited
by Donald W. Seldin and Gerhard Giebisch,
Raven Press, Ltd., New York © 1989.

13

Diuretics and Potassium

Christopher S. Wilcox

*Departments of Medicine, Pharmacology and Therapeutics,
University of Florida College of Medicine,
Gainesville, Florida 32610*

Diuretic Therapy
Primary Tubular Actions of Diuretics
    Osmotic Diuretics • Carbonic Anhydrase Inhibitors • Loop Diuretics • Thiazides • Potassium-Sparic Diuretics
Secondary Actions of Diuretics on Potassium Excretion
    Intrarenal Mechanisms • Hormonal Mechanisms • Changes in Blood Composition • Structural Changes in the Nephron
Changes in Potassium During Diuretic Therapy
    Effects of Hypokalemia • Mechanisms of Hypokalemia • Diuretic Braking Phenomenon • Factors Affecting Potassium Depletion • Prevention or Treatment of Hypokalemia
References

DIURETIC THERAPY (17–27)

Diuretics have an established position as drugs of first choice in the treatment of hypertension and edema. The primary aim of diuretic therapy is to produce a negative salt balance. Since the osmolality of the extracellular fluid is closely regulated by appropriate adjustments in water intake (thirst) or excretion (free water clearance), any reduction in extracellular NaCl content normally is followed by a parallel reduction in extracellular fluid volume (ECV). In the treatment of edema or hypertension, a reduction in ECV or a fall in blood pressure (BP) can be achieved by restricting dietary salt intake or by diuretic administration. Modest restriction of the dietary salt intake within the range of 75 to 125 mmoles per day in patients with mild essential hypertension has approximately additive antihypertensive effects to standard doses of thiazide diuretics. Thus, the physician who prescribes diuretic therapy should always give due attention to regulation of salt intake. This normally should include a quantitative assessment of dietary salt (from review of diet or from measurement of renal sodium [Na] excretion before diuretic therapy), establishment of a goal for permissible level of Na intake, and some advice about how to achieve this goal. Consequently, this review considers the effects of diuretics and salt restriction on potassium (K) homeostasis.

Diuretics have retained their popularity because they are both effective and relatively nontoxic. Patients occasionally develop a drug allergy or idiosyncracy, e.g., drug fever, skin rash, or blood dyscrasia. However, a more frequent problem is adverse effects that are related to the major renal actions of the drug, e.g., untoward volume and electrolyte depletion with hypotension, azotemia, and electrolyte disturbances or alterations in blood sugar, lipid, or uric acid concentrations. One of the major clinical concerns is production of hypokalemia and K depletion because of the association of hypokalemia with the production of dangerous or even lethal cardiac dysrhythmias.

The major groups of diuretic drugs used in clinical practice, together with representative values for peak natriuretic and kaliuretic responses likely to be encountered with the first administration of these drugs in their usual clinical doses, are shown in Table 1. Of the diuretics used for long-term therapy, loop diuretics and thiazides are the most potent natriuretic agents and are the most widely prescribed. Therefore, these drugs receive particular emphasis in this chapter. The kaliuretic response is particularly prominent with the first dose of carbonic anhydrase inhibitors and osmotic diuretics, but all diuretics, except the potassium-sparing agents, increase renal K excretion (Table 1).

A change in K excretion produced by a diuretic can be ascribed either to a primary action of the drug on its specific tubular target transport mechanism

TABLE 1. *Peak rates of electrolyte excretion with different diuretics in humans*[a]

	$U_{Na}V$ ($\mu mol \cdot min^{-1}$)	U_KV ($\mu mol \cdot min^{-1}$)
Control	50	15
Osmotic diuretic (e.g., mannitol)	900	150
Carbonic anhydrase inhibitor (e.g., acetazolamide)	200	200
Thiazide diuretic (e.g., hydrochlorothiazide)	450	75
Loop diuretic (e.g., furosemide)	1100	75
Potassium-sparing diuretic (e.g., amiloride)	250	10

[a]Data are representative values, not precise figures, of those expected for a normal human subject at peak diuresis with the first dose of the diuretic.

in the nephron or to a secondary action that is a consequence of its inhibitory effect on tubular NaCl or fluid reabsorption upstream of its direct action on a tubule segment. These secondary actions of diuretics include changes in tubule fluid flow and composition at nephron segments that are downstream from the primary site of action of the diuretic. In addition, changes mediated by hormones released in response to the drug, changes in blood composition, and possible structural adaptations in the nephron during prolonged diuretic therapy have to be considered.

For a more detailed description of the normal mechanisms that subserve tubular ion fluxes and the mechanisms of diuretic action, the reader is referred to a number of excellent reviews (17–27).

PRIMARY TUBULAR ACTIONS OF DIURETICS (1,2,5,10,12)

Diuretics affect renal K excretion directly by altering tubular K reabsorption or secretion. Effects on renal blood flow or glomerular filtration rate (GFR) normally are of lesser importance. This section is confined to a discussion of the direct tubular actions of these drugs.

Osmotic Diuretics

Osmotic diuretics are biochemically inactive substances whose physiologic actions depend on generation of osmotic gradients across cell membranes. They are filtered freely at the renal glomerulus but are reabsorbed little or not at all. Thus, they are concentrated in tubule fluid. Accordingly, their concentration increases progressively with distance down the nephron. Fluid reabsorption from the proximal tubule and the loop of Henle is dependent on the development of favorable osmotic gradients from the peritubular (interstitial) to luminal compartments developed by reabsorption of solutes. Therefore, osmotic diuretics have their major actions in these nephron segments, where they inhibit fluid reabsorption. At higher concentrations, the marked inhibition of tubular fluid reabsorption leads to a fall in tubule fluid sodium (Na) concentration and to the development of an unfavorable chemical gradient opposing Na reabsorption, thereby inhibiting a substantial fraction of fluid and Na reabsorption in the proximal nephron. As a consequence, there is a sharp increase in the delivery of fluid and NaCl to the more distal nephron sites. K normally is extensively reabsorbed by the proximal tubule and the loop of Henle; the late distal tubule and the collecting ducts are the main sites of K secretion. Since K is reabsorbed isotonically in the proximal tubule in rough proportion to fluid transport, inhibition of fluid reabsorption in the proximal tubule and the loop of Henle causes proportionate inhibition of

K reabsorption. This results in increased rates of K delivery to the distal nephron.

Mannitol is the hypertonic solute used most commonly as an osmotic diuretic. Mannitol produces profound, dose-dependent diuresis, natriuresis, and kaliuresis. The degree of body fluid and electrolyte depletion induced by an infusion of mannitol may be underestimated because of the osmotic action of the drug on the fluxes of fluid and electrolytes. Mannitol raises the plasma osmolality and thereby draws water from the intracellular to the extracellular compartments. Cellular dehydration increases the intracellular K concentration and the efflux of K from the cell into the extracellular compartment. Thus, the serum potassium concentration (serum K) may be maintained or even increased despite external K losses into the urine. The full consequences of the osmotic diuresis may become apparent only later when the mannitol has been excreted and fluid and K reenter cells, thereby unmasking the underlying extracellular depletion of fluid and K. A similar sequence of events can occur in patients with diabetic ketoacidosis undergoing an osmotic diuresis due to glucose. It may be only after correction of the plasma hypertonicity and acidosis by appropriate fluid and insulin therapy that severe K depletion becomes manifest as hypokalemia.

Carbonic Anhydrase Inhibitors

Acetazolamide, benzolamide, and ethoxolamide inhibit the enzymic reaction between carbon dioxide and water that leads to the formation of carbonic acid, whose nonenzymic dissociation within the tubule cell provides H and HCO_3. The intracellular proton is made available for secretion into the tubular lumen in exchange for Na (Na, H antiport mechanism), the latter being reabsorbed from the lumen to the cell cytoplasm. The bicarbonate ion leaves the cell via the peritubular cell membrane and is reabsorbed into the bloodstream. H ions secreted into the proximal tubular fluid can react with nonvolatile buffers, such as ammonia or phosphate, or with filtered bicarbonate.

The reaction between tubular fluid H and HCO_3 forms carbonic acid whose dehydration is catalyzed by carbonic anhydrase to carbon dioxide, which can penetrate the tubule cell. Therefore, the net effect of these actions of carbonic anhydrase is to facilitate H ion secretion into and Na reabsorption from the tubular fluid. Inhibition of carbonic anhydrase diminishes proximal Na and fluid reabsorption and diminishes or abolishes acidification of proximal tubule fluid. Since K is reabsorbed isotonically with fluid from the proximal tubule, inhibition of the enzyme should also diminish proximal K reabsorption. A direct effect of these drugs on K secretion by the distal tubule has been demonstrated and is most likely due to direct alkalization of the cytoplasm of K-secreting distal cells. This is a known stimulus for K secretion. A significant part of the pronounced increase in distal K secretion is due to secondary effects resulting from the inhibition of $NaHCO_3$ and fluid reabsorption in more proximal segments and the delivery of large amounts of fluid and HCO_3 into the distal tubule and collecting duct.

Loop Diuretics

The powerful loop diuretics (e.g., furosemide, bumetanide, and ethacrynic acid) can increase the GFR modestly. However, their main action is to inhibit the electroneutral cotransport of Na, K, and 2Cl in the thick ascending limb of the loop of Henle (Fig. 1). The energy for reabsorption of these ions is derived indirectly from the Na,K pump (Na,K-ATPase) located in the basolateral cell surface, which maintains a low intracellular Na concentration. Inspection of Fig. 1 demonstrates that K enters the cell from both luminal and basolateral surfaces; its exit across the luminal cell membrane is primarily by passive diffusion. Across the basolateral surface, an electroneutral cotransport process with chloride has been suggested as a possible exit mechanism, although passive K diffusion (not shown) also may be present. The primary action of loop diuretics is to diminish reabsorption of K with Na and

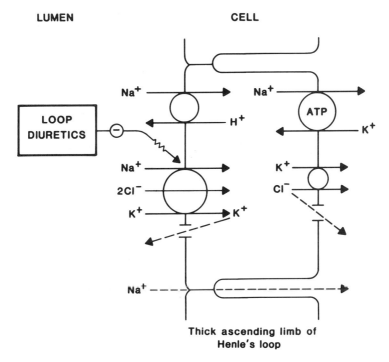

FIG. 1. Cell model of the thick ascending limb of Henle's loop and diluting segments.

2Cl in the loop segment and thereby to deliver increased quantities of K to the distal nephron. In addition, inhibition by loop diuretics of Na entry from lumen to cell lowers the intracellular Na concentration and increases the gradient for Na entry coupled to H extrusion via the Na,H antiport mechanism (Fig. 1). This may explain the finding that, in the rat at least, loop diuretics directly increase acidification of the tubule fluid in the early distal tubule.

Thiazides

The water-soluble thiazide diuretics (e.g., chlorothiazide) can inhibit carbonic anhydrase at concentrations achieved in clinical practice. These drugs will inhibit fluid, Na, HCO₃, and K reabsorption in the proximal nephron. The more lipid-soluble compounds (e.g., bendroflumethiazide) lack a major action on carbonic anhydrase but are also powerful diuretic drugs. The primary site of action of these drugs is the early distal tubule (distal convoluted tubule), where they inhibit coupled NaCl reabsorption by an electroneutral cotransport process (Fig. 2). The energy for Na reabsorption is again provided indirectly via the Na,K pump (Na,K-ATPase), which maintains a low intracellular Na concentration. This segment appears to lack a major reabsorptive flux for K, and, therefore, thiazide diuretics do not have direct effects on tubular transport. Recent studies indicate that furosemide, but not bumetanide, is also a weak inhibitor of this thiazide-sensitive cotransport process.

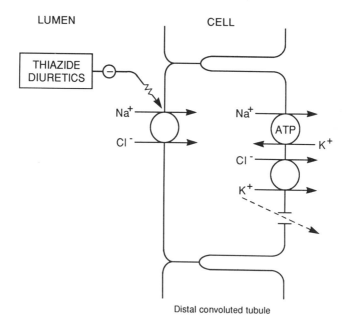

FIG. 2. Cell model of the distal convoluted tubule (early distal tubule).

Potassium-Sparing Diuretics

Diuretics of this class (e.g., triamterene and amiloride) and drugs that antagonize the actions of aldosterone (e.g., spironolactone) have the unique properties of increasing the excretion of Na while decreasing the excretion of K and H. At the concentrations encountered during diuretic therapy, the major sites of action of amiloride and triamterene are the late distal tubule (initial collecting tubule) and the cortical collecting ducts (Fig. 3). At very high concentrations, inhibition of proximal reabsorption, including Na,H exchange also may occur.

At distal nephron sites, Na enters the luminal surface of the cell down its electrochemical gradient by an amiloride-sensitive channel and exits at the basolateral surface against an electrochemical gradient driven by the action of the Na,K pump. At both the initial collecting tubule and the cortical collecting ducts, K enters the cells via the Na,K pump and can diffuse out via the luminal or peritubular cell membrane. Inhibition of luminal Na entry by potassium-sparing diuretics could diminish K excretion by one of two mechanisms. First, inhibition of Na entry from the lumen would reduce the luminal electronegativity and thereby diminish the electrical gradient favoring secretion of K and H from cell to lumen. Second, inhibition of Na entry from the lumen would reduce the intracellular Na concentration and thereby diminish the activity of the Na,K pump on the basolateral cell membrane, which is responsible for maintaining a high intracellular K concentration. The consequences of these actions are that the renal excretion of Na increases only modestly because much of the filtered Na already has been absorbed upstream, but the more striking changes are a sharp fall in K and acid excretion. The decline in H secretion is also due to the reduction of the lumen-negative potential that normally favors H secretion.

The cortical collecting duct is the major nephron site at which aldosterone increases Na absorption and K secretion. The mechanism of action of aldosterone entails an increase in Na permeability of the luminal cell membrane and increased activity of the Na,K pump at the basolateral cell membrane. Consequently, spironolactone and its metabolites, which block aldosterone receptors, may decrease Na reabsorption and K and H secretion by blocking aldosterone-stimulated Na entry at the luminal cell membrane. Their site of action is similar to that of amiloride and triamterene, although the latter two drugs do not interact with aldosterone receptors directly.

SECONDARY ACTIONS OF DIURETICS ON POTASSIUM EXCRETION (3,4,6,8,9,14)

The main primary tubular action of carbonic anhydrase inhibitors leads to decreased Na, HCO_3, fluid, and K reabsorption in the proximal tubule,

LUMEN   CELL

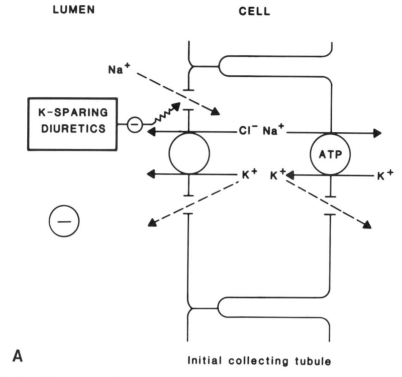

A   Initial collecting tubule

FIG. 3. Cell models of (**A**) the initial connecting tubule (late distal tubule) and (**B**) cortical collecting ducts.

whereas the primary tubular action of loop diuretics on the Na,K,2Cl co-transport system leads to inhibition of K reabsorption in the loop of Henle. The primary tubular action of K-sparing diuretics to inhibit luminal Na entry at the cortical collecting duct leads to a closely linked diminution in K secretion. On the other hand, changes in K excretion produced by other classes of diuretics cannot be ascribed to their primary tubular actions. It is clear that the major determinant of kaliuresis even with carbonic anhydrase inhibitors and loop diuretics is increased distal K secretion rather than decreased K reabsorption more proximally. Therefore, secondary actions of diuretics on K excretion are of predominant importance.

Intrarenal Mechanisms

Inhibition of tubular Na reabsorption increases the delivery of solute and fluid to downstream nephron segments. Several mechanisms are involved in the ensuing powerful stimulation of K secretion along the late distal tubule

LUMEN   CELL

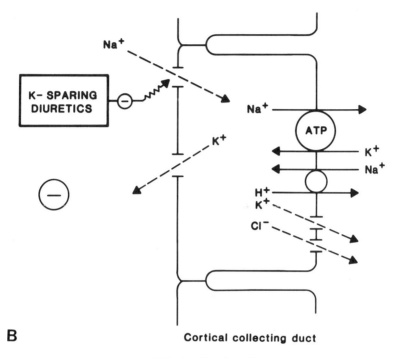

B   **Cortical collecting duct**

FIG. 3. (*Continued.*)

(initial collecting duct and cortical collecting tubule). Of pivotal importance is increased fluid and sodium delivery. Changes in the electrical potential and pH may augment K secretion. Microperfusion of superficial distal tubules at varying rates has shown that distal K secretion increases with the rate of tubular fluid flow. The concentration of Na in tubular fluid can determine K secretion by the distal nephron, particularly when the Na concentration is initially low. In the cortical collecting tubule, Na delivery has been shown to determine K secretion in a major way. Increasing flow through the distal nephron acts to increase Na delivery and also may lower K concentration in the lumen, thereby creating a more favorable gradient for K movement from cell to lumen. This provides a simple model for flow-dependent K secretion and a universal mechanism whereby diuretics acting at more proximal segments (osmotic diuretics, carbonic anyhdrase inhibitors, loop diuretics, and thiazides) promote K secretion in the distal nephron.

Additional kaliuretic mechanisms may be activated during administration of various diuretics, but their role is less well defined; e.g., infusion of Na with a poorly reabsorbed anion (e.g., sulfate) also increases the excretion of K and net acid. This increase in distal K and H secretion has been related to the development of a more favorable electrical gradient (negative in the tubular fluid) due to reabsorption of Na in the presence of the poorly permeant anion. More recently, a neutral KCl cotransport process has been identified on the luminal surface of cells in the late distal tubule (initial collecting tubule) (Fig. 3A). An alternative explanation for the increase in K secretion during increased distal delivery of poorly reabsorbed anion is the decrease in luminal Cl concentration. Thus, a fall in tubular fluid Cl concentration would favor exit from cell to lumen, which is linked to K secretion. Another relevant point is that the capacity of the distal nephron to reabsorb HCO_3 is limited, particularly after inhibition of carbonic anhydrase. Thus, administration of carbonic anhydrase inhibitors increases the distal delivery of Na with a poorly reabsorbed anion (HCO_3). Micropuncture experiments have shown that K secretion by the distal tubule increases in proportion to the alkalinity of the tubular and cellular fluid. Therefore, the sharp increase in U_KV during administration of carbonic anhydrase inhibitors can be related to three consequences of inhibition of proximal HCO_3 reabsorption: increased distal tubular fluid flow, increased distal delivery of a poorly reabsorbed anion (HCO_3) with a consequent fall in tubular fluid Cl concentration, and, increased distal tubular fluid alkalinity. It is no surprise to find that these drugs are the most potent kaliuretic diuretics (Table 1).

Hormonal Mechanisms (14)

Diuretics are powerful stimuli of the renin-angiotensin-aldosterone (RAA) system. Renin release is stimulated by ECV depletion. On the other hand, enhanced Cl reabsorption in the loop of Henle inhibits the release of renin, and inhibition of Cl reabsorption by loop diuretics can stimulate renin release even in the absence of ECV depletion. Angiotensin II (AII) is a major regulator of aldosterone secretion. Frequently, because of volume depletion, the plasma concentrations of both renin and aldosterone rise during diuretic therapy. Aldosterone can increase K and H secretion by the late distal tubule (initial connecting tubule) and the cortical collecting ducts. Prolonged hypersecretion of aldosterone, as in patients with an adrenal aldosterone-secreting tumor (Conn's syndrome) or biolateral adrenal hyperplasia, clearly decreases serum K. Activation of the RAA system by diuretics, therefore, whether due to volume depletion or inhibition of Cl reabsorption in the loop of Henle by loop diuretics, may promote diuretic-induced K losses. This is particularly important in settings in which there is preexisting hyperaldosteronism (e.g., edematous states, primary hyperaldosteronism). This aldosterone-dependent K secretion occurs in those nephron segments responsive to distal K-sparing diuretics. Such drugs as amiloride and triamterene can counter aldosterone-stimulated K loss, although they are not specific aldosterone antagonists. Spironolactone will counter this mechanism of K loss more specifically by inhibition of aldosterone receptors.

Recently, antidiuretic hormone (ADH, vasopressin) has been shown to stimulate K secretion by the superficial distal tubule. In many physiologic settings, this effect of ADH on distal K secretion may be concealed by its effects on tubular fluid flow. For example, a water diuresis has little effect on $U_K V$. This may be explained by the offsetting effects of a fall in ADH and an increase in distal flow and Na delivery. Osmotic diuretics produce much greater increase in $U_K V$. These drugs abstract water from the intracellular compartment and thereby stimulate ADH secretion powerfully. Osmotic diuretics also promote increased distal flow as well as Na and K delivery by inhibiting fluid, Na, and K reabsorption in the proximal nephron; they may further activate K secretion by enhancing the luminal electronegativity of the distal nephron if luminal Na concentration is initially low. Other classes of

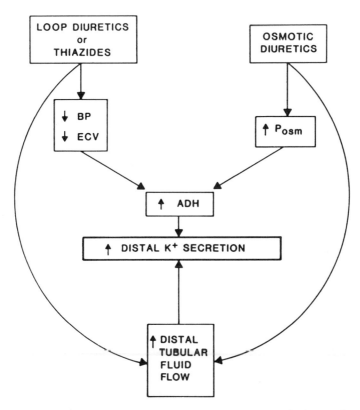

FIG. 4. Diagrammatic representation of the effects of diuretics on distal potassium secretion mediated by changes in antidiuretic hormone and distal tubular fluid flow rate.

diuretics could stimulate ADH release via the low pressure baroreceptor volume-sensing mechanism located in the atria, ventricles, large veins, and pulmonary vessels (Fig. 4). Recent studies lend support to the hypothesis that furosemide-induced ADH release stimulates K secretion, since water loading that should suppress ADH release was found to diminish the kaliuretic response to furosemide in normal human subjects despite increasing urine flow rate.

Changes in Blood Composition

Carbonic anhydrase inhibitors and distal K-sparing diuretics decrease net acid excretion and can cause a metabolic acidosis. In contract, loop diuretics and thiazides cause a metabolic alkalosis. The generation of metabolic alkalosis with loop diuretics in humans results largely from loss of NaCl and fluid from the ECV without an equivalent loss of HCO_3 (contraction alkalosis). However, loop diuretics can also stimulate distal H secretion. The metabolic alkalosis is maintained by enhanced HCO_3 reabsorption, but the mechanisms responsible during prolonged diuretic administration are not clearly defined; they probably include aldosterone-stimulated distal H secretion and enhanced HCO_3 reabsorption in response to Cl depletion. Once alkalosis occurs, it partitions K from the extracellular to the intracellular compartments and may further enhance loss of K. Thus, the fall in serum K during administration of thiazide or loop diuretics can be related, in part, to the concurrent metabolic alkalosis. Fortunately, hypokalemia, particularly when associated with a fall in cell K concentrations, inhibits renal K excretion and thereby provides some safeguard against severe K depletion. The distal K-sparing diuretics do not lead to alkalosis, since they inhibit renal H secretion. Prolonged diuretic administration can induce magnesium (Mg) depletion, which potentiates renal K loss.

Chloride depletion often accompanies diuretic-induced metabolic alkalosis, especially that due to loop diuretics. Chloride depletion can increase K excretion by stimulating renin and aldosterone release and by reducing luminal Cl concentrations, which stimulate distal K secretion directly (Fig. 3A).

Structural Changes in the Nephron

There is remarkable hypertrophy of the distal convoluted tubules of rats given large doses of loop diuretics for 5 days. The basolateral cell membrane area and Na,K-ATPase activity of this segment increase considerably. These may be structural and functional adaptations to a prolonged increase in delivery of tubular fluid to the distal nephron during blockade of reabsorption by the diuretic at upstream segments. The full significance of these changes is not yet clear, but conceivably such increased Na,K-ATPase activity developing during diuretic therapy could enhance both distal tubular Na reabsorption and K secretion.

CHANGES IN POTASSIUM DURING DIURETIC THERAPY (7,11,13–16)

Effects of Hypokalemia

Numerous studies have shown that the serum K falls by an average of 0.3–0.6 mmoles·liter^{-1} during regular therapy with thiazides or loop diuretics in hypertensive subjects not receiving concurrent therapy with other drugs or additional dietary K supplements. This fall in serum K generally develops within the first week of treatment and remains stable thereafter. However, a further sharp fall in serum K may occur during intercurrent illness that increases K losses (e.g., gastroenteritis), decreases K intake (e.g., vomiting), or

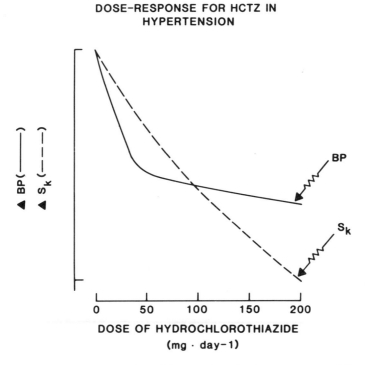

DOSE–RESPONSE FOR HCTZ IN HYPERTENSION

FIG. 5. Diagrammatic representation of the steady state dose–response relationships for changes in blood pressure and serum potassium concentration during treatment of hypertensive patients with hydrochlorothiazide. (Adapted from ref. 4a.)

redistributes K into cells (e.g., alkalosis). Overall, less than 7% of patients with uncomplicated hypertension treated with thiazides have a fall in serum K below 3.0 mmoles·liter^{-1}; the corresponding figure for loop diuretics is approximately 1%.

Severe hypokalemia (serum K below 3.0 mmoles·liter^{-1}), particularly when associated with total body K depletion, can have serious clinical consequences, particularly the development of cardiac arrhythmias. Milder degrees of hypokalemia, such as are encountered commonly during diuretic therapy for patients with hypertension, increase the risk of ventricular premature beats. However, it is not clear whether there is an increased risk of serious or lethal dysrhythmias. Hypokalemia impairs insulin release and, therefore, contributes to the deterioration in glucose tolerance that is seen in some diuretic-treated patients. For these reasons, hypokalemia should be identified and treated aggressively in patients with hypertension or cardiovascular disease receiving diuretic drugs, and attention should be given to its prevention.

Long-term studies of hypertensive patients treated with different doses of thiazides have shown that the antihypertensive response reaches a plateau at a daily dose of hydrochlorothiazide of between 25 and 50 mg (Fig. 5). In contrast, the fall in serum K increases almost linearly with increasing daily dosage. Every effort should be made, therefore, to maintain thiazide dosage within the lower range or to take steps to prevent hypokalemia in the few patients who may need a higher dosage. Long-acting thiazides (e.g., chlorthalidone) are more prone to cause serious hypokalemia than shorter-acting drugs (e.g., hydrochlorothiazide) and are not recommended for routine use.

Mechanisms of Hypokalemia

During long-term therapy with thiazide or loop diuretics in patients with hypertension, the serum K falls by an average of 15% whereas changes in total body K, measured by isotopic techniques, are much smaller and average less than 5%. In many studies, no significant changes in total body K are detectable. Studies of patients under metabolic balance conditions have shown that hypokalemia can develop in the first 3 days of furosemide administration without any detectable reduction in total body K. Thus, a major part of diuretic-induced hypokalemia represents redistribution of K from extracellular to intracellular sites rather than total body K deficiency. Diuretics increase serum levels of aldosterone and catecholamines and lead to a metabolic alkalosis. These are all factors associated with movement of K from extracellular to intracellular compartments (Fig. 6).

Of particular importance is the fall in serum K concentration of 0.3 to 1.0 mmole·liter^{-1}, that is provoked by activation of beta$_2$-adrenergic receptors by epinephrine. This catecholamine stimulates Na,K-ATPase activity in cell membranes, notably skeletal muscle. Epinephrine released in response to pain and stress could be important in explaining the abrupt fall in serum K

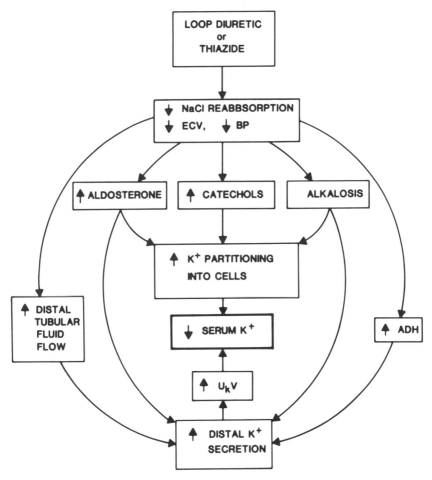

FIG. 6. Diagrammatic representation of the secondary effects of thiazide and loop diuretic drugs on serum potassium concentration.

concentration that can occur during acute myocardial infarction. Hypokalemia at this time is a particular hazard because it may provoke or perpetuate serious cardiac dysrhythmias. Preexisting diuretic-induced hypokalemia may increase the chance that serum K concentration falls into a dangerously low range in patients developing myocardial infarction.

Diuretic Braking Phenomenon

Whereas the first dose of a diuretic produces a marked increase in excretion of Na and fluid and a corresponding reduction in body weight, administration of the drug over 2 to 5 days leads to a new equilibrium; excretion now no longer exceeds intake, and a stable body weight is regained. This diuretic braking phenomenon has been related to a decreasing natriuretic and diuretic response to the drug (seen during severe dietary salt restriction) or to a period of enhanced renal Na and fluid retention in the postdiuretic phase (seen at higher levels of dietary salt intake). A similar postdiuretic phase of renal K retention (renal compensation) has been observed in normal subjects taking furosemide. The mechanism of this decreased K loss is unclear. Presumably, it is not mediated by increased levels of aldosterone or ADH or the structural changes seen in the distal nephron during prolonged therapy, all of which should promote, rather than diminish, renal K excretion.

Factors Affecting Potassium Depletion

There is an exaggerated renal K loss with furosemide in normal subjects during severe dietary Na restriction to 20 mmoles/day. This negative K balance correlates with a striking increase in plasma aldosterone concentration. In contrast, there is a diminished fall in total body K over 4 to 8 weeks of thiazide therapy for hypertension during more modest dietary Na restriction to about 75 mmoles/day. These different results with respect to K loss may relate to offsetting effects of dietary salt restriction on plasma aldosterone concentration and distal delivery of sodium and fluid (Fig. 7). Plasma aldosterone concentration rises very steeply as dietary salt restriction falls to very low levels (below 25–50 mmoles/day). At these levels, hyperaldosteronism may have a predominant effect in promoting diuretic-induced K losses. In contrast, more modest degrees of salt restriction increase plasma aldosterone levels only slightly, and the diminished distal delivery of solute and fluid may be of predominant importance in diminishing diuretic-induced K losses. Thus, moderate salt restriction in patients with uncomplicated hypertension not only increases the antihypertensive action of diuretics but also may diminish the K depletion.

The model shown in Fig. 7 implies that preexisting hyperaldosteronism might shift the relationship between K excretion and Na intake so that even mild degrees of salt restriction might increase renal K losses. This prediction has not been explored in detail. However, it is apparent that patients with edema and hyperaldosteronism (e.g., uncompensated congestive heart failure or cirrhosis of the liver) are at special risk of developing hypokalemia during dietary salt restriction and diuretic therapy.

Prevention or Treatment of Hypokalemia

Potentially serious hypokalemia or K depletion developing during diuretic therapy should be anticipated in patients with hyperaldosteronism (edema-

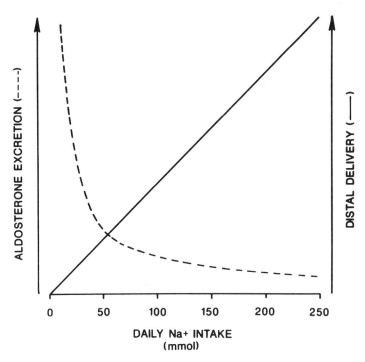

FIG. 7. Diagrammatic representation of the offsetting interrelationships between steady state levels of aldosterone secretion or delivery of filtrate to the distal nephron as they are affected by dietary Na intake.

tous conditions, such as severe cardiac failure, cirrhosis of the liver, nephrotic syndrome, malnutrition, Conn's syndrome, bilateral adrenal hyperplasia or renal vascular hypertension), with high levels of ADH (edema, syndrome of inappropriate ADH secretion), or with severe metabolic alkalosis. Deficient K intake may be anticipated in patients with diarrheal diseases or in those with poor appetite, e.g., alcoholic subjects eating a diet deficient in fresh fruit and vegetables. The diet of black hypertensive subjects is generally lower in K than that of white hypertensives. Dietary K intake can be assessed from 24 hr urine collections; this is a valuable guide to the need for supplemental K before starting diuretic therapy. Although therapy directed at increasing K intake or decreasing renal K excretion is required in the majority of these high-risk patients with edema or preexisting K depletion, its need in the routine treatment of patients with essential hypertension with thiazide diuretics is debated vigorously. Potassium replacement therapy or adjunctive measures to prevent K losses and hypokalemia are clearly indicated in diuretic-treated patients when serum K concentrations fall below 3.0 mmoles·liter^{-1}, when they are receiving digitalis glycosides, when there is danger of hepatic coma, and when there is underlying cardiac disease.

Mild degrees of hypokalemia may translate into severe hypokalemia during the stress of myocardial infarction or during concurrent illness, such as diarrhea. Since severe hypokalemia is an established risk for ventricular dysrhythmias and patients with hypertension are at increased risk for developing a myocardial infarction, most physicians take steps to prevent even mild degrees of hypokalemia. Two strategies are available. The first is to increase the K intake either by encouraging dietary intake of substances rich in K or by supplementing with KCl. Substitution of KCl for NaCl used as cooking or table salt may be useful. K must be given as the Cl salt, since oral K citrate is not retained, perhaps because of the accompanying alkalosis.

A second strategy to treat or prevent hypokalemia is to combine thiazide or loop diuretic therapy with a drug that counteracts renal K losses. Three classes of drugs have been shown to be effective (Fig. 8). Angiotensin-converting enzyme (ACE) inhibitors (e.g., captopril or enalapril) prevent generation of AII from AI and thereby block the increase in aldosterone secretion provoked by diuretic-induced renin release. Thus, these drugs often can prevent diuretic-induced hypokalemia while potentiating the antihypertensive and volume-depleting actions of the diuretics. Combined therapy with a loop diuretic or thiazide and an ACE inhibitor is attractive, since it increases the efficacy while decreasing a major toxicity of the diuretic. With increased efficacy, however, comes an increased risk of an exaggerated fall in BP or ECV, and close surveillance is required when diuretics are used in combination with ACE inhibitors.

The effects of diuretic-induced hyperaldosteronism can be counteracted by administration of a drug that blocks aldosterone receptors (e.g., spironolactone). A combined tablet with a thiazide and spironolactone is available. Spironolactone is helpful in countering diuretic-induced hypokalemia, but prolonged therapy with this drug has some undesirable side effects (e.g., gynecomastia, androgenic actions, gastrointestinal upset).

The potassium-sparing diuretics do not block aldosterone-induced distal K secretion directly, but these drugs can prevent the kaliuretic response to loop diuretics or thiazides. These drugs also diminish net acid excretion and thereby counteract the production of metabolic alkalosis with thiazides or loop diuretics. Fixed-dose combinations of thiazide and potassium-sparing diuretics are available and convenient for treatment of patients with no complications. Where preexisting K depletion is present or anticipated, increased doses of K-sparing diuretic, relative to thiazides, will be required, and fixed dose combinations would not be appropriate.

Severe or even fatal hyperkalemia can develop in patients receiving aldosterone antagonists or distal K-sparing diuretics. Hyperkalemia most often develops where K intake is high (e.g., inappropriate KCl therapy), GFR is low (e.g., elderly patients), acidosis is present (e.g., diabetic patients), or another drug that limits renal K excretion is being administered (e.g., ACE inhibitor or heparin). Therefore, spironolactone, amiloride, and triamterene

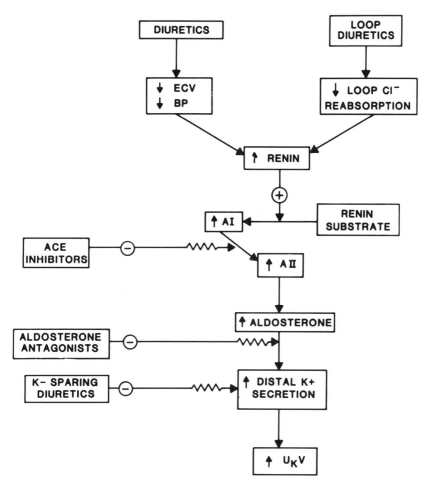

FIG. 8. Diagrammatic representation of the effects of diuretics, such as thiazides, on changes in K excretion mediated by activation of the renin-angiotensin-aldosterone system. Note that three separate classes of drugs can interrupt this mechanism.

should be used only after a careful evaluation of those factors that can predispose to hyperkalemia. Regular assessment of serum K is required, especially during initiation of therapy or intercurrent illness.

Beta-blocking drugs reduce renin secretion. In large trials, there is often a small increase in serum K during beta blocker therapy. However, this effect is usually modest and insufficient to justify the use of these drugs specifically to prevent hypokalemia.

Occasional patients develop severe Mg depletion and hypomagnesemia during prolonged diuretic therapy. Less severe degrees of Mg depletion are difficult to substantiate and may be frequent. Hypokalemia and K depletion cannot be corrected in the presence of severe Mg depletion because of ongoing renal K losses. Therefore, refractory hypokalemia should warrant a search for Mg depletion and appropriate Mg therapy.

ACKNOWLEDGMENT

The author gratefully acknowledges support from a Grant-in-Aide from the American Heart Association (Florida Affiliate) and an equipment grant from the Veterans Administration, Washington, DC, to the Gainesville GRECC, which was instrumental in performing the studies described. Investigations performed in the Clinical Research Center were supported by a grant to the Gainesville CRC from the NIH (RR 82-25). It is a pleasure to acknowledge the collaboration of many colleagues at the Brigham and Women's Hospital and the University of Florida, including W.E. Mitch, R.A. Kelly, N.J. Guzman, N.R. Loon, and P.A. Friedman, and the helpful advice of Dr. Charles C. Wingo.

REFERENCES

1. Duarte, C. G., Chomety, F., and Giebisch, G. (1971): Effects of amiloride, ouabain and furosemide on distal tubular function in the rat. *Am. J. Physiol.*, 221:632–639.
2. Field, M. J., Fowler, N., and Giebisch, G. H. (1984): Effects of enantiomers of indacrinone (MK-196) on transport by the loop of Henle and distal tubule studied by microperfusion *in vivo. J. Pharmacol. Exp. Ther.*, 230:62–68.
3. Field, M. J., Stanton, B. A., and Giebisch, G. H. (1984): Differential acute effects of aldosterone, dexamethasone and hyperkalemia on distal tubular potassium secretion in the rat kidney. *J. Clin. Invest.*, 74:1792–1802.
4. Field, M. J., Stanton, B. A., and Giebisch, G. H. (1984): Influence of ADH on renal potassium handling: A micropuncture and microperfusion study. *Kidney Int.*, 25:502–511.
4a. Hollifield, J. W. (1984): Potassium and magnesium abnormalities: Diuretics and arrhythmias in hypertension. *Am. J. Med.*, 77:28–32.
5. Hropot, M., Fowler, N., Karlmark, B., and Giebisch, G. (1985): Tubular action of diuretics: Distal effects on electrolyte transport and acidification. *Kidney Int.*, 28:477–489.
6. Kaissling, B., Bachmann, S., and Kriz, W. (1985): Structural adaptation of the distal convoluted tubule to prolonged furosemide treatment. *Am. J. Physiol.*, 248:F374–F381.
7. Kelly, R. A., Wilcox, C. S., Meyer, T. W., et al. (1983): The response of the kidney to furosemide. II. Effect of captopril on sodium balance. *Kidney Int.*, 24:233–239.
8. Khuri, R. N., Strieder, N., Wiederholt, M., and Giebisch, G. (1975): Effects of flow rate and potassium intake on distal tubule potassium transfer. *Am. J. Physiol.*, 228:1249–1261.
9. Malnic, G., Mello-Aires, M., and Giebisch, G. H. (1971): Potassium transport across renal distal tubules during acid-base disturbances. *Am. J. Physiol.*, 221:1192–1208.
10. Morgan, T., Tadokoro, M., Marvin, D., and Berliner, R. W. (1970): Effects of furosemide on Na^+ and K^+ transport studied by microperfusion of the rat nephron. *Am. J. Physiol.*, 218:292–297.
11. Ram, V. C. S., Garrett, B. N., and Kaplan, N. C. (1981): Moderate sodium restriction and various diuretics in the treatment of hypertension: Effects on potassium wastage and blood pressure control. *Arch. Intern. Med.*, 141:1015–1019.
12. Velazquez, H., and Wright, F. S. (1986): Effects of diuretic drugs on Na, Cl, and K transport by rat renal distal tubule. *Am. J. Physiol.*, 250:F1013–F1023.
13. Wilcox, C. S., Guzman, N. J., Mitch, W. E., et al. (1987): Na^+, K^+ and BP homeostasis in man during furosemide: Effects of prazosin and captopril. *Kidney Int.*, 31:135–141.

14. Wilcox, C. S., Mitch, W. E., Kelly, R. A., et al. (1984): Factors affecting potassium balance during furosemide administration. *Clin. Sci.*, 67:195–203.
15. Wilcox, C. S., Mitch, W. E., Kelly, R. A., et al. (1983): The response of the kidney to furosemide. I. Importance of salt intake and renal compensation. *J. Lab. Clin. Med.*, 102:450–458.
16. Wilkinson, P. R., Issler, H., Hesp, R., and Rafferty, E. B. (1975): Total body and serum potassium during prolonged thiazide therapy for essential hypertension. *Lancet*, 1:759–762.

General Review Articles

17. Dirks, J. H., and Sutton, R. A. L., eds. (1986): *Diuretics: Physiology Pharmacology and Clinical Use.* Saunders, Philadelphia.
18. Giebisch, G., and Koeppen, B. (1987): Transport of sodium and potassium across the epithelium of the distal nephron. In: *Diuretics: Chemistry, Pharmacology and Clinical Applications*, edited by J. P. Puschett, pp. 121–130. Elsevier, Amsterdam.
19. Hollifield, J. W. (1986): Thiazide treatment of hypertension: Effects of thiazide diuretics on serum potassium, magnesium and ventricular ectopy. *Am. J. Med.*, 80 [Suppl. 4A]:8–12.
20. Maren, T. H. (1967): Carbonic anhydrase: Chemistry, physiology and inhibition. *Physiol. Rev.*, 47:595.
21. Morgan, D. B., and Davidson, C. (1980): Hypokalemia and diuretics: An analysis of publications. *Br. Med. J.*, 1:905–908.
22. Tannen, R. L. (1985): Diuretic-induced hypokalemia. *Kidney Int.*, 28:988–1000.
23. Velazquez, H., and Wright, F. S. (1986): Control by drugs of renal potassium handling. *Annu. Rev. Pharmacol. Toxicol.*, 26:293–309.
24. Whelton, P. K., Whelton, A., and Gordon, W. W., eds. (1986): *Potassium in Cardiovascular and Renal Medicine.* Marcel Dekker, New York.
25. Wiener, I. M., and Mudge, G. H. (1985): Diuretics and other agents employed in the mobilization of edema. In: *The Pharmacological Basis of Therapeutics*, 7th ed., edited by A. G. Gilman, L. S. Goodman, T. W. Rall, and F. Murad, pp. 887–907. Macmillan, New York.
26. Wilcox, C. S. (1987): Diuretics and potassium. *Curr. Top. Membranes Transport*, 28:331–350.
27. Wilcox, C. S. (1987): Roles of renin-angiotensin-aldosterone and autonomic nervous systems in the response to diuretic drugs in man. In: *Diuretics: Chemistry, Pharmacology and Clinical Applications*, edited by J. B. Puschett, pp. 503–509. Elsevier, Amsterdam.

The Regulation of Potassium Balance, edited
by Donald W. Seldin and Gerhard Giebisch,
Raven Press, Ltd., New York © 1989.

14

High Potassium Diets Reduce Stroke Mortality and Arterial and Renal Tubular Lesions and Sometimes Even the Blood Pressure in Hypertension

Louis Tobian

Department of Medicine, University of Minnesota Hospital and School of Medicine, Minneapolis, Minnesota 55455

Clinical Studies
　　Potassium Intake and Blood Pressure in Various Populations • Effect of Dietary Potassium on Deaths Related to Strokes
Animal Studies
　　Effect of Potassium on Hypertension and Stroke • Effect of Potassium on Renal Lesions in Hypertension • Effect of Potassium on Arterial and Cardiac Hypertrophy in Hypertension • Effect of Potassium on Arterial Endothelial Cells in Hypertension • Effect of Potassium on Longevity
Possible Mechanisms of Action of Potassium in Relation to Hypertension
References

CLINICAL STUDIES (6–8,12,21,32,33)

Potassium appears to be a very important element in human nutrition. The evidence for this has been growing steadily for the last four decades. As a background to considering potassium in the diet, one should realize that prehistoric humans and hominids starting 3.5 million years ago up to around 10,000 years ago lived as pure hunter-gatherers and ate only the natural food that could be obtained from hunting or collecting vegetable materials, such as roots, fruits, tubers, nuts, grains, and seeds. This type of naturally obtained food contains not only a very low amount of sodium but also a very high amount of potassium. There are a few pockets of human beings living as hunter-gatherers in the world today, and a study of their diet indicates that they take in between 200 and 285 mEq of potassium per day. On the other hand, urban whites in the United States eat about 65 mEq per day, and certain population groups, such as blacks in the southeastern part of the United States, average around 25 to 30 mEq per day. There is a wide diversity among various peoples in the world in the habitual daily intake of potassium. However, all modern people eat far less potassium than did their prehistoric forebears, taking in much less than one-fourth the amount of potassium that was eaten by prehistoric hunter-gatherers.

During those 3.5 million years of human and hominid existence, evolutionary forces were at work, and according to darwinian principles, it is reasonable to expect that during this time human beings became exceedingly well adapted to this very high potassium diet. Such a diet could be considered the natural diet of man and is in great contrast to modern diets, which contain far less potassium. This contrast would make one suspicious that the modern low potassium intake could have some sort of adverse physiologic effect.

It may or may not be a coincidence, but groups of people in the world that are on habitually low potassium diets appear to have an increased amount of cardiovascular complications. For instance, the blacks in the southeastern part of the United States eat a very low potassium diet and also appear to have a higher stroke rate than any other geographic or ethnic group in the United States. These same blacks also have an inordinately high incidence of the type of end-stage renal disease caused by hypertension—an 18 times higher incidence than whites.

The people of Scotland, who have a relatively low potassium intake, averaging about 46 mEq per day, have a considerably greater incidence of cardiovascular disease than have the people of Southern England, France, or Italy, regions where higher levels of potassium are consumed. The people of Tibet eat a very low potassium intake, around 20 mEq per day, and have an exceedingly high incidence of strokes, far greater than found in other areas of China or in Japan. However, the stroke rate in China and Japan is very much higher than that in certain western countries and has long been considered the leading cause of death in these two countries. Recent surveys indicate that the people of China and Japan have an average intake of about 45 mEq of potassium per day, a level that could be considered low compared to average American or European Caucasians. Sasaki et al. have described two adjoining prefectures in northern Japan, the Akita and the Aamori prefectures, that have contrasting diets. Farmers living in the Aamori district eat 8 to 10 apples per day, whereas those in the Akita prefecture do not and eat more rice instead. The consumption of this many apples would provide a greater potassium intake and possibly a lower sodium intake as well, and it is clear that the people of the apple-eating district have a significantly lower stroke rate than those in the district where rice is the chief foodstuff.

Potassium Intake and Blood Pressure in Various Populations (2,4,5,11,12, 14–16,18,19,21–23,25–27,31,35,39–41)

Primitive peoples all over the world eat diets with very low amounts of sodium and very high amounts of potassium and literally have no hypertension. It is possible that the high potassium intake contributes to this, along with the low sodium intake. Several studies suggest that potassium intake may indeed have an effect on blood pressure. For instance, Langford collected 24 hr urines for 6 consecutive days in 101 black women of about 20 years of age. The blood pressure was measured three times daily for 8 days in these individuals. In this group of both genetically susceptible women and those not susceptible to hypertension, there was no significant correlation between blood pressure and the level of sodium excretion. However, there was a positive correlation between the urinary sodium/potassium ratio and the diastolic blood pressure, with a correlation coefficient of 0.37, $p<0.02$.

Walker et al. studied a large group of people in Baltimore, Maryland, and found no significant correlation between blood pressure and sodium intake. However, they did find a highly significant negative correlation between potassium excretion and recumbent diastolic blood pressure, $r=-0.23$, $p< 0.0001$.

Page et al. found that among the men of the Qash'qai tribe of Northern Iran there was a correlation of blood pressure with sodium intake. The women of that tribe did not have a significant correlation between blood pressure and sodium excretion, although their blood pressure did have a positive correlation with the sodium/potassium ratio in the urine.

There is a report from Norway of an almost perfect correlation between mean urinary sodium/potassium ratio and mean diastolic blood pressure in three different areas of the country.

Studies in Rancho Bernardo, California, on the island of St. Lucia in the Caribbean, and in Honolulu found a significant positive correlation of blood pressure with the sodium/potassium ratio in the diet and a negative correlation with the potassium/creatinine ratio in the urine and with potassium in the diet. Similarly, in Zutphen in the Netherlands, potassium intake was inversely correlated with blood pressure.

There are at least six studies in the United States indicating that blacks consume less potassium than whites. Watson et al. studied black and white females averaging 20 years of age. The 24 hr potassium excretion was 28 mEq in black females and 36 mEq in white females, a significant difference.

In Evans County, Georgia, Grim et al. reported an estimated potassium intake of 23 mEq/24 hr in black men versus 54 mEq/24 hr in white men, a highly significant difference. Black men had an average 24 hr urinary excretion of potassium of 24 mEq/day compared to 40 mEq/day for white men, once again a definitely significant difference. Similar differences were found in the women of the area. A study by Zinner et al. showed that black youths between the ages of 5 and 18 years were much more likely to have a low urinary potassium concentration than white youths.

In a study at five Veterans' Administration Hospitals, Cushman and Langford reported that the average 24 hr potassium excretion among blacks was 40 mEq versus 70 mEq for whites (p less than 0.001). Voors et al. also found that black children had a markedly lower 24 hr potassium excretion than white children, with the black children excreting only two thirds as much potassium per day as whites. Langford found similar results in Holmes County, Mississippi, with blacks eating significantly less potassium than whites. Walker et al., in a study carried out in Baltimore, confirmed that blacks take in considerably less potassium in their diets compared to whites, and Dai et al. found the same pattern of potassium intake in three U.S. cities, with blacks eating significantly less potassium per day than whites.

These differences in potassium intake, with blacks consuming less potassium than whites, may have very important implications with regard to hypertension in blacks and with the complications of hypertension. There is accumulating evidence that a low level of potassium in the diet is correlated with a somewhat higher blood pressure. There is also strong evidence in rats that a diet low in potassium appears to increase the likelihood of strokes, and there is also evidence in animals that a somewhat low potassium intake increases the likelihood of renal disease. It is known that blacks have a considerably greater incidence of hypertension that whites, and it is also known that blacks have a much greater incidence of strokes and end-stage renal disease than whites. Hence, there is a strong suspicion that the low intake of potassium in blacks may be partially responsible for their high rate of end-stage kidney disease and their marked likelihood for having strokes.

There are at least seven studies that show a decrease in the blood pressure of hypertensive patients resulting from supplementation of the diet with extra potassium. The earliest studies were those by Addison and Priddle, with both reporting a decrease in the blood pressure of their patients when they were given supplements of potassium. Iimura et al. in Japan found a marked hypotensive effect of a high potassium intake in patients with essential hypertension. MacGregor et al. of England, in a very well controlled study, also noted that potassium supplementation brought about a decrease in blood pressure of about 6 mm Hg systolic and 4 mm Hg diastolic in patients with essential hypertension. Morino et al. found that potassium supplements will reduce the blood pressure of hypertensive patients. Svetkey et al. found a reduction in blood pressure averaging 7 mm Hg systolic and 4 mm Hg diastolic when they administered potassium supplementation to patients with essential hypertension. Kaplan et al. had a number of patients with essential hypertension on treatment with small doses of thiazide diuretics. They administered potassium supplements for one treatment period and withheld potassium supplements for a contrasting treatment period. The average blood pressure was significantly lower by a factor of 7 mm Hg systolic and 4 mm Hg diastolic during those intervals in which potassium supplements were administered.

Effect of Dietary Potassium on Deaths Related to Strokes (1,3,13,20)

Khaw and Barrett-Connor have published an analysis of the relationship of potassium intake to the stroke-related death rate. They studied a group of people over 50 years of age in a retirement community in Rancho Bernardo, California. They performed a very detailed 24 hr food recall on each person, which was administered by a certified lipid research clinic dietician. The quantity of foods taken in was assessed with the use of food models. The items in this dietary recall were analyzed according to the sophisticated University of Minnesota Nutrition Coordinating Center database. Over the succeeding 12 years the incidence of stroke-related deaths was ascertained. These stroke-related deaths had a very significant negative correlation with the daily intake of potassium. For example, among women who took in less than 49 mEq of potassium per day, the stroke rate was 5.3 per 100. When the potassium intake was between 49 and 66 mEq per day, the stroke incidence was 2.1 per 100. Most striking of all, if the potassium intake was greater than 67 mEq per day there were no stroke-related deaths at all. Each of these three groups represents tertiles of potassium intake, with 168 individuals in each of the tertiles. These differences were statistically highly significant.

Among the men in the study, those taking less than 59 mEq of potassium per day had a stroke rate of 3.4 per 100, those taking between 59 and 76 mEq per day had a stroke rate of 2.4 per 100, and those taking more than 76 mEq per day had no stroke-related deaths at all. Again, these represent the tertiles of potassium intake for men, and there were 119 individuals in each of the three tertiles.

Thus, the intake of potassium appears to influence stroke-related deaths in a dose-dependent manner, with relatively low potassium intakes having the most stroke deaths, the middle category of potassium intake having an intermediate value, and a high level of potassium intake, over about 76 mEq per day, having no stroke-related deaths at all over the 12 years of the study. When the correlation of potassium with the death rate was corrected for age, for calorie intake, for systolic or diastolic blood pressure, and for the fiber, magnesium, or calcium content of the food, the results still held up as strongly as they had without correction for these various factors. Using this corrected data, it could be deduced that a 10 mEq/day increase of potassium intake would bring about a 40% decrease in the incidence of stroke-related death over the 12 years of the study. This amounts to only one full extra helping of fruits, citrus fruit juices, vegetables, or potatoes per day, which reveals that relatively small increases of potassium intake in the daily diet were associated with very marked decreases of stroke-related deaths. In this study, the same strong relationship could be seen if the influence of blood pressure was totally factored out. A similar relationship of potassium to coronary artery events could not be found in this study.

It is clear from these analyses that the reduction of stroke-related deaths was related only in a very minor, insignificant way to a reduction of blood pressure and that, instead, the protective effect of added potassium in the diet appeared to be exerted without any change in blood pressure. This was precisely the same type of result that had been found in earlier studies in rats with high blood pressure by Tobian et al. Most of the variations of potassium in the diet could be accounted for by differences in the intake of fruits and vegetables. This study, if confirmed, could be the basis for strong advice to people to increase their intake of fruits and vegetables, particularly since such advice would appear to be a perfectly safe alternative and one that might have a salutary effect on cancer as well as on cardiovascular disease.

ANIMAL STUDIES

Effect of Potassium on Renal Lesions in Hypertension (9,36)

In Dahl S rats with genetic, salt-induced high blood pressure, one finds a gradual, progressive injury to the kidney with normal levels of potassium in the diet. In Fig. 1 (left) are seen large dilated tubules filled with big casts stained with PAS that were found in the renal cortex, in the renal medulla, and in the renal papilla of Dahl S rats eating 5% NaCl and a normal amount of potassium. Another group of Dahl S rats on 4% NaCl was fed the same diet except that 1.36% K was added to it to achieve a final K concentration of 2.1% in the diet. This is about the same percentage of K in the dry diet as one would find in the diet of a prehistoric human hunter-gatherer eating only natural foods. When K was added to the 4% NaCl diet of these Dahl S rats, it did not lower the blood pressure at all. The lesions in the renal tubules were graded blindly for each rat. Despite no lowering of blood pressure, the Dahl S rats on the high K diet had a 50% improvement in lesions in the renal cortex, a 30% improvement in the lesions of the renal outer medulla, and a 43% improvement in the lesions of the renal papilla (Table 1), indicating a major protective effect.

This same protective effect can be seen in a different way. In another set of Dahl S rats fed a 4% NaCl diet for 24 weeks, there was uniformly severe hypertension both in rats on diets with no added K salts and in rats receiving K supplements up to a final concentration of 2.11% K. However, after 24 weeks on the usual K intake, the plasma flow to the renal papilla had gone down to 13.5, which is 18% lower than the papillary plasma flow found in a Dahl S rat on a low NaCl intake (Fig. 2).

This 18% reduction in plasma flow to the renal papilla in the severely hy-

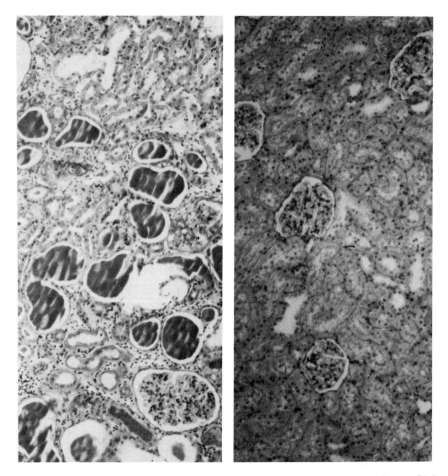

FIG. 1. Photomicrographs of the renal cortex. **Left**: Dahl S rat fed a 4% NaCl diet. **Right**: Dahl R rat fed a 4% NaCl diet. PAS stain. × 140.

pertensive Dahl S rat was probably caused by advancing renal lesions, including nephrosclerosis of the glomeruli and dilation of the tubules. However, in the Dahl S rats fed a supplement of 3.8% K citrate (2.1% total K in diet), flow to the renal papilla was not reduced at all and actually increased by 7.1% instead of decreasing, as was seen in the Dahl S rats receiving 4% NaCl diet and no added K. The addition of 3.8% K citrate to Dahl S rats on a 4% NaCl diet increased the plasma flow to the renal papilla by 34% compared to the Dahl S rats on the same 4% NaCl diet who had no added K in their diet. The addition of K citrate appeared to prevent nephron loss and, therefore, prevented the reduction in papillary plasma flow that usually accompanies nephron loss. The results of this study were in agreement with the previous study,

TABLE 1. Renal tubular dilation scores and glomerular lesion scores in Dahl salt-sensitive (S) rats and diets containing varying amounts of Na and K

Diet	BP (mm Hg)	Renal tubular dilation scores				Glomerular lesion scores
		Cortex	Outer medulla	Papilla		
4% NaCl No K added ($n = 18$)[a]	171	41	79	49		29
4% NaCl 3.8% K citrate ($n = 20$)	174	20 ($-51\%, p < 0.001$)	54 ($-32\%, p < 0.001$)	28 ($-43\%, p < 0.001$)		24 ($-17\%, p < 0.07$)
4% NaCl 2.6% KCl ($n = 20$)	173	22 ($-46\%, p < 0.001$)	58 ($-27\%, p < 0.001$)	28 ($-43\%, p < 0.001$)		23 ($-21\%, p < 0.05$)
0.3% NaCl no K added ($n = 20$)	158	24	53	26		25

[a] n = number of rats.

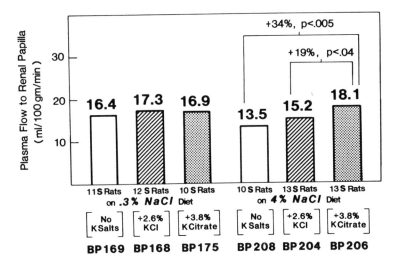

FIG. 2. Renal papillary plasma flow and mean blood pressure (BP, mm Hg) in Dahl S and R rats fed for 24 weeks on either low (0.32%) or high (4%) NaCl diets containing various K supplements.

in which the addition of K salts greatly diminished the tubular dilation lesions in NaCl-fed Dahl S rats.

Microscopic kidney slides of Dahl S rats and control Dahl R rats that are highly resistant to NaCl-induced hypertension were studied for arteriolar dimensions. As seen in Fig. 3, if a 4% NaCl diet is fed to a Dahl S rat, the rat develops hypertension, and the wall thickness of the renal arterioles increases by 38%. This is a well-known effect and was described by Volhard 73 years ago. However, when 1.36% potassium was added to the 4% NaCl diet the Dahl S rats became as hypertensive as ever, yet, the average thickness of their renal arterioles was really no thicker than the wall thickness of the Dahl R rats, who had no hypertension. Thus the added K salts greatly diminished the expected thickening of the arteriolar walls even though the blood pressure was not reduced.

The results of these studies on arteriolar wall thickness led directly to an additional series of studies. In the past, most people working in the hypertension field assumed that the thickening of the walls of arteries and arterioles in hypertension was the direct result of the presence of the high blood pressure itself. This study by Tobian et al. proved that hypertrophy was not always an inevitable result of high blood pressure. It showed that it was possible to have very high blood pressure and have no thickening of the arteriolar wall whatsoever. It was as if the extra potassium in the diet permitted the arteriole to resist the usual effects of the high blood pressure. The hyperstretching effect of the hypertension was there, but additional dietary potassium seemed to allow the artery not to notice it or be affected by it. This amounted to a

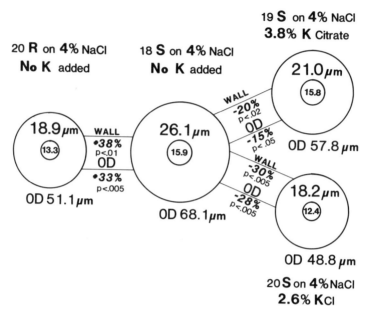

FIG. 3. Measurement of renal arteries. Average outer diameter (OD), wall thickness, and lumen size in arteries from Dahl S and R rats fed diets containing varying amounts of Na and K.

prevention of a type of arteriolar lesion in the kidney that usually results from long-standing hypertension.

The fact that potassium supplements in the diet could prevent arteriolar lesions in the kidney led to studies of whether the same type of potassium supplementation might be able to prevent certain artery diseases in other parts of the body. Strokes often result from common types of artery disease in the brain. Hypertension is a frequent forerunner of such strokes and causes damage primarily through a chronic overstretching of the walls of the cerebral arteries. This leads to a thickening of the artery wall, with possible eventual total closure of the artery lumen, leading to a brain infarct. Thrombosis in the diseased artery walls may hasten the total closure of the cerebral artery. These closures can occur also in the very small arteries of the hypertensive rat and can lead to tiny infarcts almost like lacunar lesions. On the other hand, the overstretching of the cerebral arteries also can cause local thinning of the wall and Charcot-Bouchard microaneurysms of these arteries, occurring espe-cially at the branching points of arteries. Such microaneurysms have the high wall tension that is brought about by high intraarterial pressure and larger radius. The thin-walled microaneurysm when stretched by the high arterial pressure often bursts, resulting in a cerebral hemorrhage. This is another important category of strokes that come on as a result of high blood pressure.

Both types of strokes represent classic arterial diseases that could possibly be improved with the institution of a high K diet.

Effect of Potassium on Hypertension and Stroke (37)

When stroke-prone SHR (SHRsp) rats are fed a Japanese-style diet including 4% NaCl, this rat chow increases the incidence of stroke compared to an American-style rat chow. After 17 weeks of feeding two Japanese type diets, with each diet containing 4% NaCl, 20 of the 24 SHRsp rats in the diet group with no added K (0.75% total K) had died, an 83% mortality rate. During this same period of time, 49 of the 50 rats on the same diet but with the addition of 1.36% K (2.1% total K) were still alive and showed no evidence of a non-fatal stroke. One rat had died in the final week, giving a 2% mortality rate to the K-supplemented group. The results were striking, with $p < 0.000001$. The K supplements significantly reduced blood pressure in the SHRsp rats, thus lessening the tension in the walls of the cerebral arteries. This would be expected to reduce the tendency to arterial lesions and strokes, and is a partial explanation for the remarkable protective effect of the K supplements.

The K supplements also appeared to reduce the death rate for a given level of hypertension. With two groups of SHRsp having virtually equal average blood pressures of 212 mm Hg, the group of 11 K-supplemented rats had only 1 death (9% mortality rate), whereas the group of 11 rats without K supplements had 7 deaths (64% mortality rate). In these two groups, the 86% decrease in mortality rate, 64% versus 9%, was significant (Fig. 4). This difference indicates that a supplementation in SHRsp rats is very effective for preventing death, even though blood pressure is almost identical in the two groups being compared.

In another study, after 9 weeks of feeding the high NaCl diets, 18 of 33 Dahl S rats on the diet with no K supplement (0.75% total K) had died (55% mortality rate), whereas only 2 of 45 Dahl S rats on the diets with 1.36% K supplements (2.1% total K) had died (4% mortality rate) (Fig. 5). This 93% reduction in mortality rate, 55% versus 4%, was significant, $p < 10^{-6}$.

K supplementation did effect a modest reduction in blood pressure in the Dahl S rats on an 8% NaCl diet in the later study. This modest reduction of blood pressure in the K-supplemented groups could explain some of the lowering of mortality rate in these groups. Again, however, it was possible to remove the effect of this reduction of blood pressure and still be able to analyze the influence of K supplements on mortality rate. In two groups of Dahl S rats with very closely matched blood pressures, the mortality rate was 38% (8 of 21) in the group with no K supplement versus 5% (2 of 39) in the groups with K supplementation. This 87% reduction in mortality rate was significant, $p < 0.001$.

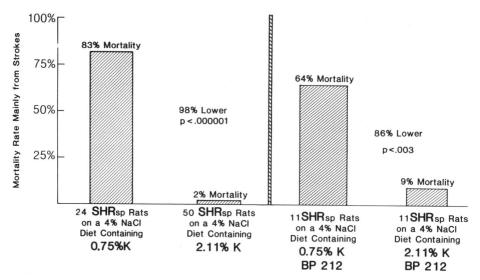

FIG. 4. The left panel indicates the remarkable 98% lowering of mortality rate when SHRsp rats are eating a high K diet (2.11% K) versus a normal K diet (0.75% K). The right panel shows that even when blood pressure was equal in the groups being compared, the SHRsp rats on the high K diet (2.11%) had an 86% lower mortality rate than the SHRsp rats on the normal K diet (0.75%).

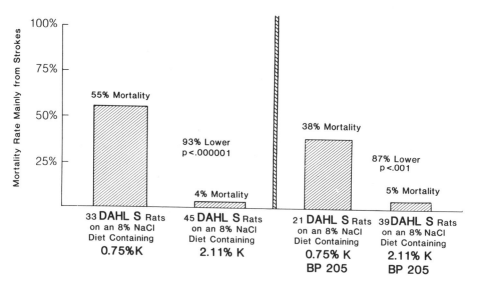

FIG. 5. The left panel indicates the remarkable 93% lowering of the mortality rate when Dahl S rats are eating a high K diet (2.11% K) versus a normal K diet (0.75% K). The right panel shows that even when blood pressure was equal in the groups being compared, the Dahl S rats on the high K diet (2.11% K) had an 87% lower mortality rate than Dahl S rats on the normal K diet (0.75%).

In a second study of SHRsp rats, after 22 weeks of the diets, 18 of 28 rats had died in the group with no added K, a 64% mortality rate. In contrast, among the SHRsp rats receiving a K supplement, only 2 of 36 had died, a 5.6% mortality rate. This represents a 91% reduction in mortality, $p < 10^{-6}$ (Fig. 6). Among the survivors in this second batch of SHRsp rats, brains were examined for spots of hemorrhage. In the group of 10 survivors not receiving

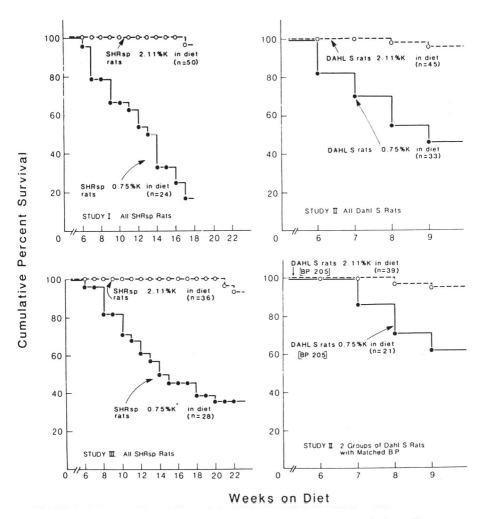

FIG. 6. This graph plots three studies as the cumulative percentage survival rate. The upper left panel plots the survival data of study I on SHRsp rats. The two right panels plot the survival data of the Dahl S rats on study II. The lower left panel plots the survival rate among a second group of SHRsp (study III). In study III there was a 64% mortality among SHRsp rats on the 0.75% normal K diet, whereas there was a 5% mortality rate among SHRsp rats on the 2.11% high K diet ($p < 0.000001$).

K supplements, 4 of 10 brains had spots of cerebral hemorrhage, a 40% incidence. Among the 34 survivors in the SHRsp rats that did receive K supplements, not a single brain had a spot of cerebral hemorrhage, a zero incidence. Thus K supplementation was associated with a striking reduction in the incidence of cerebral hemorrhage, $p < 0.0001$. This study strongly indicates that K supplements in SHRsp rats reduce the incidence of cerebral hemorrhage.

The relatively small lowerings of blood pressure that were brought about by the high K intake probably had only a minor effect in reducing the death rate. However, it is clear that anything that lowers the blood pressure in a hypertensive rat should have at least some small effect in reducing the death rate from stroke. The blood pressures described were taken using a microphonic method on the rat tail. They were repeated with an even more reliable intraarterial measurement. Moreover, blood pressures were all taken during the day, and there might have been a difference in the diurnal blood pressure at other times during the 24 hr.

In an additional study, male SHRsp rats were fed a Japanese-style diet containing 4% NaCl. Again, some of these SHRsp rats received the basic Japanese diet containing 0.75% K, and other rats received the same basic diet plus K supplementation up to a final level of 2.1% K. At the end of this study, 69% of the SHRsp rats on the normal (0.75%) K intake had died (40 of 58), most of them of a stroke (Fig. 7). In the group receiving K supplementation (2.11% K), only 2 rats of 95 had died, a 2% mortality rate. Thus the addition of K salts to the diet brought about a 98% reduction in mortality rate, $p < 0.000001$. During the 10th week on the diets, each rat was tested for intraarterial blood pressure in the femoral artery under light ether anesthesia both during the day and at night. These two pressures were averaged to obtain a mean blood pressure representative for that rat. The feeding of a high K diet reduced the mean blood pressure by 17 mm Hg, with the rats on the normal (0.75%) K diet having a mean blood pressure of 187 mm Hg, whereas the rats on the high K diet (2.11%) had a mean blood pressure of 170 mm Hg (10% difference, $p < 0.0001$) (Fig. 7).

With these data, it was possible to obtain two perfectly matching groups of rats with equal mean blood pressure by discarding some rats on the normal K intake with the highest blood pressures and some rats on the high K intake with the lowest blood pressures. Thus, a group of 47 SHRsp rats on normal K intake with a mean blood pressure of 182 mm Hg and 35 SHRsp rats on high K intake with a mean blood pressure of 182 mm Hg, two groups with exactly matching mean arterial pressures, were compared. In these matched groups, the mortality rate in the group of SHRsp rats on a normal K intake was 64%, whereas the mortality rate of the SHRsp rats on the high K intake was 6% (-91%, $p < 0.0001$). The group on the high K intake has a 91% lower mortality rate than the group on the normal K intake. It appears even more certain that the ability of the high K diet to prevent death from strokes does not depend on a lowering of the arterial pressure.

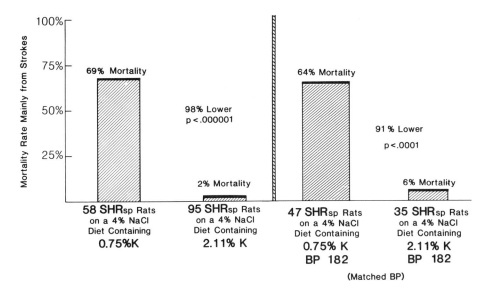

FIG. 7. Results of study IV involving SHRsp rats. There was a 69% mortality rate among the SHRsp rats eating the 0.75% normal K diet. In sharp contrast, there was a 2% mortality rate among SHRsp rats eating the 2.11% high K diet ($p<0.000001$). Blood pressures were measured intra-arterially in the femoral artery under light ether anesthesia during both daytime and nighttime hours. The day and night blood pressure were averaged for each rat. These highly accurate blood pressures helped in matching.

In another study, multiple sagittal sections of the brain were obtained at 0.5 mm intervals and examined blindly for the presence of brain infarcts. Among the surviving SHRsp rats on the normal 0.75% K intake, 13 of the 36 slides (36%) showed evidence of a brain infarct. In contrast, among the 11 surviving SHRsp rats on the 2.1% high K diet, only 1 slide of 44 showed evidence of a brain infarct, a 2% incidence. This was a 94.5% reduction of infarcts ($p<0.0001$). This study indicated clearly that the high K diet prevents brain infarcts in stroke-prone hypertensive rats.

In another series of stroke-prone SHR rats, 26 rats that were fed the normal 0.75% K diet for an 8 week period had a 72% incidence of cerebral hemorrhage, whereas 36 SHRsp rats on the high K intake had only a 5.5% incidence of brain hemorrhage, ($p<10^{-6}$) (Table 2). The rats in this study were killed after 8 weeks on the diet before any had died of a stroke. In this period, there was a strikingly high (72%) incidence of cerebral bleeding in the rats on the regular K diet and a very low (5.5%) incidence in the rats on the high K diet.

It was investigated in a group of SHRsp rats if a high K diet would protect against lethal strokes after there had been a bilateral carotid ligation. SHRsp rats were placed either on a normal 0.75% K intake or a high 2.11% K intake. After 8 weeks on these diets, blood pressures were taken intra-arterially under light ether anesthesia, and two matched groups of rats were selected with precisely matching and equal mean blood pressures of 168 mm Hg. At

TABLE 2. *Incidence of cerebral hemorrhages in stroke-prone SHRsp rats on normal K or high K diet*

No. of rats	Diet	% with brain hemorrhages[a]
25 SHRsp rats	0.75% normal K diet for 8 weeks	72
36 SHRsp rats	2.11% high K diet for 8 weeks	5.5

[a]The high K diet brought about a 92% reduction in brain hemorrhages ($p < 0.000001$).

that point, the rats underwent a bilateral carotid ligation under inactin anesthesia and were observed for 3 hr. In that 3 hr interval, 48% of the rats on the normal K intake died, whereas only 23% of the rats on the high K intake died (Table 3), a 52% reduction in mortality rate ($p<0.05$). Normal rats easily survive a bilateral carotid ligation. Among hypertensive rats, there are a number of deaths after bilateral carotid ligation because the collateral arterial vessels of hypertensive rats do not dilate in a normal fashion after there has been a ligation of some of the main arteries supplying the brain. Apparently, consumption of a high K diet enables these collateral arterial channels to dilate with a much greater degree of efficiency, thereby reducing the amount of ischemia and death from brain infarcts.

In studies of the kidney in Dahl S rats on normal and high K intakes, it was found that the high K diet prevented the usual thickening of the arteriolar walls in the kidneys of hypertensive rats. Would the same type of high K intake prevent hypertrophy of larger arteries, such as the aorta or the mesenteric arterioles? To study this, male SHRsp rats (5 weeks old) were fed 6% NaCl diets containing either 0.75% normal K ($n=25$) or 2.1% high K ($n=47$) for 8 weeks. Age-matched WKY rats ($n=15$) were fed a 6% NaCl diet with

TABLE 3. *Mortality rate within 3 hr after bilateral carotid ligation*

No. of rats	Diet	% dead within 3 hr after carotid litigation[a]
48 SHRsp rats	Normal K diet (0.75% K, BP 168)[b]	48%
26 SHRsp rats	High K diet (2.11% K, BP 168)	23%

[a]The high K diet brought about a 52% reduction in mortality ($p <0.05$).
[b]BP, blood pressure in mm Hg.

normal K (blood pressure 138). Blood pressures under inactin anesthesia in these SHRsp rats were not different: normal K, 207 mm Hg, high K, 208 mm Hg. After perfusion fixation, average medial thicknesses (m), normal K versus high K, were: aorta, 123 versus 94, -24%; mesenteric, 72 versus 58, -19%; carotid, 65 versus 56, -14%; basilar, 31 versus 25, -20% ($p<0.001$ for each). Thus, all four arteries were less hypertrophied in high K rats, with aorta and mesenterics no thicker than in normotensive WKY rats.

Effect of Potassium on Arterial and Cardiac Hypertrophy in Hypertension

In these same rats, intimal injury scores for each of nine segments of aorta (450 μm per segment) were graded blindly at a magnification of $\times 430$. Two such segments were graded for mesenterics and carotids, with 60 the worst possible score and 0 the best possible score. Average intimal injury scores, normal K versus high K, were: aorta, 28 versus 13, -54%; mesenteric, 18 versus 10, -44%; carotid, 29 versus 19, -35% ($p<0.001$ for each). In aorta and mesenterics, average intimal injury scores in high K SHRsp rats were similar to scores in normotensive WKY rats. Thus, high K diets have a highly protective effect against hypertensive arterial injury in SHRsp rats, including prevention of intimal lesions and medial hypertrophy, even though blood pressures were equally high in the normal and high K groups.

A protective effect of high K diets against endothelial cell injury could explain both intimal and medial protection, since release of endothelium, macrophage, and platelet-derived growth factors would be diminished with a healthier endothelium. This would reduce the medial hypertrophy and the intimal hypercellularity that result when medial smooth muscle cells migrate into the intimal layer in response to the chemoattraction of these growth factors. Reduced intimal lesions in the high K group probably indicate less endothelial cell injury. With less damage to endothelium, fewer macrophages would migrate into the intima, and fewer platelets would stick. Thus, release of growth factors from macrophages, damaged endothelium, and platelets would be diminished, causing less medial smooth muscle cell hypertrophy and less migration of smooth muscle cells from media to intima and less hyperplasia of these intimal smooth muscle cells. Heart weight (dry weight) to body weight (kg) ratios averaged 0.98 on 0.75% K versus 0.85 on 2.1% K, 13% less on high K ($p<0.001$), even though blood pressures were the same in the two groups. It can, therefore, no longer be considered a certainty that hypertension will lead invariably to a large thickening in the walls of arteries and arterioles. The high K diet, even with severe hypertension, can bring about a substantial reduction in wall thickening in either very large or very small arteries of SHRsp hypertensive rats. The high K diet appears to prevent severe hypertension from inducing a thickening of the artery wall, probably through a protective action on endothelial cells.

Effect of Potassium on Arterial Endothelial Cells
in Hypertension (28–30,34,38)

Recent evidence by Tobian et al. provides a much stronger link between high potassium feeding and preservation of the integrity of arterial endothelial cells. It has been known for a decade that endothelial cells secrete a relaxing factor that acts on the smooth muscle cells of the arteries and causes them to relax. Some vasodilating substances act directly on the smooth muscle cell, whereas other vasodilators act entirely by causing the endothelial cells to release this special relaxing factor, which has been termed endothelium-derived relaxing factor (EDRF) and may be nitric oxide.

Investigations in our laboratory have revealed that severe hypertension in SHRsp rats on a high NaCl diet causes injury to the endothelial cells, causing them to release much lower quantities of EDRF when they are stimulated with the vasodilator, acetylcholine. However, when other SHRsp rats on a high NaCl diet were given supplements of K citrate in the diet, it was found that the endothelial cells' capacity for releasing EDRF was completely preserved, even though the blood pressure was just as high in these rats as in the rats on a normal K intake. The addition of potassium to the diet allowed these endothelial cells to secrete as much EDRF as the endothelial cells in the aorta of a normotensive WKY rat. This study provides strong evidence that added potassium in the diet appears to prevent injury and thereby preserve normal function in the arterial endothelial cells even when they are chronically exposed to very high intraarterial pressure. It has been reported recently that EDRF released from endothelial cells inhibits platelet adhesion to endothelial cells and also inhibits platelet aggregation. Thus, a deficiency of EDRF release, such as would be found in hypertensive arteries, would encourage platelet adhesion to endothelial cells as well as platelet aggregation in the vicinity of the adhering platelets. This would strongly increase the likelihood of thrombosis on artery walls. Many infarct-type strokes in hypertensive people or rats are the result of thrombus formation in cerebral arteries. An endothelial dysfunction resulting from hypertension could, by decreasing EDRF release, encourage local thrombus formation through the increase in platelet adhesion and aggregation. High K diets greatly reduce brain infarcts in SHRsp rats and, at the same time, protect the endothelium from hypertensive dysfunction. This preservation of EDRF release could be an important factor in reducing these thrombotic infarcts. The finding of Tobian et al. that the high potassium diet prevents thickening of the intimal layer of several arteries in the SHRsp rat also provides strong evidence indicating that endothelial cells are protected by the high potassium diet, since the thickening of the intima is primarily caused by abnormal function of the endothelial cells. Thus using two separate approaches, it seems reasonably certain that the arterial endothelial cells are protected from hypertensive injury by the high potassium diet.

To explain the protective effect of high K diets, in still another study, measurements of total exchangeable sodium and total exchangeable potassium in Dahl S rats and in SHRsp rats after 23 days on either a normal or a high K diet were examined. Neither of the high K diets (KCl added or K citrate added) significantly increased total exchangeable K in the Dahl S rats or in the SHRsp rats. Moreover, in the SHRsp rats, the total exchangeable Na was not altered significantly by either high K diet. Among Dahl S rats, it was found that a high K diet resulting from the addition of KCl also did not significantly alter total exchangeable Na, even though this diet provided a very strong degree of protection against death from strokes as well as hypertensive hypertrophy of arteries. When the high K diet was achieved by the addition of K citrate, there was a 6.5% reduction of body Na in Dahl S rats ($p<0.0001$). However, both KCl and K citrate provided protection against stroke deaths in Dahl S rats, even though KCl was associated with an unchanged total body Na, whereas K citrate resulted in a reduced body Na. It is apparent that a reduction in total exchangeable Na is not a requisite for a marked prevention of death from hypertensive strokes.

It was thought that the high K diets might increase the K content in skeletal muscle or in the wall of the aorta. However, in both SHRsp rats and in Dahl S rats, the high K diet did not cause any changes in skeletal muscle K or in aortic wall K compared to similar rats on a normal K intake. It is apparent that the remarkable protective effect of the high K diet can be achieved without any changes in total body K, muscle K, aortic wall K, or plasma K.

Effect of Potassium on Longevity (24,40,42)

In both SHRsp and Dahl S rats, the addition of either KCl or K citrate strikingly reduced the death rate. This marked reduction occurred even when blood pressure was virtually equal in the two groups being compared. The K supplements reduced blood pressure considerably in SHRsp rats and modestly in Dahl S rats, and the reductions in blood pressure undoubtedly contributed somewhat to the lower death rate. The SHRsp rats were not dying of uremia and did not exhibit the ascites and edema of congestive heart failure. They often suffered a hemiplegia during the 14 days before death. It is likely that the great majority of these deaths were caused by stroke, either a rupture or a closure of a cerebral artery, caused by hypertensive lesions in the artery. In some way, extra K in the diet appears to reduce greatly the incidence of these lesions even when blood pressure is similar in the groups being compared. This could explain the 94.5% reduction of cerebral hemorrhage spots in K-supplemented SHRsp rats. The extra K in the diet allows the cerebral arteries to carry a very high arterial pressure without sustaining very much damage.

The mortality rate in the Dahl S rats on 8% NaCl was high. Werber et al. observed a similarly high mortality rate in Dahl S rats; all 37 of their Dahl S rats were dead after 18 weeks of feeding a Japanese-style chow containing 8% NaCl. Seventy-eight percent of their Dahl S rats had sustained a stroke after the 18 weeks of feeding, with a 35% incidence of cerebral hemorrhage and a 68% incidence of cerebral infarction. Meneely et al. reported a significantly reduced death rate in 5.6% NaCl-fed Sprague-Dawley rats, which resulted from the addition of 1.2% K to the control diet. This study was a 2½ year feeding experiment, and the time interval up to 50% survival was 38% longer in the K-supplemented rats, 26.9 months versus 19.5 months in the control rats. In Meneely et al.'s study, the KCl supplementation prolonged life even though the blood pressure was not reduced below control levels. In another study, Gordon et al. produced renal hypertension in rabbits, which caused a mesenteric vascular disease with many tiny hemorrhages in the mesentery. Supplements of K in these rabbits did not reduce the blood pressure but did greatly reduce the number of small hemorrhages in the mesentery, suggesting a partial prevention of some of the mesenteric vascular lesions.

POSSIBLE MECHANISMS OF ACTION OF POTASSIUM IN RELATION TO HYPERTENSION (10)

The precise mechanism by which extra dietary K reduces deaths is as yet elusive. Moderately severe hypertension can cause rents, irregularities, and severe stretching in a tense arterial endothelial layer, which could increase the permeability of the endothelial lining. Such endothelial irregularities in cerebral arteries ultimately could produce strokes. One could speculate that the high K diet preserves the integrity of endothelial cells even when they are under great tension from high blood pressure, thereby preventing artery wall lesions with subsequent cerebral hemorrhage and infarcts.

Thus, a return toward the high K levels of prehistoric cuisine might very well diminish these high attack rates of stroke and hypertensive renal failure. As these studies indicate, the added dietary K appears to retard the development of lesions in cerebral arteries exposed to high arterial pressure.

ACKNOWLEDGMENT

This work was supported by grants from the National Institutes of Health (HL 17871) and The Cargill Foundation.

REFERENCES

1. Acheson, R. M., and Williams, D. R. R. (1983): Does consumption of fruit and vegetables protect against stroke? *Lancet*, 1:1191–1193.
2. Addison, W. (1928): The uses of sodium chloride, potassium chloride, sodium bromide and

potassium bromide in cases of arterial hypertension which are amenable to potassium chloride. *Can. Med. Assoc. J.*, 18:281–285.

3. Colditz, G. A., Branch, L. G., Lipnick, R. J., et al. (1985): Increased green and yellow vegetable intake and lowered cancer deaths in an elderly population. *Am. J. Clin. Nutr.*, 41: 32–36.

4. Cushman, W. C., and Langford, H. G., for Veterans Administration Cooperative Study Group on Antihypertensive Agents (1983): Urinary electrolyte differences in black and white hypertensives (Abstr.). *Clin. Res.*, 31:843A.

5. Dai, W. S., Kuller, L. H., and Miller, G. (1984): Arterial BP and urinary electrolytes. *J. Chronic Dis.*, 37:75–84.

6. Darwin, C. (1984): *On the Origin of Species.* Harvard University Press, Cambridge.

7. Denton, D. (1982): *Hunger for Salt, an Anthropological, Physiological and Medical Analysis*, pp. 573–575. Springer-Verlag, New York.

8. Eaton, S. B., and Konner, M. (1985): Paleolithic nutrition. A consideration of its nature and current implications. *N. Engl. J. Med.*, 312:283.

9. Ganguli, M. C., Tobian, L., Iwai, J., and Johnson, M. A. (1981): Potassium citrate feeding protects against nephron loss in severe NaCl hypertension in rats. *Clin. Sci.*, 61:73–75.

10. Goldby, F. S., and Beilin, L. J. (1972): Relationship between arterial pressure and the permeability of arterioles to carbon particles in acute hypertension in the rat. *Cardiovasc. Res.*, 6:384–390.

11. Gordon, D. B., and Drury, D. R. (1956): The effect of potassium on the occurrence of petechial hemorrhages in renal hypertensive rabbits. *Circ. Res.*, 4:167–172.

12. Grim, D. E., Luft, F. C., Miller, J. Z., et al. (1980): Racial differences in blood pressure in Evans County, Georgia: Relationship to sodium and potassium intake and plasma renin activity. *J. Chronic Dis.*, 33:87–94.

13. Hirayama, T. (1979): Diet and cancer. *Nutr. Cancer*, 1:67–81.

14. Iimura, O., Kijima, T., Kikuchi, K., et al. (1981): Studies on the hypotensive effect of high potassium intake in patients with essential hypertension. *Clin. Sci.*, 61:77–80.

15. Kaplan, N. M., Carnegie, A., Raskin, P., Heller, J. A., and Simmons, M. (1985): K supplementation in hypertensive patients with diuretic-induced hypokalemia. *N. Engl. J. Med.*, 312:746–749.

16. Khaw, K. T., and Barrett-Connor, E. (1984): Dietary potassium and blood pressure in a population. *Am. J. Clin. Nutr.*, 39:963–968.

17. Khaw, K. T., and Barrett-Connor, E. (1987): Dietary potassium and stroke-associated mortality: A 12-year prospective population study. *N. Engl. J. Med.*, 316:235–240.

18. Khaw, K. T., and Rose, G. (1982): Population study of blood pressure and associated factors in St Lucia, West Indies. *Int. J. Epidemiol.*, 11:372–377.

19. Kromhout, D., Bosschieter, E. B., and Coulander, C. D. L. (1985): Potassium, calcium, alcohol intake and blood pressure: The Zutphen study. *Am. J. Clin. Nutr.*, 41:1299–1304.

20. Kushi, L. H., Lew, R. A., Stare, F. J., et al. (1985): Diet and 20-year mortality from coronary heart disease: The Ireland-Boston Diet-Heart Study. *N. Engl. J. Med.*, 312:811–818.

21. Langford, H. G. (1983): Dietary potassium and hypertension: Epidemiologic data. *Ann. Intern. Med.*, 98[Suppl]:770–772.

22. Langford, H. G. (1985): Potassium and hypertension. *Proceedings of NIH Workshop on Nutrition and Hypertension*, edited by M. J. Horan, M. Blaustein, J. B. Dunbar, et al., pp. 147–153. Biomedical Information, New York.

23. MacGregor, G. A., Smith, S. J., Markandu, N. D., Banks, R. A., and Sagnella, G. A. (1982): Moderate potassium supplementation in essential hypertension. *Lancet*, 2:567–570.

24. Meneely, G. R., and Ball, C. O. T. (1958): Experimental epidemiology of chronic NaCl toxicity and the protective effects of potassium chloride. *Am. J. Med.*, 25:713–725.

25. Morino, T., McCaa, R., and Langford, H. G. (1978): Effect of potassium on blood pressure, sodium excretion and plasma renin activity in hypertensive patients (Abstr.). *Clin. Res.*, 26:805A.

26. Page, L. B., Vandevert, D. E., Nader, K., et al. (1981): Blood pressure of Qash'qai pastoral nomads in Iran in relation to culture, diet and body form. *Am. J. Clin. Nutr.*, 34:527.

27. Priddle, W. W. (1931): Observations on the management of hypertension. *Can. Med. Assoc. J.*, 25:5–8.

28. Radomski, M. W., Palmer, R. M. J., and Moncada, S. (1987): Comparative pharmacology of endothelium-derived relaxing factor, nitric oxide and prostacyclin in platelets. *Br. J. Pharm.*, 92:181–187.

29. Radomski, M. W., Palmer, R. M. J., and Moncada, S. (1987): Endogenous nitric oxide inhibits human platelet adhesion to vascular endothelium. *Lancet*, 2:1057–1058.
30. Radomski, M. W., Palmer, R. M. J., and Moncada, S. (1987): The role of nitric oxide and cGMP in platelet adhesion to vascular endothelium. *Biochem. Biophys. Res. Commun.*, 148:1482–1489.
31. Reed, D., McGee, D., Yano, K., and Hankin, J. (1985): Diet, blood pressure, and multicollinearity. *Hypertension*, 7:405–410.
32. Rostand, S. G., Kirk, K. A., Rutsky, E. A., and Pate, B. A. (1982): Racial differences in the incidence of treatment for end-stage renal disease. *N. Engl. J. Med.*, 306:1276–1279.
33. Sasaki, N., Mitsuhashi, T., and Fukushi, S. (1959): Effects of the ingestion of large amounts of apples on blood pressure in farmers in Akita prefecture. *Igaku Seibutsugaku*, 51:103–105.
34. Sugimoto, T., Tobian, L., and Ganguli, M. C. (1988): High K diets protect against dysfunction of endothelial cells in stroke-prone SHR. *Hypertension* (in press)
35. Svetkey, L. P., Yarger, W. E., Feussner, J. R., DeLong, E., and Klotman, P. E. (1986): Placebo-controlled trial of oral potassium in the treatment of mild hypertension (Abstr.). *Clin. Res.*, 34:487A.
36. Tobian, L., MacNeill, D., Johnson, M. A., Ganguli, M. C., and Iwai, J. (1984): Potassium protection against lesions of the renal tubules, arteries and glomeruli and nephron loss in salt-loaded hypertensive Dahl S rats. *Hypertension*, 6[Suppl. 1]:170–176.
37. Tobian, L., Lange, J., Ulm, K., Wold, L., and Iwai, J. (1985): Potassium reduces cerebral hemorrhage and death in hypertensive rats even when BP is not lowered. *Hypertension*, 7:110–114.
38. Tobian, L., Sugimoto, T., Johnson, M. A., and Hanlon, S. (1988): High K diets protect against endothelial injury in stroke-prone SHR rats. *J. Hypertension* (in press)
39. Voors, A. W., Dalferes, E. R. Jr., Frank, G. C., et al. (1983): Relation between ingested potassium and sodium balance in young blacks and whites. *Am. J. Clin. Nutr.*, 37:583–594.
40. Walker, W. G., Whelton, P. K., Saito, H., et al. (1979): Relation between blood pressure and urinary sodium and potassium in 574 ambulatory subjects. *Hypertension*, 1:287–291.
41. Watson, R. L., Langford, H. G., Abernethy, J., et al. (1980): Urinary electrolytes, body weight, and blood pressure: Pooled cross-sectional results among four groups of adolescent females. *Hypertension*, 2:193–198.
42. Werber, A. H., Baumbach, G. L., Wagner, D. V., Mark, A. L., and Heistad, D. D. (1985): Factors that influence stroke in Dahl salt-sensitive rats. *Hypertension*, 1:59–64.
43. Zinner, S. H., Margolius, H. S., Rosner, B., et al. (1976): Familial aggregation of urinary kallikrein concentration in childhood: Relation to blood pressure, race and urinary electrolytes. *Am. J. Epidemiol.*, 104:124–132.

Subject Index